Mental Health
in Literature

Mental Health in Literature
Literary Lunacy and Lucidity

Glenn E. Rohrer
East Carolina University

LYCEUM
BOOKS, INC.

5758 South Blackstone Avenue
Chicago, Illinois 60637

© Lyceum Books, Inc., 2005

Published by

LYCEUM BOOKS, INC.
5758 S. Blackstone Ave
Chicago, Illinois 60637
773+643-1903 (Fax)
773+643-1902 (Phone)
lyceum@lyceumbooks.com
http://www.lyceumbooks.com

10 9 8 7 6 5 4

ISBN 0-925065-84-6

Library of Congress Cataloging-in-Publication Data

    Mental health in literature : literary lunacy and lucidity / [edited by] Glenn Rohrer.
      p. cm.
    ISBN 0-925065-84-6
    1. Mental illness—Fiction. I. Rohrer, Glenn.
    PN6120.95.M4M46 2004
    809'.933561—dc22

                                        2004014632

Permissions

The following selections are reprinted with permission.

Excerpts from THE LOST WEEKEND by Charles Jackson. Copyright © 1944 by Charles Jackson. Copyright renewed 1971 by Rhodey Jackson. Reprinted by permission of Farrar, Straus and Giroux, LLC.

Excerpts from pages 142–143 from chapter 11 of THE BELL JAR by Sylvia Plath. Copyright © 1971 by Harper & Row, Publishers, Inc. Reprinted by permission of HarperCollins Publishers Inc.

Excerpts from AN UNQUIET MIND by Kay Redfield Jamison. Copyright © 1995 by Kay Redfield Jamison. Used by permission of Alfred A. Knopf, a division of Random House, Inc.

"The End of the Party," from COLLECTED STORIES OF GRAHAM GREENE by Graham Greene. Copyright © 1929. Copyright renewed 1957 by Graham Greene. Used by permission of Viking Penguin, a division of Penguin Group (USA) Inc.

Excerpts from ACHILLES IN VIETNAM: COMBAT TRAUMA AND THE UNDOING OF CHARACTER by Jonathan Shay. Copyright © 1994 by Jonathan Shay. Reprinted with the permission of Scribner, an imprint of Simon & Schuster Adult Publishing Group.

Excerpts from THE THING ON THE DOORSTEP by H. P. Lovecraft. Reprinted by permission of the Arkham House Publishers, Inc. and Arkham's agents, JABberwocky Literary Agency, PO Box 4558, Sunnyside, New York 111040558.

Excerpts from GIRL, INTERRUPTED by Susanna Kaysen. Copyright © 1993 by Susanna Kaysen. Used by permission of Turtle Bay Books, a division of Random House, Inc.

Excerpts from ZIPPER by Caroline Janover. Used by permission of Caroline Janover.

Excerpts from MANCHILD IN THE PROMISED LAND by Claude Brown. Copyright © 1965 by Claude Brown. Reprinted with the permission of Scribner, an imprint of Simon & Schuster Adult Publishing Group.

Excerpts from WASTED: A MEMOIR OF ANOREXIA AND BULIMIA by Marya Hornbacher. Copyright © 1998 by Marya Hornbacher-Beard. Reprinted by permission of HarperCollins Publishers Inc.

This book is dedicated to all those
"Who Dream by Day": may they find peace.

Contents

Preface

Men have called me mad; but the question is not yet settled, whether madness is or is not the loftiest intelligence—whether much that is glorious—whether all that is profound—does not spring from disease of thought—from moods of mind exalted at the expense of the general intellect. They who dream by day are cognizant of many things, which escape those who dream only by night.

—From "Elnora" by Edgar Allan Poe

Literature has always been a rich source of information for human behavior. The combination of madness and genius, and the often-fine distinction between the two, has been a continuous theme in Western literature from its beginnings. Myths and legends appear in Homer, the Bible, and ancient Greek drama. Such myths contain primordial symbolizations of delusions, mania, and other bizarre forms of thought and behavior (Vernon, 1972).

This book provides the opportunity to look into the human mind through the eyes of the world's great literary writers, biographers, and more recent contemporary writers. Great writers often capture the human experience in ways that most of us simply do not have the insight and capacity to articulate. Imaginative writers from the fifth century B.C. to the present have always been concerned with madness as a revelation of processes of the human mind (Feder, 1980). Writers can offer superb insights into human conduct because often, in real life, they share a character's struggle or condition. Strange, abnormal, and deviant actions of literary characters offer an indispensable resource for investigating personality (Rieger, 1994).

Using literature to examine human behavior has many advantages over using case studies. One of the major problems with case studies is that they are often written to illustrate a diagnostic point. They lack the vitality of writings designed to develop characters without the limitations of a predescribed set of behaviors. As Rieger (1994) points out, from what better source could one learn about madness, violence, murder, deceit, betrayal, lust, greed, loneliness, and depression than from great writers? Commenting on case studies, Hartwell (1980) notes, "Editorial commentary places the characters' lives in precise psychological categories, suggesting abnormal, clinical case histories, rather than literature. The accompanying *Diagnostic and Statistical Manual*–like labels reduce the characters to one-dimensional clinical studies, forcing them to conform exactly to the current thinking regarding significant characteristics and labels. Such procedures can reduce literature's complexity to trite, simplistic observations." This book demonstrates particularly in the first chapter, literature repeatedly challenges the simplistic notion of the clear-cut difference between sanity and insanity. Literature often provides glimpses of lucidity, which the reader may have difficulty distinguishing from the view many have of the insane.

It is clear that literature questions the concept that insanity rests solely within the individual. Feder (1980) reminds us that "Madness as a theme of myth and literature has always dealt with personal responses to environmental influences, which include, political, social, and cultural pressures, or perhaps it would be more correct to say which exclude nothing." Vernon (1972) adds, "The madman, like other people, does not exist alone. He both reflects and influences those involved with him. In the study of madness in literature, psychological theory provides but one discipline that, along with others, especially literary, religious, and social history, helps elucidate the various symbolic forms into which the human mind transforms experience." Literature has made a strong and vital contribution to our understanding of behavior.

This literature presents the outward forms of psychopathology. It is my intent to utilize the insights of this literature to the fullest and not to demean these works by forcing them into the limits of current diagnostic categories. For purposes of organization and presentation, the book uses the current categories of the *Diagnostic and Statistical Manual (DSM)* of the American Psychiatric Association. Readers do not need prior experience with the *DSM* to understand this work. The works cited are not intended to meet all of the diagnostic criteria required by the current manual. The value of using these works to illustrate psychopathology is their ability to resist the oversimplification of case histories.

I hope that students of both literature and human behavior will use this work. The theme of madness or insanity in literature is a recurring one that the student of literature will encounter time and time again. There is a vast amount of literature exploring the topic of literary madness, and we have only skimmed the surface. Students are encouraged to explore this rich and complex topic in greater detail.

References

Feder, Lillian. (1980). *Madness in literature*. Princeton, NJ: Princeton University Press.

Hartwell, Charles. (1980). *Disordered personalities in literature*. New York: Longman.

Rieger, Branimir. (1994). *Dionysus in literature*. Bowling Green, OH: Bowling Green State University Press.

Vernon, John. (1973). *The garden and the map: Schizophrenia in twentieth-century literature and culture*. Champaign, IL: University of Illinois Press.

Acknowledgments

A work of this type is not accomplished without the assistance of many people. I would like to thank my colleagues in social work, psychology, and psychiatry for their assistance in locating and categorizing many of the stories utilized in this book. In addition, I would like to thank my many students who also suggested stories and who tested their developing diagnostic skills by assessing the characters in the stories on the take-home exams in my psychopathology courses. I would also like to thank my wife Lois for her love and support and for long hours spent in proofreading and correcting the manuscript. Without her vital contribution this work could not have been accomplished. Finally, I would like to thank the late Dr. Jim Lantz, who was instrumental in formulating the early plans for this book and bringing it to fruition. His advice and encouragement were sincerely appreciated, and he will be greatly missed.

Chapter 1

The Problem of Assessment and Diagnosis

We begin this work with two stories that highlight the difficult job of assessing and diagnosing emotional problems. In literature, as in real life, the line between normal and not so normal is not always clear. A primary concern for anyone who has ever attempted to assess a troubled person is to determine whether or not certain behaviors represent a normal or an aberrant condition. This age-old dilemma is the subject of numerous works of literature. Two of the best such efforts come to us from Edgar Allan Poe and E.T.A. Hoffmann.

Edgar Allan Poe (1809–1849)

Edgar Allan Poe was born in Boston in 1809. Both of his parents died before he was three years old and he was taken into the home of John and Fanny Allan in Richmond, Virginia. The Allans lived in England from 1815 to1820, where Edgar attended school. He also attended The University of Virginia and West Point—unsuccessfully.

Poe's life is marked with several personal tragedies. The death of his wife, Virginia, who was his first cousin, and whom he married when she was only thirteen, was particularly difficult for him. Poe's life was characterized by depression as a result of these losses. Throughout his life he experienced argumentative outbursts, suicidal thoughts, and well-documented alcohol and drug problems. His biological father reportedly died from alcoholic complications, and his stepfather was a heavy drinker. Drinking played a part in his expulsion from the University of Virginia and West Point and may have been a factor in his untimely death at the age of forty.

The narrators of Poe's stories are often "madmen," and his writings seem to capture the thoughts and feelings of seriously disturbed people with remarkable insight and understanding. He is given credit for inventing the detective story, and his imaginative descriptions of his characters continue to provide us with excellent pictures of the troubled human mind.

In this selection, "The System of Dr. Tarr and Prof. Fether," Poe reminds us of the difficulty in distinguishing between lunacy and lucidity.

"The System of Dr. Tarr and Prof. Fether"

During the autumn of 18—, while on a tour through the extreme southern provinces of France, my route led me within a few miles of a certain *Maison de Santé* or private madhouse, about which I had heard much, in Paris, from my medical friends. As I had never visited a place of the kind, I thought the opportunity too good to be lost; and so proposed to my traveling companion (a gentleman with whom I had made casual acquaintance a few days before), that we should turn aside, for an hour or so, and look through the establishment. To this he objected—pleading haste, in the first place, and, in the second, a very unusual horror at the sight of a lunatic. He begged of me, however, not to let any mere courtesy toward himself interfere with the gratification of my curiosity, and said that he would ride on leisurely, so that I might overtake him during the day, or, at all events, during the next. As he bade me good-bye, I bethought me that there might be some difficulty in obtaining access to the premises, and mentioned my fears on this point. He replied that, in fact, unless I had personal knowledge of the superintendent, Monsieur Maillard, or some credential in the way of a letter, a difficulty might be found to exist, as the regulations of these private madhouses were more rigid than the public hospital laws. For himself, he added, he had, some years since, made the acquaintance of Maillard, and would so far assist me as to ride up to the door and introduce me; although his feelings on the subject of lunacy would not permit of his entering the house.

I thanked him, and, turning from the main road, we entered a grass-grown by-path, which, in half an hour, nearly lost itself in a dense forest, clothing the base of a mountain. Through this dank and gloomy wood we rode some two miles, when the *Maison de Santé* came into view. It was a fantastic *chateau*, much dilapidated, and indeed scarcely tenantable through age and neglect. Its aspect inspired me with absolute dread, and, checking my horse, I half resolved to turn back. I soon, however, grew ashamed of my weakness, and proceeded.

As we rode up to the gateway, I perceived it slightly open, and the visage of a man peering through. In an instant afterward, this man came forth, accosted my companion by name, shook him cordially by the hand, and begged him to alight. It was Monsieur Maillard himself. He was a portly, fine-looking gentleman of the old school, with a polished manner, and a certain air of gravity, dignity, and authority which was very impressive.

My friend, having presented me, mentioned my desire to inspect the establishment, and received Monsieur Maillard's assurance that he would show me all attention, now took leave, and I saw him no more.

When he had gone, the superintendent ushered me into a small and exceedingly neat parlor, containing, among other indications of refined taste, many books, drawings, pots of flowers, and musical instruments. A cheerful fire blazed upon the hearth. At a piano, singing an aria from Bellini, sat a young and very beautiful woman, who at my entrance, paused in her song, and received me with graceful courtesy. Her voice was low, and her whole manner subdued. I thought, too, that I perceived the traces of sorrow in her countenance, which was excessively, although to my taste, not unpleasingly, pale. She was attired in deep mourning, and excited in my bosom a feeling of mingled respect, interest, and admiration.

I had heard, at Paris, that the institution of Monsieur Maillard was managed upon what is vulgarly termed the "system of soothing"—that all punishments were avoided—that even confinement was seldom resorted to—that the patients, while secretly watched, were left much apparent liberty, and that most of them were permitted to roam about the house and grounds in the ordinary apparel of persons in right mind.

Keeping these impressions in view, I was cautious in what I said before the young lady; for I could not be sure that she was sane; and, in fact, there was a certain restless brilliancy about her eyes which half led me to imagine she was not. I confined my remarks, therefore, to general topics, and to such as I thought would not be displeasing or exciting even to a lunatic. She replied in a perfectly rational manner to all that I said; and even her original observations were marked with the soundest good sense; but a long acquaintance with the metaphysics of *mania*, had taught me to put no faith in such evidence of sanity, and I continued to practice, throughout the interview, the caution with which I commenced it.

Presently a smart footman in livery brought in a tray with fruit, wine, and other refreshments, of which I partook, the lady soon afterward leaving the room. As she departed I turned my eyes in an inquiring manner toward my host.

"No," he said, "oh, no—a member of my family—my niece, and a most accomplished woman."

"I beg a thousand pardons for the suspicion," I replied, "but of course you will know how to excuse me. The excellent administration of your affairs here is well understood in Paris, and I thought it just possible, you know—"

"Yes, yes—say no more—or rather it is myself who should thank you for the commendable prudence you have displayed. We seldom find so much of forethought in young men; and, more than once, some unhappy *contretemps* has occurred in consequence of thoughtlessness on the part of our visitors. While my former system was in operation, and my patients were permitted the privilege of roaming to and fro at will, they were often aroused to a dangerous frenzy by injudicious persons who called to inspect the house. Hence I was obliged to enforce a rigid system of exclusion; and none obtained access to the premises upon whose discretion I could not rely."

"While your *former* system was in operation!" I said, repeating his words— "do I understand you, then, to say that the 'soothing system' of which I have heard so much is no longer in force?"

"It is now," he replied, "several weeks since we have concluded to renounce it forever."

"Indeed! You astonish me!"

"We found it, sir," he said, with a sigh, "absolutely necessary to return to the old usages. The *danger* of the soothing system was, at all times, appalling; and its advantages have been much overrated. I believe, sir, that in this house it has been given a fair trial, if ever in any. We did everything that rational humanity could suggest. I am sorry that you could not have paid us a visit at an earlier period, that you might have judged for yourself. But I presume you are conversant with the soothing practice—with its details."

"Not altogether. What I have heard has been at third and fourth hand."

"I may state the system, then, in general terms, as one in which the patients were *ménages*—humored. We contradicted *no* fancies which entered the brains of the mad. On the contrary, we not only indulged but encouraged them; and many of our most permanent cures have been thus effected. There is no argument which so touches the feeble reason of the madman as the *reductio ad absurdum*. We have had men, for example, who fancied themselves chickens. The cure was, to insist upon the thing in fact—to accuse the patient of stupidity in not sufficiently perceiving it to be a fact—and thus to refuse him any other diet for a week than that which properly appertains to a chicken. In this manner a little corn and gravel were made to perform wonders."

"But was this species of acquiescence all?"

"By no means. We put much faith in amusements of a simple kind, such as music, dancing, gymnastic exercises generally, cards, certain classes of books, and so forth. We affected to each individual as if for some ordinary physical disorder; and the word 'lunacy' was never employed. A great point was to set each lunatic to guard the actions of all the others. To repose confidence in the understanding or discretion of a madman is to gain him body and soul. In this way we were enabled to dispense with an expensive body of keepers."

"And you had no punishments of any kind?"

"None."

"And you never confined your patients?"

"Very rarely. Now and then, the malady of some individual growing to a crisis, or taking a sudden turn of fury, we conveyed him to a secret cell, lest his disorder should infect the rest, and there kept him until we could dismiss him to his friends—for with the raging maniac we have nothing to do. He is usually removed to the public hospitals."

"And you have now changed all this—and you think for the better?"

"Decidedly. The system had its disadvantages, and even its dangers. It is now, happily, exploded throughout all the *Maisons de Santé* of France."

"I am very much surprised," I said, "at what you tell me; for I made sure that, at this moment, no other method of treatment for mania existed in any portion of the country."

"You are young yet, my friend," replied my host, "but the time will arrive when you will learn to judge for yourself of what is going on in the world, without trusting to the gossip of others. Believe nothing you hear, and only one-half that you see. Now about our *Maisons de Santé*, it is clear that some ignoramus has misled you. After dinner, however, when you have sufficiently recovered from the fatigue of your ride, I will be happy to take you over the house, and introduce to you a system which, in my opinion, and that of every one who has witnessed its operation, is incomparably the most effective as yet devised."

"Your own?" I inquired—"one of your own invention?"

"I am proud," he replied, "to acknowledge that it is—at least in some measure."

In this manner I conversed with Monsier Maillard for an hour or two, during which he showed me the gardens and conservatories of the place.

"I cannot let you see my patients," he said, "just at present. To a sensitive mind there is always more or less of the shocking in such exhibitions; and I do not wish to spoil your appetite for dinner. We will dine. I can give you some veal *à la St. Menehoult*, with cauliflowers in *velouté* sauce—after that a glass of *Clos de Vougeot*—then your nerves will be sufficiently steadied."

At six, dinner was announced; and my host conducted me into a large *salle à manger*, where a very numerous company were assembled—twenty-five or thirty in all. They were, apparently, people of rank—certainly of high breeding—although their habiliments, I thought, were extravagantly rich, partaking somewhat too much of the ostentatious finery of the *ville cour*. I noticed that at least two thirds of these guests were ladies; and some of the latter were by no means accounted in what a Parisian would consider good taste at the present day. Many females, for example, whose age could not have been less than seventy, were bedecked with a profusion of jewelry, such as rings, bracelets, and earrings, and wore their bosoms and arms shamefully bare. I observed, too, that very few of the dresses were well made—or, at least, that very few of them fitted the wearers. In looking about, I discovered the interesting girl to whom Monsieur Maillard had presented me in the little parlor; but my surprise was great to see her wearing a hoop and farthingale, with high-heeled shoes, and a dirty cap of Brussels lace, so much too large for her that it gave her face a ridiculously diminutive expression. When I had first seen her, she was attired, most becomingly, in deep mourning. There was an air of oddity, in short, about the dress of the whole party, which, at first, caused me to recur to my original idea of the "soothing system," and to fancy that Monsieur Maillard had been willing to deceive me until after dinner, that I might experience no uncomfortable feelings during the repast, at finding myself dining with lunatics; but I remembered having been informed, in Paris, that the southern provincialists were a peculiarly eccentric people, with a vast number of antiquated notions;

and then, too, upon conversing with several members of the company, my apprehensions were immediately and fully dispelled.

The dining room itself, although perhaps sufficiently comfortable and of good dimensions, had nothing too much of elegance about it. For example, the floor was uncarpeted; in France, however, a carpet is frequently dispensed with. The windows, too, were without curtains; the shutters, being shut, were securely fastened with iron bars, applied diagonally, after the fashion of our shop-shutters. The apartment, I observed, formed, in itself, a wing of the *chateau*, and thus the windows were on three sides of the parallelogram, the door being at the other. There were no less than ten windows in all.

The table was superbly set out. It was loaded with plate, and more than loaded with delicacies. The profusion was absolutely barbaric. There were meats enough to have feasted the Anakim. Never, in all my life, had I witnessed so lavish, so wasteful an expenditure of the good things of life. There seemed very little taste, however, in the arrangements; and my eyes, accustomed to quiet lights, were sadly offended by the prodigious glare of a multitude of wax candles, which, in silver *candelabra*, were deposited upon the table, and all about the room, wherever it was possible to find a place. There were several active servants in attendance; and, upon a large table, at the farther end of the apartment, were seated seven or eight people with fiddles, fifes, trombones, and a drum. These fellows annoyed me very much, at intervals, during the repast, by an infinite variety of noises, which were intended for music, and which appeared to afford much entertainment to all present, with the exception of myself.

Upon the whole, I could not help thinking that there was much of the *bizarre* about every thing I saw—but then the world is made up of all kinds of persons, with all modes of thought, and all sorts of conventional customs. I had traveled, too, so much, as to be quite an adept at the *nil admirari*; so I took my seat very coolly at the right hand of my host, and, having an excellent appetite, did justice to the good cheer set before me.

The conversation, in the meantime, was spirited and general. The ladies, as usual, talked a great deal. I soon found that nearly all the company were well educated; and my host was a world of good-humored anecdote in himself. He seemed quite willing to speak of his position as superintendent of a *Maison de Santé*; and, indeed, the topic of lunacy was, much to my surprise, a favorite one with all present. A great many amusing stories were told, having reference to the *whims* of the patients.

"We had a fellow here once," said a fat little gentleman, who sat at my right—"a fellow that fancied himself a teapot; and by the way, is it not especially singular how often this particular crotchet has entered the brain of a lunatic? There is scarcely an insane asylum in France which cannot supply a human tea-pot. *Our* gentleman was a Britannia-ware teapot, and was careful to polish himself every morning with buckskin and whiting."

"And then," said a tall man just opposite, "we had here, not long ago, a person who had taken it into his head that he was a donkey—which allegorically speaking, you will say, was quite true. He was a troublesome patient; and we had much ado to keep him within bounds. For a long time he would eat nothing but thistles; but of this idea we soon cured him by insisting upon his eating nothing else. Then he was perpetually kicking out his heels—so—so—"

"Mr. De Kock! I will thank you to behave yourself!" here interrupted an old lady, who sat next to the speaker. "Please keep your feet to yourself! You have spoiled my brocade! Is it necessary, pray, to illustrate a remark in so practical a style? Our friend here can surely comprehend you without all this. Upon my word, you are nearly as great a donkey as the poor unfortunate imagined himself. Your acting is very natural, as I live."

"*Mille pardons! Ma'm'selle!*" replied Mr. De Kock, thus addressed—"a thousand pardons! I had no intention of offending. Ma'm'selle Laplace—Monsieur De Kock will do himself the honor of taking wine with you."

Here Monsieur De Kock bowed low, kissed his hand with much ceremony, and took wine with Ma'm'selle Laplace.

"Allow me, *mon ami,*" now said Monsieur Maillard, addressing myself, "allow me to send you a morsel of this veal *á la St. Menhoult*—you will find it particularly fine."

At this instant three sturdy waiters had just succeeded in depositing safely upon the table an enormous dish, or trencher, containing what I supposed to be the "*monstrum horrendum, informe, ingens, cui lumen ademptum.*" A closer scrutiny assured me, however, that it was only a small calf roasted whole, and set upon its knees, with an apple in its mouth, as is the English fashion of dressing a hare.

"Thank you, no," I replied; "to say the truth, I am not particularly partial to veal *á la St.*—what is it?—for I do not find that it altogether agrees with me. I will change my plate, however, and try some of the rabbit."

There were several sidedishes on the table containing what appeared to be the ordinary French rabbit—a very delicious *morceau,* which I can recommend.

"Pierre," cried the host, "change this gentleman's plate, and give him a sidepiece of this rabbit *au-chat.*"

"Why, thank you—upon second thoughts, no. I will just help myself to some of the ham."

There is no knowing what one eats, thought I to myself, at the tables of these people of the province. I will have none of their rabbit *au-chat*—and, for the matter of that, none of their *cat-au-rabbit* either.

"And then," said a cadaverous-looking personage, near the foot of the table, taking up the thread of conversation where it had been broken off, "and then, among other oddities, we had a patient, once upon a time, who very pertinaciously maintained himself to be a Cordova cheese, and went about, with a knife in his hand, soliciting his friends to try a small slice from the middle of his leg."

"He was a great fool, beyond doubt," interposed some one, "but not to be compared with a certain individual whom we all know, with the exception of this strange gentleman. I mean the man who took himself for a bottle of champagne, and always went off with a pop and a fizz, in this fashion."

Here the speaker, very rudely, as I thought, put his right thumb in his left cheek, withdrew it with a sound resembling the popping of a cork, and then, by dexterous movement of the tongue upon the teeth, created a sharp hissing and fizzing, which lasted for several minutes, in imitation of the frothing of champagne. This behavior, I saw plainly, was not very pleasing to Monsieur Maillard; but that gentleman said nothing, and the conversation was resumed by a very lean little man in a big wig.

"And then there was an ignoramus," said he, "who mistook himself for a frog; which, by the way, he resembled in no little degree. I wish you could have seen him sir,"—here the speaker addressed myself—"it would have done your heart good to see the natural airs that he put on. Sir, if that man was *not* a frog, I can only observe that it is a pity he was not. His croak thus—o-o-o-o-gh—o-o-o-o-gh—was the finest note in the world—B flat; and when he put his elbows upon the table thus—after taking a glass or two of wine—and distended his mouth, thus, and rolled up his eyes, thus, and winked them with excessive rapidity, thus, why then, sir, I take it upon myself to say, positively, that you would have been lost in admiration of the genius of the man."

"I have no doubt of it," I said.

"And then," said somebody else, "then there was Petit Gaillard, who thought himself a pinch of snuff, and was truly distressed because he could not take himself between his own finger and thumb."

"And then there was Jules Desoulieres, who was a very singular genius, indeed, and went mad with the idea that he was a pumpkin. He persecuted the cook to make him up into pies—a thing which the cook indignantly refused to do. For my part, I am by no means sure that a pumpkin pie *à la Desoulieres* would not have been very capital eating indeed!"

"You astonish me!" said I; and I looked inquisitively at Monsieur Maillard.

"Ha! ha! ha!" said that gentleman—"he! he! he!-hi! hi! hi!—ho! ho! ho!—hu! hu! hu!!—very good indeed! You must not be astonished, *mon ami*; our friend here is a wit—a *drôle*—you must not understand him to the letter."

"And then," said some other one of the party,—"then there was Bouffon Le Grand—another extraordinary personage in his way. He grew deranged through love, and fancied himself possessed with two heads. One of these he maintained to be the head of Cicero; the other he imagined a composite one, being Demosthenes' from the top of the forehead to the mouth, and Lord Brougham's from the mouth to the chin. It is not impossible that he was wrong; but he would have convinced you of his being in the right; for he was a man of great eloquence. He had an absolute passion for oratory, and could not refrain from display. For example, he used to leap upon the dinner-table thus, and—and—"

Here a friend, at the side of the speaker, put a hand upon his shoulder and whispered a few words in his ear; upon which he ceased talking with great suddenness, and sank back within his chair.

"And then," said the friend who had whispered, "there was Boullard, the teetotum. I call him the teetotum because, in fact, he was seized with the droll, but not altogether irrational, crotchet, that he had been converted into a teetotum. You would have roared with laughter to see him spin. He would turn round upon one heel by the hour, in this manner—so—"

Here the friend whom he had just interrupted by a whisper, performed an exactly similar office for himself.

"But then," cried an old lady, at the top of her voice, "your Monsieur Boullard was a madman, and a very silly madman at best; for who, allow me to ask you, ever heard of a human teetotum? The thing is absurd. Madame Joyeuse was a more sensible person, as you know. She had a crotchet, but it was instinct with common sense, and gave pleasure to all who had the honor of her acquaintance. She found, upon mature deliberation, that, by some accident, she had been turned into a chicken-cock; but, as such, she behaved with propriety. She flapped her wings with prodigious effect—so—so—so—and, as for her crow, it was delicious! Cock-a-doodle-doo!—cock-a-doodle-do—cock-a doodle-de-doo-doo-doo-doo-o-o-o-o-o-o!"

"Madame Joyeuse, I will thank you to behave yourself!" here interrupted our host, very angrily. "You can either conduct yourself as a lady should do, or you can quit the table forthwith—take your choice."

The lady (whom I was much astonished to hear addressed as Madame Joyeuse, after the description of Madame Joyeuse she had just given) blushed up to the eyebrows, and seemed exceedingly abashed at the reproof. She hung down her head, and said not a syllable in reply. But another and younger lady resumed the theme. It was my beautiful girl of the little parlor.

"Oh, Madame Joyeuse *was* a fool!" she exclaimed, "but there was really much sound sense, after all, in the opinion of Eugenie Salsafette. She was a very beautiful and painfully modest young lady, who thought the ordinary mode of habiliment indecent, and wished to dress herself, always, by getting outside instead of inside of her clothes. It is a thing very easily done, after all. You have only to do so—and then so—so—so—and then so—so—so—and then—"

"Mon dieu! Ma'm'selle Salsafette!" here cried a dozen voices at once. "What *are* you about?—forbear!—that is sufficient!—we see, very plainly, how it is done!—hold! hold!" and several persons were already leaping from their seats to withhold Ma'm'selle Salsafette from putting herself upon a par with the Medicean Venus, when the point was very effectually and suddenly accomplished by a series of loud screams, or yells, from some portion of the main body of the *chateau*.

My nerves were very much affected, indeed, by these yells; but the rest of the company I really pitied. I never saw any set of reasonable people so thoroughly frightened in my life. They all grew as pale as so many corpses, and, shrinking within their seats, sat quivering and gibbering with terror, and listening for a repetition of the sound. It came again—louder and seemingly nearer—and then a third time *very* loud, and then a fourth time with a vigor evidently diminished. At this apparent dying away of the noise, the spirits of the company were immediately regained, and all was life and anecdote as before. I now ventured to inquire the cause of the disturbance.

"A mere *bagatelle*," said Monsieur Maillard. "We are used to these things, and care really very little about them. The lunatics, every now and then, get up a howl in concert; one starting another, as is sometimes the case with a bevy of dogs at night. It occasionally happens, however, that the *concerto* yells are succeeded by a simultaneous effort at breaking loose; when, of course, some little danger is to be apprehended."

"And how many have you in charge?"

"At present we have not more than ten, altogether."

"Principally females, I presume?"

"Oh, no—every one of them men, and stout fellows, too, I can tell you."

"Indeed! I have always understood that the majority of lunatics were of the gentler sex?"

"It is generally so, but not always. Some time ago, there were about twenty-seven patients here; and, of that number, no less than eighteen were women; but lately, matters have changed very much, as you see."

"Yes—have changed very much as you see," here interrupted the gentleman who had broken the shins of Ma'm'selle Laplace.

"Yes—have changed very much, as you see!" chimed in the whole company at once.

"Hold your tongues, every one of you!" said my host, in a great rage. Whereupon the whole company maintained a dead silence for nearly a minute. As for one lady, she obeyed Monsieur Maillard to the letter, and thrusting out her tongue, which was an excessively long one, held it very resignedly, with both hands, until the end of the entertainment.

"And this gentlewoman," said I, to Monsieur Maillard, bending over and addressing him in a whisper—"this good lady who has just spoken, and who gives us the cock-a-doodle-de-doo—she, I presume, is harmless—quite harmless, eh?"

"Harmless!" ejaculated he, in unfeigned surprise, "why—why. What *can* you mean?"

"Only slightly touched?" said I, touching my head. "I take it for granted that she is not particularly—not dangerously affected, eh?"

"*Mon dieu!* what *is* it you imagine? This lady, my particular old friend Madame Joyeuse, is as absolutely sane as myself. She has her little eccentricities, to be sure—but then, you know, all old women—all *very* old women—are more or less eccentric!"

"To be sure," said I—"to be sure—and then the rest of these ladies and gentlemen—"

"Are my friends and keepers," interrupted Monsieur Maillard, drawing himself up with hauteur—"my very good friends and assistants."

"What! All of them?" I asked—"the women and all?"

"Assuredly," he said—"we could not do at all without the women; they are the best lunatic nurses in the world; they have a way of their own, you know; their bright eyes have a marvelous effect,—something like the fascination of the snake, you know."

"To be sure," said I,—"to be sure! They behave a little odd, eh?—they are a little *queer,* eh?—don't you think so?"

"Odd!—queer!—why, do you *really* think so? We are not very prudish, to be sure, here in the South—do pretty much as we please—enjoy life, and all that sort of thing, you know—"

"To be sure," said I,—"to be sure."

"And then, perhaps, this *Clos de Vougeot* is a little heady, you know—a little *strong*—you understand, eh?"

"To be sure," said I,—"to be sure. By the by, Monsieur, did I understand you to say that the system you have adopted in place of the celebrated soothing system was one of very rigorous severity?"

"By no means. Our confinement is necessarily close; but the treatment— the medical treatment, I mean—is rather agreeable to the patients than otherwise."

"And the new system is one of your own invention?"

"Not altogether. Some portions of it are referable to Doctor Tarr, of whom you have, necessarily, heard; and, again, there are modifications in my plan which I am happy to acknowledge as belonging of right to the celebrated Fether, with whom, if I mistake not, you have the honor of an intimate acquaintance."

"I am quite ashamed to confess," I replied, "that I have never even heard the names of either gentleman before."

"Good heavens!" ejaculated my host, drawing back his chair abruptly, and uplifting his hands. "I surely do not hear you aright! You did not intend to say, eh? that you had never *heard* either of the learned Doctor Tarr, or of the celebrated Professor Fether?"

"I am forced to acknowledge my ignorance," I replied; "but the truth should be held inviolate above all things. Nevertheless, I feel humbled to the dust, not to be acquainted with the works of these, no doubt, extraordinary men. I will seek out their writings forthwith, and peruse them with deliberate care. Monsieur Maillard, you have really—I must confess it—you have *really*—made me ashamed of myself!"

And this was the fact.

"Say no more, my good young friend," he said kindly, pressing my hand,— "join me now in a glass of Sauterne."

We drank. The company followed our example without stint. They chatted—they jested—they laughed—they perpetuated a thousand absurdities—the fiddles shrieked—the drum row-de-dowed—the trombones bellowed like so many brazen bulls of Phalaris—and the whole scene, growing gradually worse and worse, as the wines gained the ascendancy, became at length a sort of pandemonium *in petto*. In the meantime, Monsieur Maillard and myself, with some bottles of Sauterne and Vougeot between us, continued our conversation at the top of the voice. A word spoken in an ordinary key stood no more chance of being heard than the voice of a fish from the bottom of Niagara Falls.

"And, sir," said I, screaming in his ear, "you mentioned something before dinner about the danger incurred in the old system of soothing. How is that?"

"Yes," he replied, "there was, occasionally, very great danger indeed. There is no accounting for the caprices of madmen; and, in my opinion as well as that of Dr. Tarr and Professor Fether, it is *never* safe to permit them to run at large unattended. A lunatic may be 'soothed,' as it is called, for a time, but, in the end, he is very apt to become obstreperous. His cunning, too, is proverbial and great. If he has a project in view, he conceals his design with a marvelous wisdom; and the dexterity with which he counterfeits sanity presents, to the metaphysician, one of the most singular problems in the study of mind. When a madman appears *thoroughly* sane, indeed, it is high time to put him in a straitjacket."

"But the *danger*, my dear sir, of which you were speaking—in your own experience—during your control of this house—have you had practical reason to think liberty hazardous in the case of a lunatic?"

"Here?—in my own experience?—why, I may say, yes. For example—no *very* long while ago, a singular circumstance occurred in this very house. The 'soothing system,' you know, was then in operation, and the patients were at large. They behaved remarkably well—especially so—any one of sense might have known that some devilish scheme was brewing from that particular fact, that the fellows behaved so *remarkably* well. And, sure enough, one fine morning the keepers found themselves pinioned hand and foot, and thrown into the cells, where they were attended, as if *they* were the lunatics, by the lunatics themselves, who had usurped the offices of the keepers."

"You don't tell me so! I never heard of any thing so absurd in my life!"

"Fact—it all came to pass by means of a stupid fellow—a lunatic—who, by some means, had taken it into his head that he had invented a better system of government than any ever heard of before—of lunatic government, I mean. He wished to give his invention a trial, I suppose, and so he persuaded the rest of the patients to join him in a conspiracy for the overthrow of the reigning powers."

"And he really succeeded?"

"No doubt of it. The keepers and the kept were soon made to exchange places. Not that exactly either, for the madmen had been free, but the keepers were shut up in cells forthwith, and treated, I am sorry to say, in a very cavalier manner."

"But I presume a counterrevolution was soon effected. This condition of things could not have long existed. The country people in the neighborhood—visitors coming to see the establishment—would have given the alarm."

"There you are out. The head rebel was too cunning for that. He admitted no visitors at all—with the exception, one day, of a very stupid-looking young gentleman of whom he had no reason to be afraid. He let him in to see the place—just by way of variety—to have a little fun with him. As soon as he had gammoned him sufficiently, he let him out, and sent him about his business."

"And *how* long, then, did the madmen reign?"

"Oh, a very long time, indeed—a month certainly—how much longer I can't precisely say. In the meantime, the lunatics had a jolly season of it—that you may swear. They doffed their own shabby clothes, and made free with the family wardrobe and jewels. The cellars of the *chateau* were well stocked with wine; and these madmen are just the devils that know how to drink it. They lived well, I can tell you."

"And the treatment—what was the particular species of treatment which the leader of the rebels put into operation?"

"Why, as for that, a madman is not necessarily a fool, as I have already observed; and it is my honest opinion that his treatment was a much better treatment than that which it superseded. It was a very capital system indeed—simple—neat—no trouble at all—in fact it was delicious—it was—"

Here my host's observations were cut short by another series of yells, of the same character as those which had previously disconcerted us. This time, however, they seemed to proceed from persons rapidly approaching.

"Gracious heavens!" I ejaculated—"the lunatics have most undoubtedly broken loose."

"I very much fear it is so," replied Monsieur Maillard, now becoming excessively pale. He had scarcely finished the sentence, before loud shouts and imprecations were heard beneath the windows; and, immediately afterward, it became evident that some persons outside were endeavoring to gain entrance into the room. The door was beaten with what appeared to be a sledgehammer, and the shutters were wrenched and shaken with prodigious violence.

A scene of the most terrible confusion ensued. Monsieur Maillard, to my excessive astonishment, threw himself under the sideboard. I had expected more resolution at his hands. The members of the orchestra, who, for the last fifteen minutes, had been seemingly too much intoxicated to do duty, now sprang all at once to their feet and to their instruments, and, scrambling upon their table, broke out, with one accord, into, "Yankee Doodle," which they performed, if not exactly in tune, at least with an energy superhuman, during the whole of the uproar.

Meantime, upon the main dining table, among the bottles and glasses, leaped the gentleman who, with such difficulty, had been restrained from leaping there before. As soon as he fairly settled himself, he commenced an oration, which, no doubt, was a very capital one, if it could only have been heard. At the same moment, the man with the teetotum predilection, set himself to spinning around the apartment, with immense energy, and with arms outstretched at right angles with his body; so that he had all the air of a teetotum in fact, and knocked everybody down that happened to get in his way. And now, too, hearing an incredible pooping and fizzing of champagne, I discovered at length, that it proceeded from the person who performed the bottle of that delicate drink during dinner. And then, again, the frog-man croaked away as if the salvation of his soul depended upon every note that he uttered. And, in the midst of all this, the continuous braying of a donkey arose over all. As for my old friend, Madame Joyeuse, I really could have wept for the poor lady, she appeared so terribly perplexed. All she did, however, was to stand up in a corner, by the fireplace, and sing out incessantly at the top of her voice, "Cock-a-doodle-de-dooooooh!"

And now came the climax—the catastrophe of the drama. As no resistance, beyond whooping and yelling and cock-a-doodling, was offered to the encroachments of the party without, the ten windows were very speedily, and almost simultaneously, broken in. But I shall never forget the emotions of wonder and horror with which I gazed, when, leaping through these windows, and down among us *pele-mele*, fighting, stamping, scratching, and howling, there rushed a perfect army of what I took to be chimpanzees, Ourang-Outangs, or big black baboons of the Cape of Good Hope.

I received a terrible beating—after which I rolled under a sofa and lay still. After lying there some fifteen minutes, however during which time I listened with all my ears to what was going on in the room, I came to same satisfactory *denouement* of this tragedy. Monsieur Maillard, it appeared, in giving me the account of the lunatic who had excited his fellows to rebellion, had been merely relating his own exploits. This gentleman had, indeed, some two or three years before, been the superintendent of the establishment; but grew crazy himself, and so became a patient. This fact was unknown to the travelling companion who introduced me. The keepers, ten in number, having been suddenly overpowered, were first well tarred, then carefully feathered, and then shut up in underground cells. They had been so imprisoned for more than a month, during which period Monsieur Maillard had generously allowed them not only tar and feathers (which constituted his "system"), but some bread and abundance of water. The latter was pumped on them daily. At length, one escaping through a sewer, gave freedom to all the rest.

The "soothing system," with important modifications, has been resumed at the *chateau*; yet I cannot help agreeing with Monsieur Maillard, that his own "treatment" was a very capital one of its kind. As he justly observed, it was "simple—neat—and gave no trouble at all—not the least."

I have only to add that, although I have searched every library in Europe for the works of Doctor *Tarr* and Professor *Fether*, I have, up to the present day, utterly failed in my endeavors to produce a copy.

E. T. A. Hoffmann (1776–1822)

Hoffmann was a German writer, composer, caricaturist, and painter. He was best known for his stories in which supernatural characters reveal the hidden secrets of people. Hoffmann's early career was devoted to music and painting. He wrote a symphony, nine operas, and two masses. He did not become interested in writing until later in his life. His most popular story is *The Nutcracker and the Mouse King*, which, set to music by Tchaikovsky, has become a Christmas classic. Hoffmann's short stories are among the first fiction related to horror and fantasy. His works often deal with insanity, the occult, and truths about reality. His work influenced such well-known psychologists as Carl Jung and Sigmund Freud. The selection noted here is from *The Serapion Brethren*, written in 1818–21 it clearly deals with insanity and raises probing questions about the nature of reality.

"The Story of Serapion" (from *The Serapion Bretheren)*

"You know that some years ago I spent a considerable time in B___, a place in one of the pleasantest districts of the South of Germany. As my habit is, I used to take long walks in the surrounding country by myself, without any guide, though I should often have been better for one. On one of these occasions I got into a piece of thickly wooded country and lost my way; the further I went, the less could I discover the smallest vestige of a human footstep. At last the wood grew less thick, and I saw, not far from me, a man in a hermit's brown robe, with a broad straw hat on his head, and a long, wild black beard, sitting on a rock by the side of a deep ravine, gazing, with folded hands, thoughtfully into the distance. This sight had something so strange, unexpected, and out of the common about it that I felt a shiver of eeriness and awe. One can scarcely help such a feeling when what one has only heretofore seen in pictures, or read of in books, suddenly appears before one's eyes in actual, everyday life. Here was an anchorite of the early ages of Christianity, in the body, seated in one of Salvator Rosa's wild mountain scenes. But it soon occurred to me that probably a monk on his peregrinations was nothing uncommon in that part of the country. So I walked up to him, and asked him if he could tell me the shortest way out of the wood to the high road leading to B___. He looked at me from head to foot with gloomy glance, and said, in a hollow and solemn voice:

"'I know well that it is merely an idle curiosity to see me, and to hear me speak which has led you to this desert. But you must perceive that I have no time to talk with you now. My friend Ambrosius of Camaldoli is returning to Alexandria. Travel with him.'

"With which he rose and walked down into the ravine."

"I felt as if I must be in a dream. Presently I heard the sound of wheels close by. I made my way through the thickets, and found myself in a forest track, where I saw a countryman going along in a cart. I overtook him, and he shortly brought me to the high road leading to B___. As we went along I told him of my adventure, and asked if he knew who the extraordinary man in the forest was.

"'Oh, sir,' he said, 'that was the worthy man who calls himself Priest Serapion, who has been living in these woods for some years, in a little hut he built himself. People say he's not quite right in his head, but he is a nice, good gentleman, never does any harm, and edifies us of the village with pious discourses, giving us all the good advice that he can.'

"I had come across the anchorite some six or eight miles from B___, so I concluded that something must be known of him there, and this proved to be the case. Dr. S___ told me all the story. This hermit had once been one of the most brilliant intellects, one of the most universally accomplished men in M___; and belonging, as he did, to a very distinguished family, he was naturally appointed to an important diplomatic post as soon as he had completed his studies: the duties of his office he discharged with great ability and energy. Moreover, he had remarkable poetical gifts, and everything he wrote was inspired by a most brilliant fancy, a mind and imagination which sounded the profoundest depths of all subjects. His incomparable humor, and the unusual charm of his character made him the most delightful of companions imaginable. He had risen from step to step of his career, and was on the point of being dispatched on an important diplomatic mission, when he disappeared, in the most incomprehensible fashion, from M___. All searching for him was fruitless, and conjecture and inquiry were baffled by a combination of circumstances.

"After a time there appeared amongst the villages, in the depths of the Tyrolese mountains, a man in a brown robe, who preached in these hamlets, and then went away into the wildest parts of the forests, where he lived the life of a hermit. It chanced one day that Count P___ saw this man (who called himself Priest Serapion), and at once recognized him as his unfortunate nephew, who had disappeared from M___. He was taken into custody, became violent, and all the skill of the best doctors in M___ could do nothing to alleviate his terrible condition. He was taken to the lunatic asylum at B___ , and there the methodical system, based upon profound psychological knowledge, pursued by the medical man then in charge of that institution, succeeded in bringing about a condition of much less excitement, and greater quietness in the form of the malady. Whether this doctor, true to his theory, gave the patient an opportunity of escaping, or whether he himself found the means of doing so, escape he did, and was lost sight of for a considerable time.

"Serapion appeared, ultimately, in the country some eight miles from B___, where I had seen him; and the doctor declared that if any true compassion was to be shown him, he should not be again driven into a condition of wild excitement; but that, if he was to be at peace, and, after his fashion, happy, he should be left in these woods in perfect freedom, to do just as he liked; in which case he, the doctor, would be responsible for the consequences. Accordingly, the police authorities were content to leave him to a distant imperceptible supervision by the officials of the nearest village, and the result bore out what the doctor had said. Serapion built himself a little hut, pretty, and, under the circumstances, comfortable. He made chairs and tables, wove mats of rushes to lie upon, and laid out a garden where he grew flowers and vegetables. In all that did not touch the idea that he was the hermit Serapion who fled into the Theban desert in the days of the Emperor Decius, and suffered martyrdom in Alexandria, his mind was completely unaffected. He could carry on the most intellectual conversation, and often showed traces of the brilliant humor and charming individuality of character for which he had been remarkable in his former life. The aforesaid doctor declared him to be completely incurable, and strongly depreciated all attempts to restore him to the world and to his former pursuits and duties.

"You will readily understand that I could not drive this anchorite of mine out of my thoughts, and that I experienced an irresistible longing to see him again. But just picture to yourselves the excess of my folly. I had no less an undertaking in my mind than of attacking Serapion's fixed idea at its very roots. I read Pinel, Reil, every conceivable book on insanity which I could lay my hands on. I fondly believed that it might be reserved for *me*, an amateur psychologist and doctor, to cast some rays of light into Serapion's darkened intelligence. And I did not omit, either, to make myself acquainted with the stories of all the Serapions (there were no fewer than eight of them) treated of in the histories of saints and martyrs.

"Thus equipped, I set out one fine morning in search of my anchorite.

"I found him working in his garden with hoe and spade, singing a devotional song. Wild pigeons, for which he had strewed an abundant supply of food, were fluttering and cooing round him, and a young deer was peeping through the leaves on the trellis. He was evidently living in the closest intimacy with the woodland creatures. Not the faintest trace of insanity was visible in his face; it bore a quiet expression of remarkable serenity and happiness; and all this confirmed what Dr. S___ in B___ had told me. When he heard of my projected visit to the anchorite, he advised me to go some fine, bright, pleasant morning, because he said, his mind would be less troubled then and he would be more inclined to talk to a stranger, whereas at evening he would shun all intercourse with mankind.

"As soon as he saw me he laid down his spade, and came towards me in a kind and friendly manner. I said that, being weary with a longish journey, I should be glad if he would allow me to rest with him for a little while.

"'You are heartily welcome,' he said. 'The little which I can offer you in the shape of refreshment is at your service.'

"And he took me to a seat of moss in front of his hut, brought out a little table, set on bread, magnificent grapes, and a can of wine, and hospitably begged me to eat and drink. He sat down opposite to me, and ate bread with much appetite, washing it down with draughts of water.

"In good sooth I did not see how I was going to lead the conversation to my subject—how I was to bring my psychological science to bear upon this peaceful, happy man. At last I pulled myself together and began:

"'You style yourself Serapion, reverend sir?'

"' Yes, certainly,' he answered. 'The church has given me that name.'

"'Ancient ecclesiastical history,' I continued, 'mentions several celebrated holy men of that name. An abbot Serapion, known for his good works—the learned Bishop Serapion alluded to by Hieronimus in his book *De Viris Illustribus*. There was also a monk Serapion, who (as Heraclides relates in his *Paradise*) on one occasion, coming from the Theban desert to Rome, ordered a virgin, who had joined him—saying she had renounced the world and its pleasures—to prove this by walking with him naked in the streets of Rome, and repulsed her when she hesitated, saying, "You still live the life of Nature, and are careful for the opinions of mankind. Think not that you are anything great or have overcome the world." If I am not mistaken, reverend sir, this was the "filthy monk" (Heraclides himself so styles him) who suffered a terrible martyrdom under the Emperor Decius—his limbs being torn asunder at the joints, and his body thrown down from a lofty rock.'

"'That was so,' said Serapion, turning pale, and his eyes glowing with a somber fire. 'But Serapion the martyr had no connection with that monk, who, in the fury of his asceticism, did battle against human nature. *I* am Serapion the martyr, to whom you allude.'

"What?' I cried, with feigned surprise. 'You believe that you are that Serapion who suffered such a hideous martyrdom so many hundred years ago?'

"'That,' said Serapion with much calmness, 'may appear incredible to you, and I admit that it must sound very wonderful to many who cannot see further than the points of their noses. However, it is as I tell you. God's omnipotence permitted me to survive my martyrdom and to recover from its effects, because it was ordained, in His mysterious providence, that I had still to pass a certain period of my existence to His praise and glory, here in the Theban desert. There is nothing now to remind me of the tortures which I suffered except sometimes a severe headache, and occasional violent cramps and twitchings in my limbs.'

"'Now,' thought I, 'is the time to commence my cure.'

"I made a wide circumbendibus, and talked in an erudite style concerning the malady of 'Fixed Idea,' which attacks people, marring, like one single discord, the otherwise harmonious organisms. I spoke of the scientific man who could not be induced to rise from his chair for fear he would break the windows across the street with his nose. I mentioned the Abbot Molanus, who conversed most rationally upon every subject but would not leave his room because he thought he was a barleycorn and the hens would swallow him. I came to the fact that to confound oneself with some historical character was a frequent form of fixed Idea. 'Nothing more absurd and preposterous,' I said, 'could possibly be imagined than that a little bit of woodland country eight miles from B___, daily frequented by country folk, sportsmen, and people walking for exercise was the Theban desert, and he himself that ascetic who suffered martyrdom many centuries ago.'

"Serapion listened in silence. He seemed to feel what I said, and to be struggling with himself in deep reflection. So that I thought it was time to strike my decisive blow. I stood up, took him by both hands, and cried loudly and emphatically:

"'Count P___, awake from the pernicious dream which is enthralling you; throw off that abominable dress, and come back to your family which mourns your loss, and to the world where you have such important duties to discharge.'

Serapion gazed at me with a somber, penetrating gaze. Then a sarcastic smile played about his lips and cheeks, and he said, slowly and solemnly:

"'You have spoken, sir, long, and, as *you* consider, wisely and well. Allow *me*, in turn, to say a few words in reply. Saint Anthony, and all the men of the church who have withdrawn from the world into solitude, were often visited by vexing spirits, who, envying the inward peace and contentment of their souls, carried on with them lengthy contests, until they had to lie down conquered in the dust. And such is *my* fortune also. Every now and then there appear to me emissaries, sent by Satan, who try to persuade me that I am Count P___ of M___, and that I ought to betake myself to the life of Courts, and all sorts of unholiness. Were it not for the efficacy of prayer, I should take these people by the shoulders, turn them out of my little garden, and carefully barricade it against them. But I need not do so in your case; for *you* are, most unmistakably, the very feeblest of all the adversaries who have ever come to me, and I can vanquish *you* with your own weapons—those of ratiocination. It is insanity that is question between us. But if one of us two is suffering from that sad malady, it is evident that *you* are so in a much greater degree than I. You maintain that it is a case of Fixed Idea that I believe myself to be Serapion the martyr—and I am quite aware that many persons hold the same opinion, or pretend that they do. Now, if I am really insane, none but a lunatic can think that he could *argue* me out of the Fixed Idea which insanity has engendered in me. Were such a proceeding possible, there would soon be no madmen on the face of the earth, for men would be able to rule, and command, their mental power, which is not their own, but merely lent to them for a time by that Higher Power which disposes of them. But if I am *not* mad, and if I am really Serapion the martyr, it is insane to set about arguing me out of that, and leading me to adopt the Fixed Idea that I am Count P___ of M___. You say that Serapion the martyr lived several centuries ago, and that, consequently, I cannot be that martyr, presumably for the reason that human beings cannot remain so long on this earth. Well, as regards this, the notion of time is just as *relative* a notion as that of number; and I may say to you that, according to the notion of time which I have in *me*, it is scarcely three *hours* (or whatever appellation you may choose to give to divisions of time) since I was put to martyrdom by the Emperor Decius. But, leaving this on one side, can you assert, in opposition to me, that a life of such length as I say I have lived, is unexampled and contrary to human nature? Have you cognizance of the precise length of the life of every human being who has existed in all this wide world, that you can employ the expression 'unexampled' in this pert and decisive manner? Do you compare God's omnipotence to the wretched art of the clockmaker, who can't save his lifeless machinery from destruction? You say this place where we are is not the Theban desert, but a little woodland district eight miles from B___, daily frequented by country folk, sportsmen and others. *Prove* that to me.'

"Here I thought I had my man.

"Come with me,' said I, 'and in a couple of hours we shall be in B___, and what I assert will be proved.'

"'Poor blinded fool,' said Serapion. 'What a wide distance lies between us and B___! But put the case that I went with you to some town which you call B___; would you be able to convince me that we had been traveling for two hours only, and the place we had arrived at was really B___? If I were to assert that you were insane, and suppose the Theban desert is a little bit of wooded country, and far-away Alexandria the town of B___ in the south of Germany, what would you say in reply? Our old discussion would go on forever. Then there is another point which you ought seriously to consider. You must, I should suppose, perceive that I, who am talking with you, am leading the peaceful and happy life of a man reconciled with God. It is only after having passed through martyrdom that such a life dawns upon the soul. And if it has pleased the Almighty to cast a veil over what happened before my martyrdom, it is not a terrible and diabolical action to try to tear that veil away?'

"With all my wisdom, I stood confounded and silenced in the presence of this insane man! With the very rationality of his irrationality he had beaten me completely out of the field, and I saw the folly of my undertaking in all its fullness. Still more than that, I felt the reproach contained in what he had last said as deeply as I was astounded at the dim remembrance of his previous life which shone through it like some lofty, invulnerable higher spirit.

"Serapion seemed to be reading my thoughts, and, looking me full in the face with an expression of the greatest kindliness, he said:

"'I never took you for an evil-disposed adversary, and I see I was not mistaken. You may have been instigated by somebody—perhaps by the Evil One himself—to come here to vex and try me, but I am sure it was not a spontaneous act of yours. And perhaps the fact that you found me other than you expected, may have strengthened you in your expression of the doubts which you have suggested. Although I in no sense deviate from the devoutness beseeming him who has given up his life to God and the Church, that cynicism of asceticism into which many of my brethren have fallen—thereby giving proof of the weakness, nay, utter destruction of their mental vigor, instead of its boasted strength—is utterly foreign to me! You expected to find the Monk Serapion pale and haggard, wasted with fast and vigil, all the horror of visions, terrible as those which drove even St. Anthony to despair, in his somber face, with quivering knees scarce able to support him, in a filthy robe, stained with his blood. You find a placid, cheerful man. But I, too, have passed through those tortures, and have overcome them and survived. And when I awoke with shattered limbs and fractured skull, the spirit dawned, and shone bright within me, restoring my mind and my body to health. May it please Heaven speedily to grant to *you* also, my brother, even here on earth, a peace and happiness such as those which daily refresh and strengthen *me*. Have no dread of the terror of the deepest solitude. It is only there that a life like this can dawn upon the pious soul.'

"Serapion, who had spoken with genuine priestly unction, raised, in silence, his eyes to Heaven with an expression of blissful gratitude. How could I feel otherwise than awe-struck! A madman, congratulating himself on his condition, looking upon it as a priceless gift from Heaven, and, from the depths of his heart, wishing me a similar fate!

"I was on the point of leaving him, but he began in an altered tone, saying:

"'You would, probably, scarcely suppose that this wild inhospitable desert is often almost too full of the noise and bustle of life to be suitable for my silent meditations. Every day I receive visits from the most remarkable people of the most diverse kinds. Aristo was here yesterday, and Dante and Petrarch afterwards. And this evening I expect Evagrus, the celebrated father, with whom I shall discuss the most recent ecclesiastical affairs, as I did poetry yesterday. I often go up to the top of that hill there, whence the towers of Alendria are to be seen distinctly in clear weather, and the most wonderful and interesting events happen before my eyes. Many people have thought *that* incredible, too, and considered that I only *fancy* I see before me, in actual life, what is merely born in my mind and imagination. Now I say *that* is the most incomprehensible piece of folly that can exist. What is it, except the mind, which takes cognizance of what happens around us in time and space? What is it that hears, and feels, and sees? Is it not the lifeless mechanism which we call eyes, ears, hands, etc., and not the mind? Does the mind give form and shape to that peculiar world of its own which has space and time for its conditions of existence, and *then* hand over the functions of seeing, hearing, etc., to some *other* principle inherent in us? How illogical! Therefore, if it is the mind only which takes cognizance of events around us, it follows that that which it has taken cognizance of *has* actually occurred. Last evening only, Aristo was speaking of the images of his fancy, and saying he had created in his brain forms and events which had never existed in time and space. I at once denied the possibility of this, and he was obliged to allow that it was only from lack of a higher knowledge that a poet would box up within the narrow limits of his brain that which, by virtue of his peculiar seer gift, he was enabled to see in full life before him. But the complete acquirement of this higher knowledge only comes after martyrdom, and is strengthened by the life in profound solitude. You don't appear to agree with me; probably you don't understand me here. Indeed how could a child of this world, however well disposed, understand an anchorite consecrated in all his works and ways to God. Let me tell you what happened before my eyes, as I was standing this morning at sunrise at the top of that hill.'

"He then related a regular romance, with a plot and incidents such as only the most imaginative poet could have constructed. The characters and events stood out with such a vivid, plastic relief, that it was impossible—carried away as one was by the magic spell of them—to help believing, as if in the species of dream, that Serapion had actually witnessed them from the hilltop. This romance was succeeded by another, and that by another, by which time the sun stood high above us in noontide sky, Serapion then rose from his seat, and looking into the distance, said: 'Yonder comes my brother Hilarion, who, in his overstrictness, always blames me for being too much given to the society of strangers.'

"I understood the hint, and took my leave, asking if I should be allowed to pay him another visit. Serapion answered with a gentle smile, 'My friend, I thought you would be eager to get away from this wilderness, so little adapted to your mode of life. But if it is your pleasure to take up your abode for a time in my neighborhood, you will always be welcome to my cottage and my little garden. Perhaps it may be granted to convert him who came to me as an adversary. Farewell, my friend.'

"I am wholly unable to characterize the impression which my visit to him had made upon me. Whilst his condition, his methodical madness in which he found the joy of his life, produced the weirdest effect upon me, his extraordinary poetical genius filled me with amazement, and his kindly, peaceful happiness, instinct with the quietest resignation of the purest mind, touched me unspeakably. I thought of Ophelia's sorrowful words:

"'O what a noble mind is here o'erthrown! etc.'

Yet I could not make plaint against the Omnipotence, which probably had, in this mysterious fashion, steered his bark away from reefs, which might have wrecked it, into this secure haven.

"The oftener I went to see him, the more attached to him I became. I always found him happy, and disposed to converse, and I took great care never again to essay my role of the psychological doctor. It was wonderful with what acuteness and penetration he spoke of life in all its aspects, and most remarkable of all, how he deduced historical events from causes wholly remote from all ordinary theories on the subject. When sometimes—notwithstanding the striking acuteness of those divinations of his—I took it upon me to object that no work on history made any mention of the circumstances which he alluded to, he would answer, with his quiet smile, that probably no historian in the world knew as much about them as he did, seeing that he had them from the very lips of the people concerned, when they came to see him.

"I was obliged to leave B___ and it was three years before I could go back there. It was late in Autumn, about the middle of November—the 14[th,] if I do not mistake—when I set out to pay my anchorite a visit. Whilst I was still at a distance, I heard the sound of the little bell which hung above his hut, and was filled with gloomy forebodings, without apparent cause. At last I reached the cottage and went in.

"Serapion was lying on his mat, with his hands folded on his breast. I thought he was sleeping, and went softly up to him. Then I saw that he was dead."

Discussion Questions

1.   At what point in the story of Dr. Tarr and Professor Fether did you first begin to suspect that all was not well at the Maison de Santé? What specific behaviors first raised your suspicions? A significant consideration in completing a mental status examination includes an assessment of affect and mood. Write an assessment of the affect and mood of three of the characters at the Maison de Santé.

2.   Is it possible that the exact same behavior can be considered both normal and abnormal? How? When? Why? Give two specific examples of such behavior from each story in this chapter.

3.   Discuss the reasons that Serapion abandoned his life of responsibility and authority for the life of a hermit. Do you consider his reasoning to be logical or irrational? Why or why not?

4.   Cultural awareness is an important factor in assessment and diagnosis. What issues related to Serapion's cultural background should be considered in regard to making a diagnostic assessment in his case?

5.   If you were to consider Serapion's behavior disturbed, what would be your diagnosis of his behavior? List the specific behaviors from the story that you would use to make your diagnosis.

Chapter 2

Cognitive Disorders

The cognitive impairments include three disorders: delirium, dementia, and amnestic disorders. Cognitive impairment is the basic symptom of these disorders. Memory loss, disorientation, poor judgment, confusion, and general loss of intellectual functions are the basic problems experienced.

Delirium

Delirium in Latin means "to rave" or "to be crazy." Disorientation and recent memory loss characterize delirium. The basic symptom is impairment in consciousness and a reduced awareness of the environment. Delirium is related to an underlying etiological factor, which may or may not be recognized. Causes include a general medical condition such as an infection, substance-induced delirium, or multiple problems occurring simultaneously, such as head trauma and cardiac disease. Delirium has a sudden onset, a brief and fluctuating course, and rapid improvement if the underlying cause is found and treated. Delirium is most often a reversible condition. The presence of delirium is a bad prognostic sign, with a one-year mortality rate being reported as high as 50 percent.

Charles Dickens (1812–1870)

Charles Dickens was born in Landport, Hampshire, England in 1812. His father, John Dickens, was chronically in debt and was imprisoned at the Marshalsea debtors' prison in 1824, when Charles was only twelve years old. He was removed from school and sent to work at a boot-blacking factory earning six shillings a week to help support the family. Later Dickens reflected on this period as the most terrible time of his life. His childhood poverty and feelings of abandonment greatly influenced his views on social reform and were often reflected in his works.

Dickens began his career as a fiction writer in 1833 when his articles and short stories began to appear in periodicals. Dickens was a keen observer of people, which helped him to create the colorful characters for which he became famous. Many of his novels first appeared in monthly installments, including *The Pickwick Papers*, excerpted here, which appeared from April 1836 to November 1837.

Dickens spent much time traveling, writing, and lecturing against many of the social evils of his day, including debtors' prisons and child labor. He wrote fifteen major novels and countless short stories and articles before his death in 1870. In this selection Dickens provides us with a wonderfully written account of the delirium often encountered in the alcoholic.

"The Stroller's Tale" (from *The Pickwick Papers*)

"There is nothing of the marvelous in what I am going to relate," said the dismal man; "there is nothing even uncommon in it. Want and sickness are too common in many stations of life, to deserve more notice than is usually bestowed on the most ordinary vicissitudes of human nature. I have thrown these few notes together, because the subject of them was well known to me for many years. I traced his progress downwards, step by step, until at last he reached that excess of destitution from which he never rose again.

"The man of whom I speak was a low pantomime actor; and, like many people of his class, an habitual drunkard. In his better days, before he had become enfeebled by dissipation and emaciated by disease, he had been in receipt of a good salary, which, if he had been careful and prudent, he might have continued to receive for some years—not many; because these men either die early, or, by unnaturally taxing their bodily energies, lose, prematurely, those physical powers on which alone they can depend for subsistence. His besetting sin gained so fast upon him, however, that it was found impossible to employ him in the situations in which he really was useful to the theater. The public-house had a fascination for him which he could not resist. Neglected disease and hopeless poverty were as certain to be his portion as death itself, if he persevered in the same course; yet he *did* persevere, and the result may be guessed. He could obtain no engagement, and he wanted bread.

"Everybody who is at all acquainted with theatrical matters knows what a host of shabby, poverty-stricken men hang about the stage of a large establishment—not regularly engaged actors, but ballet people, procession men, tumblers, and so forth, who are taken on during the run of a pantomime, or an Easter piece, and are then discharged, until the production of some heavy spectacle occasions a new demand for their services. To this mode of life the man was compelled to resort; and taking the chair every night, at some low theatrical house, at once put him in possession of a few shillings more weekly, and enabled him to gratify his old propensity. Even this resource shortly failed him; his irregularities were too great to admit of his earning the wretched pittance he might thus have procured, and he was actually reduced to a state bordering on starvation, only procuring a trifle occasionally by borrowing it of some old companion, or by obtaining an appearance at one or other of the commonest of the minor theaters; and when he did earn anything, it was spent in the old way.

"About this time, and when he had been existing for upwards of a year no one knew how, I had a short engagement at one of the theatres on the Surrey side of the water, and here I saw this man, whom I had lost sight of for some time; for I had been traveling in the provinces, and he had been skulking in the lanes and alleys of London. I was dressed to leave the house, and was crossing the stage on my way out, when he tapped me on the shoulder. Never shall I forget the repulsive sight that met my eye when I turned round. He was dressed for the pantomime, in all the absurdity of a clown's costume. The spectral figures in the Dance of Death, the most frightful shapes that the ablest painter ever portrayed on canvas, never presented an appearance half so ghastly. His bloated body and shrunken legs—their deformity enhanced a hundred fold by the fantastic dress—the glassy eyes, contrasting fearfully with the thick white paint with which the face was besmeared: the grotesquely-ornamented head, trembling with paralysis, and the long skinny hands, rubbed with white chalk—all gave him a hideous and unnatural appearance, of which no description could convey an adequate idea, and which, to this day, I shudder to think of. His voice was hollow and tremulous, as he took me aside, and in broken words recounted a long catalogue of sickness and privations, terminating, as usual, with an urgent request for the loan of a trifling sum of money. I put a few shillings in his hand, and, as I turned away, I heard the roar of laughter which followed his first tumble on to the stage.

"A few nights afterwards, a boy put a dirty scrap of paper in my hand, on which were scrawled a few words in pencil, intimating that the man was dangerously ill, and begging me, after the performance, to see him at his lodgings in some street—I forget the name of it now—at no great distance from the theater. I promised to comply, as soon as I could get away; and, after the curtain fell, sallied forth on my melancholy errand.

"It was late, for I had been playing in the last piece; and, as it was a benefit night, the performances had been protracted to an unusual length. It was a dark cold night, with a chill damp wind, which blew the rain heavily against the windows and house-fronts. Pools of water had collected in the narrow and little-frequented streets, and as many of the thinly-scattered oil-lamps had been blown out by the violence of the wind, the walk was not only a comfortless, but most uncertain one. I had fortunately taken the right course, however, and succeeded, after a little difficulty, in finding the house to which I had been directed—a coal shed, with one story above it, in the back room of which lay the object of my search.

"A wretched-looking woman, the man's wife, met me on the stairs, and, telling me that he had just fallen into a kind of doze, led me softly in, and placed a chair for me at the bed-side. The sick man was lying with his face turned towards the wall; and as he took no heed of my presence, I had leisure to observe the place in which I found myself.

"He was lying on an old bedstead, which turned up during the day. The tattered remains of a checked curtain were drawn round the bed's head, to exclude the wind, which however made its way into the comfortless room through the numerous chinks in the door, and blew it to and fro every instant. There was a low cinder fire in a rusty unfixed grate; and an old three-cornered stained table, with some medicine-bottles, a broken glass, and a few other domestic articles, was drawn out before it. A little child was sleeping on a temporary bed which had been made for it on the floor, and the woman sat on a chair by its side. There were a couple of shelves, with a few plates and cups and saucers: and a pair of stage shoes and a couple of foils hung beneath them. With the exception of little heaps of rags and bundles which had been carelessly thrown into the corners of the room, these were the only things in the apartment.

"I had had time to note these little particulars, and to mark the heavy breathing and feverish startings of the sick man, before he was aware of my presence. In his restless attempts to procure some easy resting-place for his head, he tossed his hand out of the bed, and it fell on mine. He started up, and stared eagerly in my face.

"'Mr. Hutley, John,' said his wife; 'Mr. Hutley, that you sent for to-night, you know.'"

"'Ah! said the invalid, passing his hand across his forehead; 'Hutley—Hutley—let me see.' He seemed endeavoring to collect his thoughts for a few seconds, and then grasping me tightly by the wrist, said, 'Don't leave me—don't leave me, old fellow. She'll murder me; I know she will.'

"'Has he been long so?' said I, addressing his weeping wife.

"' Since yesterday night,' she replied. 'John, John, don't you know me?'

"'Don't let her come near me,' said the man, with a shudder, as she stooped over him. 'Drive her away; I can't bear her near me.' He stared wildly at her, with a look of deadly apprehension, and then whispered in my ear, 'I beat her, Jem; I beat her yesterday, and many times before. I have starved her, and the boy too; and now I am weak and helpless, Jem, she'll murder me for it; I know she will. If you'd seen her cry, as I have, you'd know it too. Keep her off.' He relaxed his grasp, and sunk back exhausted on the pillow.

"I knew but too well what all this meant. If I could have entertained any doubt of it, for an instant, one glance at the woman's pale face and wasted form would have sufficiently explained the real state of the case. 'You had better stand aside,' said I to the poor creature. 'You can do him no good. Perhaps he will be calmer, if he does not see you.' She retired out of the man's sight. He opened his eyes, after a few seconds, and looked anxiously round.

"'Is she gone?' he eagerly inquired.

"'Yes—yes,' said I, 'she shall not hurt you.'

"'I'll tell you what, Jem,' said the man, in a low voice, 'she *does* hurt me. There's something in her eyes wakes such a dreadful fear in my heart, that it drives me mad. All last night, her large staring eyes and pale face were close to mine; wherever I turned, they turned; and whenever I started up from my sleep, she was at the bed-side looking at me.' He drew me closer to him, as he said in a deep, alarmed whisper—Jem, she must be an evil spirit—a devil! Hush! I know she is. If she had been a woman, she would have died long ago. No woman could have borne what she has.'

"I sickened at the thought of the long course of cruelty and neglect which must have occurred to produce such an impression on such a man. I could say nothing in reply; for who could offer hope, or consolation, to the abject being before me?

"I sat there for upwards of two hours, during which time he tossed about, murmuring exclamations of pain or impatience, restlessly throwing his arms here and there, and turning constantly from side to side. At length he fell into that state of partial unconsciousness, in which the mind wanders uneasily from scene to scene, and from place to place, without the control of reason, but still without being able to divest itself of an indescribable sense of present suffering. Finding from his incoherent wanderings that this was the case, and knowing that in all probability the fever would not grow immediately worse, I left him, promising his miserable wife that I would repeat my visit next evening, and, if necessary, sit up with the patient during the night.

"I kept my promise. The last four-and-twenty hours had produced a frightful alteration. The eyes, though deeply sunk and heavy, shone with a luster, frightful to behold. The lips were parched, and cracked in many places: the dry hard skin glowed with a burning heat, and there was an almost unearthly air of wild anxiety in the man's face, indicating even more strongly the ravages of the disease. The fever was at its height.

"I took the seat I had occupied the night before, and there I sat for hours, listening to sounds which must strike deep to the heart of the most callous among human beings—the awful ravings of a dying man. From what I had heard of the medical attendant's opinion, I knew there was no hope for him: I was sitting by his death-bed. I saw the wasted limbs, which a few hours before had been distorted for the amusement of a boisterous gallery, writhing under the tortures of a burning fever—I heard the clown's shrill laugh, blending with the low murmurings of the dying man.

"It is a touching thing to hear the mind reverting to ordinary occupations and pursuits of health, when the body lies before you weak and helpless; but when those occupations are of a character the most strongly opposed to anything we associate with grave or solemn ideas, the impression produced is infinitely more powerful. The theatre, and the public-house, were the chief themes of the wretched man's wanderings. It was evening, he fancied; he had a part to play that night; it was late, and he must leave home instantly. Why did they hold him, and prevent his going—he should lose the money—he must go. No! they would not let him. He hid his face in his burning hands, and feebly bemoaned his own weakness, and the cruelty of his persecutors. A short pause, and he shouted out a few doggerel rhymes—the last he had ever learnt. He rose in bed, drew up his withered limbs, and rolled about in uncouth positions; he was acting—he was at the theatre. A minute's silence, and he murmured the burden of some roaring song. He had reached the old house at last; how hot the room was. He had been ill, very ill, but he was well now, and happy. Fill up his glass. Who was that, that dashed it from his lips? It was the same persecutor that had followed him before. He fell back upon his pillow, and moaned aloud. A short period of oblivion, and he was wandering through a tedious maze of low arched rooms—so low, sometimes, that he must creep upon his hands and knees to make his way along; it was close and dark, and every way he turned, some obstacle impeded his progress. There were insects too, hideous crawling things, with eyes that stared upon him, and filled the very air around: glistening horribly amidst the thick darkness of the place. The walls and ceiling were alive with reptiles—the vault expanded to an enormous size—frightful figures flitted to and fro—and the faces of men he knew, rendered hideous by gibing and mouthing, peered out from among them; they were searing him with heated irons, and binding his head with cords till the blood started; and he struggled madly for life.

"At the close of one of these paroxysms, when I had with great difficulty held him down in his bed, he sank into what appeared to be a slumber. Overpowered with watching and exertion, I had closed my eyes for a few minutes, when I felt a violent clutch on my shoulder. I awoke instantly. He had raised himself up, so as to seat himself in bed—a dreadful change had come over his face, but consciousness had returned, for he evidently knew me. The child who had been long since disturbed by his ravings, rose from its little bed, and ran towards its father, screaming with fright—the mother hastily caught it in her arms, lest he should injure it in the violence of his insanity: but, terrified by the alteration of his features, stood transfixed by the bed-side. He grasped my shoulder convulsively, and, striking his breast with the other hand, made a desperate attempt to articulate. It was unavailing—he extended his arm towards them, and made another violent effort. There was a rattling noise in the throat—a glare of the eye—a short stifled groan—and he fell back—dead!"

Dementia

Dementia—from the Latin *demens*, meaning "out of one's mind," is characterized by a loss of intellectual abilities, especially memory, general intelligence, learning, problem solving, orientation, perception, attention, judgment, abstract thinking, language skills, concentration, and social abilities. There are often changes in personality and impulse control, making some individuals difficult to manage. The course of dementia is generally an onset in the patient's fifties or sixies, with consistent slow loss of functioning over five to ten years leading eventually to death. The long course of this disorder has led to it's being labeled "the long good-bye."

Subtypes of Dementia:

1. Dementia of the Alzheimer's Type
2. Vascular Dementia
3. Dementias Due to Other General Medical Conditions
4. Substance-Induced Persisting Dementia

Theodore Dreiser (1871–1945)

Theodore Dreiser was born, the ninth of ten children, in Sullivan, Indiana. Prior to his birth his father had attempted to establish his own woolen mill, which was destroyed in a fire, leaving the family impoverished. Dreiser left home at the age of sixteen and worked at numerous jobs. His literary career began in 1892 when he got a job at the *Chicago Globe*. Later he also worked for the *St. Louis Globe-Democrat*.

Dreiser made his debut as a novelist with *Sister Carrie* (1900), an account of a young working girl's rise to success and her slow decline. Frank Doubleday, the president of the company that published *Sister Carrie*, disapproved of Dreiser's work, and as a result no attempt was made to promote *Sister Carrie*. In 1907 *Sister Carrie* was reissued and became one of the most famous novels in literary history.

Much of Dreiser's work reflected his personal experiences with poverty. His novels depict real-life subjects often portrayed in harsh circumstances. In 1919 Sherwood Anderson wrote about Dreiser, "Something gray and bleak and hurtful, that has been in the world perhaps forever, is personified in him."

In the selection utilized here, Theodore Dreiser tells a tale of dementia, most likely of the Alzheimer's type. Henry Reifsneider has difficulty accepting life without his beloved "Phoebe," and as the story unfolds he slips deeper and deeper into dementia.

"The Lost Phoebe"

. . . Old Henry Reifsneider and his wife Phoebe were a loving couple. You perhaps know how it is with simple natures that fasten themselves like lichens on the stones of circumstance and weather their days to a crumbling conclusion. The great world sounds widely, but it has no call for them. They have no soaring intellect. The orchard, the meadow, the cornfield, the pig-pen, and the chicken-lot measure the range of their human activities. When the wheat is headed it is reaped and threshed; when the corn is browned and frosted it is cut and shocked; when the timothy is in full head it is cut, and the hay-cock erected. After that comes winter, with the hauling of grain to market, the sawing and splitting of wood, the simple chores of fire-building, meal-getting, occasional repairing, and visiting. Beyond these and the changes of weather—the snows, the rains, and the fair days—there are no immediate, significant things. All the rest of life is a far-off, clamorous phantasmagoria, flickering like Northern lights in the night, and sounding as faintly as cow-bells tinkling in the distance.

Old Henry and his wife Phoebe were as fond of each other as it is possible for two old people to be who have nothing else in this life to be fond of. He was a thin old man, seventy when she died, a queer, crotchety person with coarse gray-black hair and beard, quite straggly and unkempt. He looked at you out of dull, fishy, watery eyes that had deep-brown crow's-feet at the sides. His clothes, like the clothes of many farmers, were aged and angular and baggy, standing out at the pockets, not fitting about the neck, protuberant and worn at elbow and knee. Phoebe Ann was thin and shapeless, a very umbrella of a woman, clad in shabby black, and with a black bonnet for her best wear. As time had passed, and they had only themselves to look after, their movements had become slower and slower, their activities fewer and fewer. The annual keep of pigs had been reduced from five to one grunting porker, and the single horse which Henry now retained was a sleepy animal, not overnourished and not very clean. The chickens, of which formerly there was a large flock, had almost disappeared, owing to ferrets, foxes, and the lack of proper care, which produces disease. The former healthy garden was now a straggling memory of itself, and the vines and flower-beds that formerly ornamented the windows and dooryard had now become choking thickets. A will had been made which divided the small tax-eaten property equally among the remaining four, so that it was really of no interest to any of them. Yet these two lived together in peace and sympathy, only that now and then old Henry would become unduly cranky, complaining almost invariably that something had been neglected or mislaid which was of no importance at all.

"Phoebe, where's my corn-knife? You ain't never minded to let my things alone no more."

"Now you hush, Henry," his wife would caution him in a cracked and squeaky voice. "If you don't, I'll leave yuh. I'll git up and walk out of here some day, and then where would y' be? Y' ain't got anybody but me to look after yuh, so yuh just behave yourself. Your corn-knife's on the mantel where it's allus been unless you've gone an' put it summers else."

Old Henry, who knew his wife would never leave him in any circumstances, used to speculate at times as to what he might do if she were to die. That was the one leaving that he really feared. As he climbed on the chair at night to wind the old, long-pendulumed, double-weighted clock, or went finally to the front and the back door to see that they were safely shut in, it was a comfort to know that Phoebe was there, properly ensconced on her side of the bed, and that if he stirred restlessly in the night, she would be there to ask what he wanted.

"Now, Henry, do lie still! You're as restless as a chicken."

"Well, I can't sleep, Phoebe."

"Well, yuh needn't roll so, anyhow. Yuh kin let me sleep."

This usually reduced him to a state of somnolent ease. If she wanted a pail of water, it was a grumbling pleasure for him to get it; and if she did rise first to build the fires, he saw that the wood was cut and placed within easy reach. They divided this simple world nicely between them.

As the years had gone on, however, fewer and fewer people had called. They were well-known for a distance of as much as ten square miles as old Mr. and Mrs. Reifsneider, honest, moderately Christian, but too old to be really interesting any longer. The writing of letters had become an almost impossible burden too difficult to continue or even negotiate via others, although an occasional letter still did arrive from the daughter in Pemberton County. Now and then some old friend stopped with a pie or cake or a roasted chicken or duck, or merely to see that they were well; but even these kindly minded visits were no longer frequent.

One day in the early spring of her sixty-fourth year Mrs. Reifsneider took sick, and from a low fever passed into some indefinable ailment which, because of her age, was no longer curable. Old Henry drove to Swinnerton, the neighboring town, and procured a doctor. Some friends called, and the immediate care of her was taken off his hands. Then one chill spring night she died, and old Henry, in a fog of sorrow and uncertainty, followed her body to the nearest graveyard, an unattractive space with a few pines growing in it. Although he might have gone to the daughter in Pemberton or sent for her, it was really too much trouble and he was too weary and fixed. It was suggested to him at once by one friend and another that he come stay with them awhile, but he did not see fit. He was so old and fixed in his notions and so accustomed to the exact surroundings he had known all his days, that he could not think of leaving. He wanted to remain near where they had put his Phoebe; and the fact that he would have to live alone did not trouble him in the least. The living children were notified and the care of him offered if he would leave, but he would not.

"I kin make a shift for myself," he continually announced to old Dr. Morrow, who had attended his wife in this case, "I kin cook a little, and besides, it don't take much more'n coffee an' bread in the mornin's to satisfy me. I'll get along now well enough. Yuh just let me be." And after many pleadings and proffers of advice, with supplies of coffee and bacon and baked bread duly offered and accepted, he was left to himself. For a while he sat idly outside his door brooding in the spring sun. He tried to revive his interest in farming, and to keep himself busy and free from thought by looking after fields, which of late had been much neglected. It was a gloomy thing to come in of an evening, however, or in the afternoon and find no shadow of Phoebe where everything suggested her. By degrees he put a few of her things away. At night he sat beside his lamp and read in the papers that were left him occasionally or in a Bible that he had neglected for years, but he could get little solace from these things. Mostly he held his hand over his mouth and looked at the floor as he sat and thought of what had become of her, and how soon he himself would die. He made a great business of making his coffee in the morning and frying himself a little bacon at nigh; but his appetite was gone. The shell in which he had been housed so long seemed vacant, and its shadows were suggestive of immedicable griefs. So he lived quite dolefully for five long months, and then a change began.

It was one night, after he had looked after the front and the back door, wound the clock, blown out the light, and gone through all the self-same motions that he had indulged in for years, that he went to bed not so much to sleep as to think. It was a moonlight night. The green-lichen-covered orchard just outside and to be seen from his bed where he now lay was a silvery affair, sweetly spectral. The moon shone through the east windows, throwing the pattern of the panes on the wooden floor, and making the old furniture, to which he was accustomed, stand out dimly in the room. As usual he had been thinking of Phoebe and the years when they had been young together, and of the children who had gone, and the poor shift he was making of his present days. The house was coming to be in a very bad state indeed. The bed-clothes were in disorder and not clean, for he made a wretched shift of washing. It was a terror to him. The roof leaked, causing things, some of them, to remain damp for weeks at a time, but he was getting into that brooding state where he would accept anything rather than exert himself. He preferred to pace slowly to and fro or to sit and think.

By twelve o'clock of this particular night he was asleep, however, and by two had waked again. The moon by this time had shifted to a position on the western side of the house, and it now shone in through the windows of the living-room and those of the kitchen beyond. A certain combination of furniture—a chair near a table, with his coat on it, the half-open kitchen door casting a shadow, and the position of a lamp near a paper—gave him an exact representation of Phoebe leaning over the table as he had often seen her do in life. It gave him a great start. Could it be she—or her ghost? He had scarcely ever believed in spirits, and still—He looked at her fixedly in the feeble half-light, his old hair tingling oddly at the roots, and then he sat up. The figure did not move. He put his thin legs out of the bed and sat looking at her, wondering if this could really be Phoebe. They had talked of ghosts often in their lifetime, of apparitions and omens; but they had never agreed that such things could be. It had never been a part of his wife's creed that she could have a spirit that could return to walk the earth. Her after-world was quite a different affair, a vague heaven, no less, from which the righteous did not trouble to return. Yet here she was now, bending over the table in her black skirt and gray shawl, her pale profile outlined against the moonlight.

"Phoebe," he called, thrilling from head to toe and putting out one bony hand, "have yuh come back?"

The figure did not stir, and he arose and walked uncertainly to the door, looking at it fixedly the while. As he drew near, however, the apparition resolved itself into its primal content—his old coat over the high-backed chair, the lamp by the paper, the half-open door.

"Well," he said to himself, his mouth open, "I thought shore I saw her." And he ran his hand strangely and vaguely through his hair, the while his nervous tension relaxed. Vanished as it had, it gave him the idea that she might return.

Another night, because of his first illusion, and because his mind was now constantly on her and he was old, he looked out of the window that was nearest his bed and commanded a hen-coop and pig-pen and a part of the wagon-shed, and there, a faint mist exuding from the damp of the ground, he thought he saw her again. It was one of those little wisps of mist, one of those faint exhalations of the earth that rise in a cool night after a warm day, and flicker like small white cypress of fog before they disappear. In life it had been a custom of hers to cross this lot from her kitchen door to the pig-pen to throw in any scrap that was left from her cooking, and here she was again. He sat up and watched it strangely, doubtfully, because of his previous experience, but inclined, because of the nervous titillation that passed over his body, to believe that spirits really were, and that Phoebe, who would be concerned because of his lonely state, must be thinking about him, and hence returning. What other way would she have? How otherwise could she express herself? It would be within the province of her charity so to do, and like her loving interest in him. He quivered and watched it eagerly; but, a faint breath of air stirring, it wound away toward the fence and disappeared.

A third night, as he was actually dreaming, some ten days later, she came to his bedside and put her hand on his head.

"Poor Henry!" she said. "It's too bad."

He roused out of his sleep, actually to see her, he thought, moving from his bed-room into the living-room, her figure a shadowy mass of black. The weak straining of his eyes caused little points of light to flicker about the outlines of her form. He arose, greatly astonished, walked the floor in the cool room, convinced that Phoebe was coming back to him. If he only thought sufficiently, if he made it perfectly clear by his feeling that he needed her greatly, she would come back, this kindly wife, and tell him what to do. She would perhaps be with him much of the time, in the night, anyhow; and that would make him less lonely, this state more endurable.

In age and with the feeble it is not such a far cry from the subtleties of illusion to actual hallucination and in due time this transition was made for Henry. Night after night he waited, expecting her return. Once in his weird mood he thought he saw a pale light moving about the room, and another time he thought he saw her walking in the orchard after dark. It was one morning when the details of his lonely state were virtually unendurable that he woke with the thought that she was not dead. How he had arrived at this conclusion it is hard to say. His mind had gone. In its place was a fixed illusion. He and Phoebe had had a senseless quarrel. He had reproached her for not leaving his pipe where he was accustomed to find it, and she had left. It was an aberrated fulfillment of her old jesting threat that if he did not behave himself she would leave him.

"I guess I could find yuh ag'in," he had always said. But her crackling threat had always been:

"Yuh'll not find me if I ever leave yuh. I guess I kin git some place where yuh can't find me."

This morning when he arose he did not think to build the fire in the customary way or to grind his coffee and cut his bread, as was his wont, but solely to meditate as to where he should search for her and how he should induce her to come back. Recently the one horse had been dispensed with because he found it cumbersome and beyond his needs. He took down his soft crush hat after he had dressed himself, a new glint of interest and determination in his eye, and taking his black crook cane from behind the door, where he had always placed it, started out briskly to look for her among the nearest neighbors. His old shoes clumped soundly in the dust as he walked, and his gray-black locks, now grown rather long, straggled out in a dramatic fringe or halo from under his hat. His short coat stirred busily as he walked, and his hands and face were peaked and pale.

"Why, hello, Henry! Where're yuh goin' this mornin'?" inquired Farmer Dodge, who, hauling a load of wheat to market, encountered him on the public road. He had not seen the aged farmer in months, not since his wife's death, and he wondered now, seeing him looking so spry.

"Yuh ain't seen Phoebe, have yuh?" inquired the old man, looking up quizzically.

"Phoebe who?" inquired Farmer Dodge, not for the moment connecting the name with Henry's dead wife.

"Why, my wife Phoebe, o' course. Who do yuh s'pose I mean?" He stared up with a pathetic sharpness of glance from under his shaggy, gray eyebrows.

"Wall, I'll swan, Henry, yuh ain't jokin', are yuh?" said the solid Dodge, a pursy man, with a smooth hard, red face. "It can't be your wife yuh're talkin' about. She's dead."

"Dead! Shucks!" retorted the demented Reifsneider. "She left me early this mornin', while I was sleepin'. She allus got up to build the fire, but she's gone now. We had a little spat last night, an' I guess that's the reason. But I guess I kin find her. She's gone over to Matilda Race's; that's where she's gone."

He started briskly up the road, leaving the amazed Dodge to stare in wonder after him.

"Well, I'll be switched!" he said aloud to himself. "He's clean out'n his head. That poor old feller's been livin' down there till he's gone outen his mind. I'll have to notify the authorities." And he flicked his whip with great enthusiasm. "Geddap!" he said, and was off.

Reifsneider met no one else in this poorly populated region, until he reached the whitewashed fence of Matilda Race and her husband three miles away. He had passed several other houses en route, but these not being within the range of his illusion were not considered. His wife, who had known Matilda well, must be here. He opened the picket-gate which guarded the walk, and stamped briskly up to the door.

"Why, Mr. Reifsneider," exclaimed old Matilda herself, a stout woman, looking out of the door in answer to his knock, "what brings yuh here this mornin'?"

"Is Phoebe here?" he demanded eagerly.

"Phoebe who? What Phoebe?" replied Mrs. Race, curious as to this sudden development of energy on his part.

"Why, my Phoebe, o'course. My wife Phoebe. Who do yuh s'pose? Ain't she here now?"

"Lawsy me!" exclaimed Mrs. Race, opening her mouth. "Yuh pore man! So you're clean out'n your mind now. Yuh come right in and sit down. I'll git yuh a cup o'coffee. O'course your wife ain't here; but yuh come in an' sit down. I'll find her fer yuh after a while. I know where she is."

The old farmer's eyes softened, and he entered. He was so thin and pale a specimen, pantalooned and patriarchal, that he aroused Mrs. Race's extremest sympathy as he took off his hat and laid it on his knees quite softly and mildly.

"We had a quarrel last night, an' she left me," he volunteered.

"Laws! laws!" sighed Mrs. Race, there being no one present with whom to share her astonishment as she went to her kitchen. "The pore man! Now somebody's just got to look after him. He can't be allowed to run around the country this way lookin' for his dead wife. It's turrible."

She boiled him a pot of coffee and brought in some of her new-baked bread and fresh butter. She set out some of her best jam and put a couple of eggs to boil, lying whole-heartedly the while.

"Now yuh stay right there, Uncle Henry, till Jake comes in, an' I'll send him to look for Phoebe. I think its more'n likely she's over to Swinnerton with some o'her friends. Anyhow, we'll find out. Now yuh just drink this coffee an' eat this bread. Yuh must be tired. Yuh've had a long walk this mornin'." Her idea was to take counsel with Jake, "her man," and perhaps have him notify the authorities.

She bustled about, meditating on the uncertainties of life, while old Reifsneider thrummed on the rim of his hat with his pale fingers and later ate abstractedly of what she offered. His mind was on his wife, however, and since she was not here, or did not appear, it wandered vaguely away to a family by the name of Murray, miles away in another direction. He decided after a time that he would not wait for Jake Race to hunt his wife but would seek her for himself. He must be on, and urge her to come back.

"Well, I'll be goin', " he said, getting up and looking strangely about him. "I guess she didn't come here after all. She went over to the Murrays', I guess. I'll not wait any longer, Mis' Race. There's a lot to do over to the house today." And out he marched in the face of her protests taking to the dusty road again in the warm spring sun, his cane striking the earth as he went.

It was two hours later that this pale figure of a man appeared in the Murrays' doorway, dusty, perspiring, eager. He had tramped all of five miles, and it was noon. An amazed husband and wife of sixty heard his strange query, and realized also that he was mad. They begged him to stay to dinner, intending to notify the authorities later and see what could be done; but though he stayed to partake of a little something, he did not stay long, and was off again to another distant farmhouse, his idea of many things to do and his need of Phoebe impelling him. So it went for that day and the next, and the next, the circle of his inquiry ever widening.

The process by which a character assumes the significance of being peculiar, his antics weird, yet harmless, in such a community is often involute and pathetic. This day, as has been said, saw Reifsneider at other doors, eagerly asking his unnatural question, and leaving a trail of amazement, sympathy, and pity in his wake. Although the authorities were informed—the county sheriff, no less—It was not deemed advisable to take him into custody; for when those who knew old Henry, and had for so long, reflected on the condition of the county insane asylum, a place which, because of the poverty of the district, was of staggering aberration and sickening environment, it was decided to let him remain at large; for, strange to relate, it was found on investigation that at night he returned peaceably enough to his lonesome domicile there to discover whether his wife had returned, and to brood in loneliness until the morning. Who would lock up a thin, eager, seeking old man with iron-gray hair and an attitude of kindly, innocent inquiry, particularly when he was well known for a past of only kindly servitude and reliability? Those who had known him best rather agreed that he should be allowed to roam at large. He could do no harm. There were many who were willing to help him as to food, old clothes, the odds and ends of his daily life—at least at first. His figure after a time became not so much a common-place as an accepted curiosity, and the replies, "Why, no, Henry; I ain't seen her," or "No, Henry; she ain't been here today," more customary.

For several years thereafter then he was an odd figure in the sun and rain, on dusty roads and muddy ones, encountered occasionally in strange and unexpected places, pursuing his endless search. Undernourishment, after a time, although the neighbors and those who knew his history gladly contributed from their store, affected his body; for he walked much and ate little. The longer he roamed the public highway in this manner, the deeper became his strange hallucination; and finding it harder and harder to return from his more and more distant pilgrimages, he finally began taking a few utensils with him from his home, making a small package of them, in order that he might not be compelled to return. In an old tin coffee-pot of large size he placed a small tin cup, a knife, fork, and spoon, some salt and pepper, and to the outside of it, by a string forced through a pierced hole, he fastened a plate, which could be released, and which was his woodland table. It was no trouble for him to secure the little food that he needed, and with a strange, almost religious dignity, he had no hesitation in asking for that much. By degrees his hair became longer and longer, his once black hat became an earthen brown, and his clothes threadbare and dusty.

For all of three years he walked, and none knew how wide were his per-ambulations, nor how he survived the storms and cold. They could not see him, with homely rural understanding and forethought, sheltering himself in hay-cocks, or by the sides of cattle, whose warm bodies protected him from the cold, and whose dull understandings were not opposed to his harmless presence. Overhanging rocks and trees kept him at times from the rain, and a friendly hay-loft or corn-crib was not above his humble consideration.

The involute progression of his hallucination is strange. From asking at doors and being constantly rebuffed or denied, he finally came to the conclusion that although his Phoebe might not be in any of the houses at the doors of which he inquired, she might nevertheless be within the sound of his voice. And so, from patient inquiry, he began to call sad, occasional cries, that ever and anon waked the quiet landscapes and ragged hill regions, and set to echo-ing his thin "O-o-o Phoebe! O-o-o Phoebe!" It had a pathetic, albeit insane, ring, and many a farmer or plowboy came to know it even from afar and say, "There goes old Reifsneider."

Another thing that puzzled him greatly after a time and after many hun-dreds of inquiries was, when he no longer had any particular dooryard in view and no special inquiry to make, which way to go. These crossroads, which oc-casionally led in four or even six directions, came after a time to puzzle him. But to solve this knotty problem, which became more and more of a puzzle, there came to his aid another hallucination. Phoebe's spirit or some power of the air or wind or nature would tell him. If he stood at the center of the parting of the ways, closed his eyes, turned thrice about, and called "O-o-o Phoebe!" twice, and then threw his cane straight before him, that would surely indicate which way to go for Phoebe, or one of these mystic powers would surely govern its direction and fall! In whichever direction it went, even though, as was not infrequently the case, it took him back along the path he had already come, or across fields, he was not so far gone in his mind but that he gave himself ample time to search before he called again. Also the halluci-nation seemed to persist that at some time he would surely find her. There were hours when his feet were sore, and his limbs weary, when he would stop in the heat to wipe his seamed brow, or in the cold to beat his arms. Some-times, after throwing away his cane, and finding it indicating the direction from which he had just come, he would shake his head wearily and philo-sophically, as if contemplating the unbelievable or an untoward fate, and then start briskly off. His strange figure came finally to be known in the farthest reaches of three or four counties. Old Reifsneider was a pathetic character. His fame was wide.

Near a little town called Watersville, in Green County, perhaps four miles from that minor center of human activity, there was a place or precipice locally known as the Red Cliff, a sheer wall of red sandstone, perhaps a hundred feet high, which raised its sharp face for half a mile or more above the fruitful corn-fields and orchards that lay beneath, and which was surmounted by a thick grove of trees. The slope that slowly led up to it from the opposite side was covered by a rank growth of beech, hickory, and ash, through which threaded a number of wagon-tracks crossing at various angles. In fair weather it had become old Reifsneider's habit, so inured was he by now to the open, to make his bed in such patch of trees as this to fry his bacon or boil his eggs at the foot of some tree before laying himself down for the night. Occasionally, so light and inconsequential was his sleep, he would walk at night. More often, the moonlight or some sudden wind stirring in the trees or a reconnoitering animal arousing him, he would sit up and think, or pursue his quest in the moonlight or the dark, a strange, unnatural, half wild, half savage-looking but utterly harmless creature, calling at lonely road crossings, staring at dark and shuttered houses, and wondering where, where Phoebe could really be.

That particular lull that comes in the systole-diastole of this earthly ball at two o'clock in the morning invariably aroused him, and though he might not go any farther he would sit up and contemplate the darkness or the stars, wondering. Sometimes in the strange process of his mind he would fancy that he saw moving among the trees the figure of his lost wife, and then he would get up to follow, taking his utensils, always on a string, and his cane. If she seemed to evade him too easily he would run, or plead, or, suddenly losing track of the fancied figure, stand awed or disappointed, grieving for the moment over the almost insurmountable difficulties of his search.

It was in the seventh year of these hopeless peregrinations, in the dawn of a similar springtime to that in which his wife had died, that he came at last one night to the vicinity of this self-same patch that crowned the rise to the Red Cliff. His far-flung cane, used as a divining-rod at the last cross-roads, had brought him hither. He had walked many, many miles. It was after ten o'clock at night, and he was very weary. Long wandering and little eating had left him but a shadow of his former self. It was a question now not so much of physical strength but of spiritual endurance which kept him up. He had scarcely eaten this day, and now exhausted he set himself down in the dark to rest and possibly to sleep.

Curiously on this occasion a strange suggestion of the presence of his wife surrounded him. It would not be long now, he counseled with himself, although the long months had brought him nothing, until he should see her, talk to her. He fell asleep after a time, his head on his knees. At midnight the moon began to rise, and at two in the morning, his wakeful hour, was a large silver disk shining through the trees to the east. He opened his eyes when the radiance became strong, making a silver pattern at his feet and lighting the woods with strange lusters and silvery, shadowy forms. As usual, his old notion that his wife must be near occurred to him on this occasion, and he looked about him with a speculative, anticipatory eye. What was it that moved in the distant shadows along the path by which he had entered—a pale, flickering will-o'-the-wisp that bobbed gracefully among the trees and riveted his expectant gaze? Moonlight and shadows combined to give it a strange form and a stranger reality, this fluttering of bogfire or dancing of wandering fire-flies. Was it truly his lost Phoebe? By a circuitous route it passed about him, and in his fevered state he fancied that he could see the very eyes of her, not as she was when he last saw her in the black dress and shawl but now a strangely younger Phoebe, gayer, sweeter, the one whom he had known years before as a girl. Old Reifsneider got up. He had been expecting and dreaming of this hour all these years, and now as he saw the feeble light dancing lightly before him he peered at it questioningly, one thin hand in his gray hair.

Of a sudden there came to him now for the first time in many years the full charm of her girlish figure as he had known it in boyhood, the pleasing, sympathetic smile, the brown hair, the blue sash she had once worn about her waist at a picnic, her gay, graceful movements. He walked around the base of the tree, straining with his eyes, forgetting for once his cane and utensils, and following eagerly after. On she moved before him, a will-o'-the wisp of the spring, a little flame above her head, and it seemed as though among the small saplings of ash and beech and the thick trunks of hickory and elm that she signaled with a young, a light-some hand.

"O Phoebe! Phoebe!" he called. "Have yuh really come? Have yuh really answered me?" And hurrying faster, he fell once, scrambling lamely to his feet, only to see the light in the distance dancing illusively on. On and on he hurried until he was fairly running, brushing his ragged arms against the trees, striking his hands and face against impending twigs. His hat was gone, his lungs were breathless, his reason quite astray, when coming to the edge of the cliff he saw her below among a silvery bed of apple-trees now blooming in the spring.

"O Phoebe!" he called. "O Phoebe! Oh, no don't leave me!" And feeling the lure of a world where love was young and Phoebe as this vision presented her, a delightful epitome of their quondam youth, he gave a cry of "Oh, wait, Phoebe!" and leaped.

Some farmer-boys, reconnoitering this region of bounty and prospect some few days afterward, found first the tin utensils tied together under the tree where he had left them, and then later at the foot of the cliff, pale, broken, but elate, a molded smile of peace and delight upon his lips, his body. His old hat was discovered lying under some low-growing saplings the twigs of which had held it back. No one of all the simple population knew how eagerly and joyously he had found his lost mate.

Amnestic Disorders

Amnestic disorders are characterized by memory impairment. The memory impairment may result from the direct physiological effects of a medical condition such as head trauma or the persisting effects of a substance. Such individuals are impaired in their ability to learn new information or are unable to recall previously learned information.

Charles Jackson (1902–1968)

The Lost Weekend is Charles Jackson's semiautobiographical tale of alcoholism. At the time of Jackson's landmark work, alcoholism was portrayed in books, movies, and television primarily as a weakness in the drinker. Jackson's book became a bestseller, and Billy Wilder's film version initiated a new public perception of the alcoholic. Prior to *The Lost Weekend*, alcoholism was a hidden topic, but after its commercial success the topic began to be addressed more honestly and openly.

Although the Hollywood studios were reluctant to take on the subject of alcoholism, *The Lost Weekend* became a huge hit. The film won Academy Awards for Best Picture, Best Director, Best Screenplay, and Best Actor.

Jackson had conquered his own battle with alcoholism and thrived on the success of his first novel. However, in 1946, after almost ten years of sobriety, he relapsed and slipped back into alcoholism. From that point onward his life and career spiraled downward, and he faded from the literary scene until his final book in 1967. In 1968, Jackson took his own life with an overdose of sleeping pills. At the time of his death he was working on a sequel to *The Lost Weekend*.

In this selection, Don Bernam has experienced repeated episodes of amnesia and is beginning to have difficulties with learning new information. As his drinking continues, his symptoms of amnesia continue to worsen.

The Lost Weekend

The windows were blue-white. Was it early morning, or evening? He lay watching the panes between the curtains and wondered if they would whiten into daylight or thicken into dusk. He wondered what time it was, what day. The clock said 6:10 but that told him nothing.

He had awakened fully dressed on the couch in the living room. His feet burned. He reached down and unlaced his shoes and kicked them off. He rose to a sitting position and pulled off his coat and vest, untied his tie and loosened his collar. Automatically his hand groped beside the couch for the pint on the floor. His heart sank as he found it, and found it empty.

Had he been sleeping all night, or all the next day? There was no way of telling till the light changed outside, for better or worse. If it were evening, thank Christ. He could go out and buy another, a dozen more. But if morning—

He feared to find out; for if it were morning, dawn, he would be cut off till nine or after and so made to suffer the punishment he always promised himself to avoid. It would be like the dreaded Sunday, always (at these times) the day most abhorred of all the week; for on Sundays the bars did not open till two in the afternoon and the liquor stores did not open at all. Once again he had not been clever enough to provide a supply against this very thing; again he had lost all perspective and forgotten his inescapable desperation of the morning, so much more urgent and demanding than any need of the evening before. Last night it had been merely drink. It was medication now.

He lifted the empty pint to his mouth. One warm drop crawled like slow syrup through the neck of the bottle. It lay on his tongue, useless, all but impossible to swallow. He thought of all the mornings (and as he thought of them he knew he was in for another cycle of harrowing mornings) when, at such times as these, he would drag himself into the kitchen and examine the line-up of empty quarts and pints on the floor under the sink, pick them up separately and hold them upside down over a small glass, one by one for minutes at a time, extracting a last sticky drop from one bottle, two drops from another, maybe nothing from a third, and so on through a long patient nerve-wracking process till he had collected enough, perhaps, to cover the bottom of the glass. It was like a rite—the slow drinking of it still more so; and it was never enough.

Though he hated this need of his, hated this dependency on the pick-up, so often impossible to get—hated it for what it did to him till he got it—all the same he had a profound and superior contempt for those who spurned liquor on the morning after, whose stomachs, shaken as they were by the dissipation of the night, turned and retched at the very thought of it. How often he had been dumbfounded—at first incredulous, then contemptuous—to hear someone say, after a night of drinking, "God, take it away, I don't want to smell it, I don't want to *see* it even, take it out of my sight!"—this at the very moment when he wanted and needed it most. How different that reaction was from his own, and how revealing. Clearly it was the difference between the alcoholic and the non-. He was angry to know this, but he knew it; he knew it far better than others; and he kept the knowledge to himself. It would tell them too much about him, tell them he was the drinker who couldn't stop—an abhorrent thing, more shocking to the man who went in for the occasional heavy weekend spree than it ever was to the abstainer. The hair of the dog was no lighthearted joke with him as it was with the others; but he could kid about it with the rest, if need be, hiding his agonized impatience till such time as he was able to sneak a drink or, if offered one as a dare in the presence of others (dare!), quench his thirst with affected bravery amid the shudders of his hung-over friends.

Thirst—there was a misnomer. He could honestly say he had never had a thirst for liquor or a craving for drink as such, no, not even in hangover. It wasn't because he was thirsty that he drank, and he didn't drink because he liked the taste (actually whisky was dreadful to the palate; he swallowed at once to get it down as quickly as possible): he drank for what it did to him. As for quenching his thirst, liquor did exactly the opposite. To quench is to slake or satisfy, to give you enough. Liquor couldn't do that. One drink led inevitably to the next, more demanded more, they became progressively easier and easier, culminating in the desperate need, no longer easy, that shook him on days such as these. His need to breathe was not more urgent.

Today wasn't as bad as that. He could stand it. He had only been drinking one night, this time. Tomorrow or the day after would be a different story, but—now it was hangover, nothing more; and he could stand it till he was able to get another pint. What possessed him now even more than his need for a drink was that inevitable and familiar accompaniment to the first morning after: remorse (how readily he recognized it; how humbly, from old habit, he accepted it as his just due)—remorse merely for drinking, for having drunk at all, any; but even as he acknowledged the first sickening symptom of anguish and guilt, he knew it was only a tiny twinge or pang to the hounding relentless remorse that would drive him to hell and worse a few days hence.

What had happened yesterday, last night, that he should feel so guilty now? Nothing. It was always the same, regardless of what he had done. He remembered little after he started drinking; but what he recalled up to the time he had gone down to the Village, or up to his call at Mrs. Wertheim's laundry, was enough. Merely to have started again, when he was only just safely out of the other bat, was enough now to make him sick with despair and regret.

* * *

Like a fish of the deep rising to the surface of bright air and sun, he swam up to consciousness out of a dead blank into a whiter world than he had ever seen. The daylight was blinding. He heard voices very near at hand, as if just behind his ear, talking together quietly in a business-like way against a background medley of babblings and shrieks, moans and mutterings. He was lying prone and someone was working on his back—fingers probed at his spine. He flopped over, like a fish out of water, and found himself in a low bed, little more than a mattress, so low that the two men who worked over him were kneeling on the edge.

As surprised as he, they looked at him in impersonal silence, and then recovered themselves.

"Just a moment, take it easy, turn over again, please," one of them said; and the other: "Take it easy, baby."

They must have anticipated what he was going to say because here he was saying it—saying it all in a rush as if he hadn't heard or as if he were too exasperated, angered, and offended to take it easy. "What's going on here, where am I, what are you doing to me!"

"Just lie back again, it'll only take a second," the first man said; and the second murmured the classic "It won't hurt a bit" as he himself cried out the still-more-classic "Where am I" again.

"You're in the hospital."

"What for!"

"Take it easy, baby."

"*What* hospital?"

"The alcoholic ward."

He didn't get this, not any of it. He had awakened fighting-mad, or at least bitterly offended and indignant because he couldn't figure out where he was, because he was being taken advantage of, because he didn't know who these two men were and what right had *they* to touch him? Now he heard the bedlam going on in the background and he was outraged at this further intrusion on his peace. "What's all that racket!"

"The others."

"Other *what?*"

"Patients. Now just turn over and relax, it won't take a moment."

"What do you think you are doing! Who are you!"

"We want to draw off a little of the spinal fluid. Relieve the pressure on the brain."

"Spinal tap, baby."

He suddenly understood. "Oh *no* you're not!" He drew up his knees against his chest, and as he did so his head exploded in pain above his eyes.

Both men straightened and stood back from the bed. One of them put his hands on his hips. The other's already were.

He saw now the syringe and needle and also saw the two men more or less clearly for the first time. One was small, baldish, pleasant-looking, in his middle forties. Probably the doctor, though he looked more like a professor or teacher. The other was a big strapping fellow around thirty, broad and well built but far from muscular. With a frame like a hammer- thrower, he was yet soft, just this side of fat. He stood looking down with a half-smile on his face, and the impression he gave was that of an enormous sleepy tomcat, indifferent, self-sufficient, yet predatory.

"What's the matter, what are you afraid of," the teacherish man said.

"I'm not afraid of anything!"

"Then why won't you let us do it?"

"Because I won't have it! You're not going to do that to me!"

"A spinal tap won't hurt you any. We do it all the time."

"Not on *me* you don't!" He had a horror of the spinal puncture because when it had been used in the TB sanatorium as a means of anesthesia some years ago, a friend of his had been paralyzed by it; not temporarily, which had been the idea, but permanently.

"You must listen to reason. You have too much alcohol in your system. This will help clear your brain, take some of the pressure off. Do you understand?"

"*Sure* I understand, what do you think I am!"

"Besides that, you have a fractured skull."

"Fractured *skull!*"

"A slight fracture, between the right temple and eye."

"I don't believe you!" His splitting head denied this disbelief but he didn't believe it all the same.

"The X-ray showed it very clearly. It's not serious, however. There's no real concussion."

"But where did I get—"

"Don't ask us, baby," the bigger man said, smiling. "That's what you came in with."

"How did I get here? I didn't ask to be—"

"You were brought in by the ambulance. Now let's go ahead with this. It's the best thing for you. It'll make you feel a lot better."

"I feel all right, right now!" He didn't. His head was bursting with pain, but—hadn't it often, didn't it always, on such mornings as this?

"You refuse?" the professor-like man said.

"I certainly do! You're not going to do that to me!"

The small man turned to the other and spoke as if Don weren't there at all, or as if he didn't understand English. "I guess there's nothing to do then, Bim. We can't give it to him without his consent, now that he's conscious. The patient seems to be in his right mind, capable of deciding for himself."

"Try him, Doctor."

The doctor turned back to Don. "What's your name?"

"Don Birnam," he answered, almost haughty.

"Where do you live?"

"Three-one-one East Fifty-Fifth."

"Manhattan?"

"Certainly!"

"What do you do?"

"Do? I—well, I'm not doing anything, at the moment."

"Unemployed?"

"He didn't look unemployed to me," the other said with a smile. "Not from the clothes he was wearing."

Don automatically looked down at himself. He had on a short white gown that barely reached to the knees; made of a heavy cloth as stiff and rough as canvas. It was tied in the back: he could feel the thick knot, now, between his shoulder blades. He was outraged at the spectacle he must present of himself, outraged that the man should smile. But the smiler was not smiling at him, he noticed; it was just a habit, a fixed expression of the sleepy cat-like face.

"What year is it?" the doctor went on.

"Why are you asking me these fool questions!"

"What year is it?"

"Nineteen thirty-six!"

"What month?"

"October."

"What day is today?"

Oh-oh. This is something he couldn't be sure of.

"What day is it?"

"I—I'm sorry, I guess I don't know. Monday or Tuesday, maybe, but I—" God if it were Tuesday he had to be back home, had to be safely back and in bed and finished with the weekend before Wick came in. He had to get out of here and quick.

"What's your name?"

"I *told* you. Don Birnam."

"Where do you live?"

"Three-one-one East Fifty-Fifth. Man*hat*tan!"

"Three-eleven?"

"Three-one-one, I said! That's three-eleven in *any* language, isn't it? Or it was when *I* went to school."

The doctor turned again to the other. "Okay, Bim. Give him some paraldehyde and let him go. Ten grains. I'll be in the women's ward." He started down the room.

Don suddenly couldn't let him go like that. "Doctor!" he called out. "Wait a minute!"

The doctor went on without turning back.

The big fellow was looking down at him, squinting faintly. "What did you want?"

"What day is it?"

"Sunday."

"Oh." He sank back, relieved.

"You were brought in here yesterday afternoon."

"Really in an ambulance?"

"I'll say. You were out like a lamp. You've got an awful black eye."

Instinctively Don raised his hand and touched the eye with his fingers.

"Too bad. Such nice eyes, too. Really awful nice." The voice had no fiber or resonance at all. It was the audible but whispered intimacy of one who spoke from a pillow in the dead of night. "Want to see what you look like?" From a pocket in his jacket he drew out a small round mirror and held it between thumb and forefinger.

Don pulled away. "No thank you."

"What's the matter?"

"Nothing."

"What's the matter, baby?"

In anger, Don glanced up again. But he was in no position to be angry. He had to bear with this until he got out of here, or at least until he got his clothes. "Are you a doctor?" he said, to say something.

"No."

"Orderly?"

"No."

"What."

"Nurse." He smiled. Then, barely audible: "Is that all right?"

"All right what?"

"All right with you," He smiled as if he were privately amused—a little wryly but still amused—at some secret slight joke of his own. Nothing to laugh about; just sort of muse over, continually.

Don was too uncomfortable to face him. "What's the other guy," he said, looking away.

"That's Doctor Stevens. Did you like him?"

"Listen. Didn't he say I could go?"

"Okay, baby. Hold your water. I'll go get it."

"My clothes?"

"Your paraldehyde. You'll love it." He moved silently away.

When he was at a safe distance, Don turned on the mattress to watch him go. He moved down the ward with a noiseless casual tread as if in carpet-slippers on his way to his own bathroom at home, indescribably nonchalant and at ease. It was infuriating. But you didn't have to watch him, did you? He lay on the mattress face down, refusing to look further.

Though he couldn't believe the business about the fractured skull, he began to realize the spot he was in. The alcoholic ward. So here he was at last. Inevitably he would wind up in this place and the only wonder was that he hadn't been here before. This was your natural home and you might as well take it. Take it and lie low and wait for your chance to get out again—and then forever afterward watch your step. But it wasn't happening, either—not any of it. You had a bad head but you certainly didn't feel the pain you knew you had, didn't shake (no more than usual), didn't sweat (no more than usual). It was all so unreal that you weren't even suffering; you were merely biding your time, in a time-out. He began to look about him.

It was a long high-ceilinged room with a concrete floor bare of anything but beds, most of them so low they were little more than pallets. Only three or four were of normal height, and these were boarded up at the sides like babies' cribs. The idea, he supposed, was to keep you from falling out; or, in the case of the low beds, from hurting yourself if you did fall.

On the mattress next to his, a man who looked like some kind of crank messiah (but only because of the gaunt and hollow face) lay staring at the ceiling. He had a three- or four-days' growth of beard, his cheeks were sunken, his eyes large and sad. His white legs stuck out below the pathetically short gown like a cadaver in the morgue. He might have been dead, but that his entire frame—all over, all at once—quivered. It shook with tiny tremors, regular, precise, constant, as if a fine motor operated somewhere beneath him, in the mattress itself.

Farther off, a middle-aged Negro babbled God knows what at the top of his lungs, and no one paid enough notice to find out what he was complaining about. In the bed across the way another Negro got up on his knees, lifted his gown, and urinated on the floor. No one seemed to notice or mind that, either, least of all the intelligent-looking man who leaned against the wall a few feet away in a stiff faded robe held together by a safety-pin, looking about as casually as he could and being very careful to avoid every returning glance. His self-consciousness was painful see. Don felt that the man had been looking at him, but by the time he noticed the fellow, he had shifted his gaze an inch or two to the left. You couldn't have caught his eye if you'd tried. Other men in faded robes or short gowns open at the back moved restlessly up and down the aisle or went in and out of the two rooms at the end where most of the shouting seemed to be coming from. There was a strong smell of disinfectant and dirty feet.

It wasn't possible that he was here or that he had come to this place in an ambulance, clang-clanging through the streets like the ambulances in the movies or like the one he had seen yesterday tearing in and out among the pillars of the L. You couldn't ride in one of those things and not know it. But you had. You had been rushed zig-zagging through the city streets while an interne sat at your side taking your pulse or your temperature and bracing himself for the turns. But how had you got into it in the first place? Where had you been picked up—by whom? What or who had given you a fractured skull—if you had one? All he remembered was the bottle left behind on the living room table.

Discussion Questions

1.   In delirium an underlying cause is generally assumed. Discuss the apparent underlying cause in "The Stroller's Tale" by Dickens. Do some research and list several additional causes of delirium.

2.   The "authorities" in the story of "The Lost Phoebe" allowed Henry to remain in the community instead of confining him to the county home. This decision ultimately provided Henry the freedom to roam the countryside and ultimately to fall to his death. Discuss the ethical versus humanitarian issue of the decision of the "authorities."

3.   Don Birnam is beginning to experience memory loss due to his drinking. Two serious versions of alcohol-induced persisting amnestic disorder are often seen in chronic alcoholics: Wernicke's encephalopathy and Kosakoff's syndrome. Do some research on these disorders and write a short description of each of them. In your opinion, is Don in danger of developing either of these serious disorders? Why or why not?

4.   Some of the symptoms related to dementia of the Alzheimer's type include impairments in memory and judgment, deterioration of personal self-care, and delusions. Document each of these symptoms as exhibited by Henry in "The Lost Phoebe."

Chapter 3

Substance-Related Disorders

The use of mood-altering chemicals has been a problem in most societies throughout recorded history. Virtually every known society has been forced to deal with the problem of recreational chemical use.

Substance abuse problems are related to significant societal issues including crime, various medical conditions, suicide, homicide, motor vehicle accidents, domestic violence, child abuse, infant mortality, loss of job productivity, and destruction of property.

Substances can affect both mood and behavior. The use of substances can produce symptoms that are indistinguishable from regularly seen symptoms of emotional problems. Since these symptoms are identical to those seen in emotional disturbances of all types, the clinician must rule out substance abuse prior to assessing for other psychiatric disorders. *Substance dependence* (addiction) is the term applied to those with the most severe problems.

Substances commonly abused include alcohol, amphetamines, caffeine, cannabis, cocaine, hallucinogens, inhalants, nicotine, opioids, phencyclidine, sedatives, hypnotics, and anxiolytics.

Alcohol Dependence

Alcohol abuse is by far the most common substance-related disorder in the United States. Problems related to alcohol misuse are the most costly in terms of social, economic, and related health care problems. Estimates of the direct and indirect costs associated with alcoholism vary widely and run into the billions of dollars annually when all related costs are calculated. Calculations that include alcohol-related deaths place such deaths among the leading causes of death in the United States, following closely behind heart disease and cancer. Alcohol plays a major role in homicides, suicides, fatal automobile accidents, child abuse, and incidents of domestic violence.

Jack London (1876–1916)

Jack London was born in San Francisco in 1876. London had little formal education: he attended school through the eighth grade and continued to educate himself by reading at public libraries. In the mid-1890s he returned to high school, graduated, and was admitted to the University of California at Berkeley, where he stayed only six months.

London's literary career began with the publication of his first short stories in the *Overland Monthly* in 1899. He was proud of the fact that he was a highly disciplined writer, writing his daily 1,000 words in the early morning. Between 1900 and 1916, Jack London completed over fifty books, including both fiction and nonfiction, hundreds of short stories, and numerous articles on a wide variety of topics. London's best-known books are *The Call of the Wild, White Fang,* and *The Sea Wolf.* His classic short stories include "To Build A Fire," and "The White Silence."

London was among the most publicized figures of his day. He was one of the first writers to work in the movie industry. His novel *The Sea Wolf* became the first full-length American movie. London was also one of the first celebrities to endorse commercial products. Many of London's books and short stories are classics and are still widely read around the world. Some of his works have been translated into as many as seventy different languages.

Jack London was often troubled by physical ailments. In the current selection, an excerpt from the novel *John Barleycorn* (1913), London provides in insight into alcoholism that comes from personal experience. There is little doubt that London is telling his own story in *John Barleycorn,* and while his narrator denies that he is an alcoholic, his alcohol dependence is obvious.

Jack London developed kidney disease in his thirties and died at the age of forty. There is some controversy as to his cause of death: reports vary as to whether it was renal failure or suicide. In either case, the extensive level of drinking that he documents in *John Barleycorn* would have played a role in his health problems and early death.

John Barleycorn

There are, broadly speaking, two types of drinkers. There is the man whom we all know, stupid, unimaginative, whose brain is bitten numbly by numb maggots; who walks generously with wide-spread, tentative legs, falls frequently in the gutter, and who sees, in the extremity of his ecstasy, blue mice and pink elephants. He is the type that gives rise to the jokes in the funny papers.

The other type of drinker has imagination, vision. Even when most pleasantly jingled, he walks straight and naturally, never staggers nor falls, and knows just where he is and what he is doing. It is not his body but his brain that is drunken. He may bubble with wit, or expound with good fellowship. Or he may see intellectual spectres and phantoms that are cosmic and logical and that take the forms of syllogisms. It is when in this condition that he strips away the husks of life's healthiest illusions and gravely considers the iron collar of necessity welded about the neck of his soul. This is the hour of John Barleycorn's subtlest power. It is easy for any man to roll in the gutter. But it is a terrible ordeal for a man to stand upright on his two legs unswaying, and decide that in all the universe he finds for himself but one freedom—namely, the anticipating of the day of his death. With this man this is the hour of the white logic (of which more anon), when he knows that he may know only the laws of things—the meaning of things never. This is his danger hour. His feet are taking hold of the pathway that leads down into the grave.

All is clear to him. All these baffling head-reaches after immortality are but the panics of souls frightened by the fear of death, and cursed with the thrice-cursed gift of imagination. They have not the instinct for death, they lack the will to die when the time to die is at hand. They trick themselves into believing they will outwit the game and win to a future, leaving the other animals to the darkness of the grave or the annihilating hearts of the crematory. But he, this man in the hour of his white logic, knows that they trick and outwit themselves. The one event happeneth to all alike. There is no new thing under the sun, not even that yearned-for bauble of feeble souls—immortality. But he knows, *he* knows, standing upright on his two legs unswaying. He is compounded of meat and wine and sparkle, of sun-mote and world-dust, a frail mechanism made to run for a span, to be tinkered at by doctors of divinity and doctors of physic, and to be flung into the scrap-heap at the end.

Of course, all of this is soul-sickness, life-sickness. It is the penalty the imaginative man must pay for his friendship with John Barleycorn. The penalty paid by the stupid man is simpler, easier. He drinks himself into sottish unconsciousness. He sleeps a drugged sleep, and, if he dreams, his dreams are dim and inarticulate. But to the imaginative man, John Barleycorn sends the pitiless, special syllogisms of the white logic. He looks upon life and all its affairs with the jaundiced eye of a pessimistic German philosopher. He sees through all illusions. He transvalues all values. Good is bad, truth is a cheat, and life is a joke. From his calm-mad heights, with the certitude of a god, he beholds all life as evil. Wife, children, friends—in the clear, white light of his logic they are exposed as frauds and shams. He sees through them, and all that he sees is their frailty, their meagreness, their sordidness, their pitifulness. No longer do they fool him. They are miserable little egotisms, like all the other little humans, fluttering their Mayfly life-dance of an hour. They are without freedom. They are puppets of chance. So is he. He realizes that. But there is one difference. He sees; he knows. And he knows his one freedom: he may anticipate the day of his death. All of which is not good for a man who is made to live and love and be loved. Yet suicide, quick or slow, a sudden spill or a gradual ooz-ing away through the years, is the price John Barleycorn exacts. No friend of his ever escapes making the just due payments.

* * *

I was five years old the first time I got drunk. It was on a hot day, and my father was ploughing in the field. I was sent from the house, half a mile away, to carry to him a pail of beer. "And be sure you don't spill it," was the parting injunction.

It was, as I remember it, a lard pail, very wide across the top, and without a cover. As I toddled along, the beer sopped over the rim upon my legs. And as I toddled I pondered. Beer was a very precious thing. Come to think of it, it must be wonderfully good. Else why was I never permitted to drink of it in the house? Other things kept from me by the grown-ups I had found good. Then this, too, was good. Trust the grown-ups. They knew. And, anyway, the pail was too full. I was slopping it against my legs and spilling it on the ground. Why waste it? And no one would know whether I had drunk or spilled it.

I was so small that, in order to negotiate the pail, I sat down and gathered it into my lap. First I sipped the foam. I was disappointed. The preciousness evaded me. Evidently it did not reside in the foam. Besides, the taste was not good. Then I remembered seeing the grown-ups blow the foam away before they drank. I buried my face in the foam and lapped the solid liquid beneath. It wasn't good at all. But still I drank. The grown-ups knew what they were about. Considering my diminutiveness, the size of the pail in my lap, and my drinking out of it with my breath held and my face buried to the ears in foam, it was rather difficult to estimate how much I drank. Also, I was gulping it down like medicine, in nauseous haste to get the ordeal over.

I shuddered when I started on, and decided that the good taste would come afterwards. I tried several times more in the course of that long half-mile. Then, astounded by the quantity of beer that was lacking, and remembering and remembering having seen stale beer made to foam afresh, I took a stick and stirred what was left till it foamed to the brim.

And my father never noticed. He emptied the pail with the wide thirst of the sweating ploughman, returned it to me, and started up the plough. I en-deavoured to walk beside the horses. I remember tottering and falling against their heels in front of the shining share, and that my father hauled back on the lines so violently that the horses nearly sat down on me. He told me afterward that it was only a matter of inches that I escaped disembowelling. Vaguely, too, I remember, my father carried me in his arms to the trees on the edge of the field, while all the world reeled and swung about me, and I was aware of deadly nausea mingled with an appalling conviction of sin.

I slept the afternoon away under the trees, and when my father roused me at sundown it was a very sick little boy that got up and dragged wearily home-ward. I was exhausted, oppressed by the weight of my limbs, and in my stomach was a harp-like vibrating that extended to my throat and brain. My condition was like that of one who had gone through a battle with poison. In truth, I had been poisoned.

In the weeks and months that followed I had no more interest in beer than in the kitchen stove after it had burned me. The grown-ups were right. Beer was not for children. The grown-ups didn't mind it; but neither did they mind taking pills and castor oil. As for me, I could manage to get along quite well without beer. Yes, and to the day of my death I could have managed to get along quite well without it. But circumstances decreed otherwise. At every turn in the world in which I lived, John Barleycorn beckoned. There was no escaping him. All paths led to him. And it took twenty years of contact, of exchanging greetings and passing on with my tongue in cheek, to develop in me a sneaking liking for the rascal.

* * *

. . . I abandoned myself to the life, and developed the misconception that the secret of John Barleycorn lay in going on mad drunks, rising through the successive stages that only an iron constitution could endure to final stupefaction and swinish unconsciousness. I did not like the taste, so I drank for the sole purpose of getting drunk, of getting hopelessly, helplessly drunk. And I, who had saved and scraped, traded like a Shylock and made junkmen weep; I who had stood aghast when French Frank, at a single stroke, spent eighty cents for whiskey for eight men; I turned myself loose with a more lavish disregard for money than any of them.

I remember going ashore one night with Nelson. In my pocket were one hundred and eighty dollars. It was my intention, first to buy me some clothes, after that, some drinks. I needed the clothes. All I possessed were on me, and they were as follows: a pair of sea-boots that providentially leaked the water out as fast as it ran in, a pair of fifty-cent overalls, a forty-cent cotton shirt, and a sou'wester. I had no hat, so I had to wear the sou'wester, and it will be noted that I have listed neither underclothes nor socks. I didn't own any.

To reach the stores where clothes could be bought, we had to pass a dozen saloons. So I bought me the drinks first. I never got to the clothing stores. In the morning, broke, poisoned, but contented, I came back on board, and we set sail. I possessed only the clothes I had gone ashore in, and not a cent remained of the one hundred and eighty dollars. It might well be deemed impossible, by those who have never tried it, that in twelve hours a lad can spend all of one hundred and eighty dollars for drinks, I know otherwise.

* * *

. . . But what gave immediacy to my decision to move on was a trick John Barleycorn played on me—a monstrous, incredible trick that showed abysses of intoxication hitherto undreamed. At one o'clock in the morning, after a prodigious drunk, I was tottering aboard a sloop at the end of the wharf, intending to go to sleep. The tides sweep through Carquinez Straits as in a mill-race, and the full ebb was on when I stumbled overboard. There was nobody on the wharf, nobody on the sloop. I was borne away by the current. I was not startled. I thought the misadventure delightful. I was a good swimmer, and in my inflamed condition the contact of the water with my skin soothed me like cool linen.

And then John Barleycorn played me his maniacal trick. Some maundering fancy of going out with the tide suddenly obsessed me. I had never been morbid. Thoughts of suicide had never entered my head. And now that they entered, I thought it fine, a splendid culminating, a perfect rounding off of my short but exciting career. I, who had never known girl's love, nor woman's love, nor the love of children; who had never played in the wide joy-fields of art, nor climbed the star-cool heights of philosophy, nor seen with my eyes more than a pinpoint's surface of the gorgeous world; I decided that this was all, that I had seen all, lived all, been all, that was worth while, and that now was the time to cease. This was the trick of John Barleycorn, laying me by the heels of my imagination and in a drug-dream dragging me to death.

Oh, he was convincing. I had really experienced all of life, and it didn't amount to much. The swinish drunkenness in which I had lived for months (this was accompanied by the sense of degradation and the old feeling of conviction of sin) was the last and best, and I could see for myself what it was worth. There were all the broken-down old bums and loafers I had bought drinks for. That was what remained of life. Did I want to become like them? A thousand times no; and I wept tears of sweet sadness over my glorious youth going out with the tide. (And who has not seen the weeping drunk, the melancholic drunk? They are to be found in all the bar-rooms, if they can find no other listener, telling their sorrows to the barkeeper, who is paid to listen.)

The water was delicious. It was a man's way to die. John Barleycorn changed the tune he played in my drink maddened brain. Away with tears and regret. It was a hero's death, and by the hero's own hand and will. So I struck up my death-chant and was singing it lustily, when the gurgle and splash of the current-riffles in my ears reminded me of my more immediate situation.

Below the town of Benicia, where the *Solano* wharf projects, the Straits widen out into what bay-farers call that "Bright of Turner's Shipyard." I was in the short-tide that swept under the *Solano* wharf and on into the bight. I knew of old the power of the suck which developed when the tide swung around the end of Dead Man's Island and drove straight for the wharf. I didn't want to go through those piles. It wouldn't be nice, and I might lose an hour in the bight on my way out with the tide.

I undressed in the water and struck out with a strong, single-overhand stroke, crossing the current at right-angles. Nor did I cease until, by the wharf lights, I knew I was safe to sweep by the end. Then I turned over and rested. The stroke had been a telling one, and I was a little time in recovering my breath.

I was elated, for I had succeeded in avoiding the suck. I started to raise my death-chant again—a purely extemporized farrago of a drug-crazed youth. "Don't sing—yet," whispered John Barleycorn. "The *Solano* runs all night. There are railroad men on the wharf. They will hear you, and come out in a boat and rescue you, and you don't want to be rescued." I certainly didn't. What? Be robbed of my hero's death? Never. And I lay on my back in the starlight, watching the familiar wharf-lights go by, red and green and white, and bidding sad sentimental farewell to them, each and all.

When I was well clear, in mid-channel, I sang again. Sometimes I swam a few strokes, but in the main I contented myself with floating and dreaming long drunken dreams. Before daylight, the chill of the water and the passage of the hours had sobered me sufficiently to make me wonder what portion of the Straits I was in, and also to wonder if the turn of the tide wouldn't catch me and take me back ere I had drifted out into San Pablo Bay.

Next I discovered that I was very weary and very cold, and quite sober, and that I didn't in the least want to be drowned. I could make out the Selby Smelter on the Contra Costa shore and the Mare Island lighthouse. I started to swim for the Solano shore, but was too weak and chilled, and made so little headway, and at the cost of such painful effort, that I gave it up and contented myself with floating, now and then giving a stroke to keep my balance in the tide-rips which were increasing their commotion on the surface of the water. And I knew fear. I was sober now, and I didn't want to die. I discovered scores of reasons for living. And the more reasons I discovered, the more liable it seemed that I was going to drown anyway.

Daylight, after I had been four hours in the water, found me in a parlous condition in the tide-rips off Mare Island light, where the swift ebbs form Vallejo Straits and Carquinez Straits were fighting with each other, and where, at that particular moment, they were fighting the flood tide setting up against them from San Pablo Bay. A stiff breeze had sprung up, and the crisp little waves were persistently lapping into my mouth, and I was beginning to swallow salt water. With my swimmer's knowledge, I knew the end was near. And then the boat came—a Greek fisherman running for Vallejo, and again I had been saved from John Barleycorn by my constitution and physical vigour.

And, in passing, let me note that this maniacal trick John Barleycorn played on me is nothing uncommon. An absolute statistic of the percentage of suicides due to John Barleycorn would be appalling. In my case, healthy, normal, young, full of the joy of life, the suggestion to kill myself was unusual; but it must be taken into account that it came on the heels of a long carouse, when my nerves and brain were fearfully poisoned, and that the dramatic, romantic side of my imagination, drink-maddened to lunacy, was delighted with the suggestion. And yet, the older, more morbid drinkers, more jaded with life and more disillusioned, who kill themselves, do so usually after a long debauch, when their nerves and brains are thoroughly poison-soaked.

* * *

. . . John Barleycorn, by inhibiting morality, incited to crime. Everywhere I saw men doing, drunk, what they would never dream of doing sober. And this wasn't the worst of it. It was the penalty that must be paid. Crime was destructive. Saloon-mates I drank with, who were good fellows and harmless, sober, did most violent and lunatic things when they were drunk. And then the police gathered them in and they vanished from our ken. Sometimes I visited them behind bars and said good-bye ere they journeyed across the bay to put on the felon's stripes. And time and again I heard the one explanation: "*If I hadn't been drunk I wouldn't a-done it.*" And sometimes, under the spell of John Barleycorn, the most frightful things were done—things that shocked even my case-hardened soul.

The other phase of the death-road was that of the habitual drunkards, who had a way of turning up their toes without apparent provocation. When they took sick, even with trifling afflictions that any ordinary man could pull through, they just pegged out. Sometimes they were found unattended and dead in their beds; on occasion their bodies were dragged out of the water; and sometimes it was just plain accident, as when Bill Kelley, unloading cargo while drunk, had a finger jerked off, which, under the circumstances, might just as easily have been his head.

* * *

. . . And when Saturday night came, and the week's work was over until Monday morning, I knew only one desire besides the desire to sleep, and that was to get drunk. This was the second time in my life that I had heard the unmistakable call of John Barleycorn. The first time it had been because of brain-fag. But I had no overworked brain now. On the contrary, all I knew was the dull numbness of a brain that was not worked at all. That was the trouble. My brain had become so alert and eager, so quickened by the wonder of the new world the books had discovered to it, that it now suffered all the misery of stagnancy and inaction.

And I, the long-time intimate of John Barleycorn, knew just what he promised me—maggots of fancy, dreams of power, forgetfulness, anything and everything save whirling washers, revolving mangles, humming centrifugal wringers, and fancy starch and interminable processions of duck trousers moving in steam under my flying iron. And that's it. John Barleycorn makes his appeal to weakness and failure, to weariness and exhaustion. He is the easy way out. And he is lying all the time. He offers false strength to the body, false elevation to the spirit, making things seem what they are not and vastly fairer than what they are.

But it must not be forgotten that John Barleycorn is protean. As well as to weakness and exhaustion, does he appeal to too much strength, to superabundant vitality, to the ennui of idleness. He can tuck in his arm the arm of any man in any mood. He can throw the net of his lure over all men. He exchanges new lamps for old, the spangles of illusion for the drabs of reality, and in the end cheats all who traffic with him.

*　*　*

. . . Well as soon as I got out in the company of others I was driven to melancholy and spiritual tears. I could neither laugh with nor at the solemn utterances of men I esteemed ponderous asses; nor could I laugh, nor engage in my old time lightsome persiflage, with the silly superficial chatterings of women, who, underneath all their silliness and softness, were as primitive, direct, and deadly in their pursuit of biological destiny as the monkeys women were before they shed their furry coats and replaced them with the furs of other animals.

And I was not pessimistic. I swear I was not pessimistic. I was merely bored. I had seen the same show too often, listened too often to the same songs and the same jokes. I knew too much about the box office receipts. I knew the cogs of the machinery behind the scenes so well that the posing on the stage, and the laughter and the song, could not drown the creaking of the wheels behind.

It doesn't pay to go behind the scenes and see the angel-voiced tenor beat his wife. Well, I'd been behind, and I was paying for it. Or else I was a fool. It is immaterial which was my situation. The situation is what counts, and the situation was that social intercourse for me was getting painful and difficult. On the other hand, it must be stated that on rare occasions, on very rare occasions, I did meet rare souls, or fools like me, with whom I could spend magnificent hours among the stars, or in the paradise of fools. I was married to a rare soul, or a fool, who never bored me and who was always a source of new and unending surprise and delight. But I could not spend all my hours solely in her company. Nor would it have been fair, nor wise to compel her to spend all her hours in my company. Besides, I had written a string of successful books, and society demands some portion of the recreative hours of a fellow that writes books. And any normal man, of himself and his needs, demands some hours of his fellow men.

And now we begin to come to it. How to face the social intercourse game with glamour gone? John Barleycorn. The ever patient one had waited a quarter of a century and more for me to reach my hand out in need of him. His thousand tricks had failed, thanks to my constitution and good luck, but he had more tricks in his bag. A cocktail or two, or several, I found, cheered me up for the foolishness of foolish people. A cocktail, or several, before dinner, enabled me to laugh whole-heartedly at things which had long since ceased being laughable. The cocktail was a prod, a spur, a kick, to my jaded mind and bored spirits. It recrudesced the laughter and the song, and put a lilt into my own imagination so that I could laugh and sing and say foolish things with the liveliest of them, or platitudes with verve and intensity to the satisfaction of the pompous mediocre ones who knew no other way to talk.

A poor companion without a cocktail, I became a very good companion with one. I achieved a false exhilaration, drugged myself to merriment. And the thing began so imperceptibly that I, old intimate of John Barleycorn, never dreamed whither it was leading me. I was beginning to call for music and wine; soon I should be calling for madder music and more wine.

It was at this time I became aware of waiting with expectancy for the one pre-dinner cocktail. I *wanted* it, and I was *conscious* that I wanted it. I remember, while war-corresponding in the Far East, being irresistibly attracted to a certain home. Besides accepting all invitations to dinner, I made a point of dropping in almost every afternoon. Now, the hostess was a charming woman, but it was not for her sake that I was under her roof so frequently. It happened that she made by far the finest cocktail procurable in that large city where drink-mixing on the part of the foreign population was indeed an art. Up at the club, down at the hotels, and in other private houses, no such cocktails were created. Her cocktails were subtle. They were masterpieces. They were the least repulsive to the palate and carried the most "kick." And yet, I desired her cocktails only for sociability's sake, to key myself to sociable moods. When I rode away from that city, across hundreds of miles of rice-fields and mountains, and through months of campaigning, and on with the victorious Japanese into Manchuria, I did not drink. Several bottles of whisky were always to be found on the backs of my pack-horses. Yet I never broached a bottle for myself, never took a drink by myself, and never knew a desire to take such a drink. Oh, if a white man came into my camp, I opened a bottle and we drank together according to way of men, just as he would open a bottle and drink with me if I came into his camp. I carried that whisky for social purposes, and I so charged it up in my expense account to the newspaper for which I worked.

Only in retrospect can I mark the almost imperceptible growth of my desire. There were little hints then that I did not take, little straws in the wind that I not see, little incidents the gravity of which I did not realize.

For instance, for some years it had been my practice each winter to cruise for six or eight weeks on San Francisco Bay. My stout sloop yacht, the *Spray*, had a comfortable cabin and a coal stove. A Korean boy did the cooking, and I usually took a friend or so along to share the joys of the cruise. Also, I took my machine along and did my thousand words a day. On the particular trip I have in mind, Cloudesley and Toddy came along. This was Toddy's first trip. On previous Cloudesley had elected to drink beer; so I had kept the yacht supplied with beer and had drunk beer with him.

But on this cruise the situation was different. Toddy was so nicknamed because of his diabolical cleverness in concocting toddies. So I brought whisky along—a couple of gallons. Alas! Many another gallon I bought, for Cloudesley and I got into the habit of drinking a certain hot toddy that actually tasted delicious going down and that carried the most exhilarating kick imaginable.

I *liked* those toddies. I grew to look forward to the making of them. We drank them regularly, one before breakfast, one before dinner, one before supper, and one when we went to bed. We never got drunk. But I will say that four times a day we were very genial. And when, in the middle of the cruise, Toddy was called back to San Francisco on business, Cloudesley and I saw to it that the Korean boy mixed toddies regularly for us according to formula.

But that was only on the boat. Back on the land, in my house, I took no before breakfast eye-opener, no bed-going nightcap. And I haven't drunk hot toddies since, and that was many a year ago. But the point is, I *liked* those toddies. The geniality of which they were provocative was marvelous. They were eloquent proselytisers for John Barleycorn in their own small insidious way. They were tickles of the something destined to grow into daily and deadly desire. And I didn't know, never dreamed—I, who had lived with John Barleycorn for so many years and laughed at all his unavailing attempts to win me.

* * *

. . . But the time was at hand, rhymeless and reasonless so far as I can see, when I was to begin to pay for my score of years of dallying with John Barleycorn. Occasionally guests journeyed to the ranch and remained a few days. Some did not drink. But to those who did drink, the absence of alcohol on the ranch was a hardship. I could not violate my sense of hospitality by compelling them to endure hardship. I ordered in a stock—for my guests.

I was never interested enough in cocktails to know how they were made. So I got a bar-keeper in Oakland to make them in bulk and ship them to me. When I had no guests I didn't drink. But I began to notice, when I finished my morning's work, that I was glad if there were a guest, for then I could drink a cocktail with him.

Now I was so clean of alcohol that even a single cocktail was provocative of pitch. A single cocktail would glow the mind and tickle a laugh for the few minutes prior to sitting down to table and starting the delightful process of eating. On the other hand, such was the strength of my stomach, of my alcoholic resistance, that the single cocktail was only the glimmer of a glow, the faintest tickle of a laugh. One day, a friend frankly and shamelessly suggested a second cocktail. I drank the second one with him. The glow was appreciably longer and warmer, the laughter deeper and more resonant. One does not forget such experiences. Sometimes I almost think that it was because I was so very happy that I started on my real drinking.

I remember one day Charmian and I took a long ride over the mountains on our horses. The servants had been dismissed for the day, and we returned late at night to a jolly chafing-dish supper. Oh, it was good to be alive that night while the supper was preparing, the two of us alone in the kitchen. I, personally, was at the top of life. Such things as the books and ultimate truth did not exist. My body was gloriously healthy, and healthily tired from the long ride. It had been a splendid day. The night was splendid. I was with the woman who was my mate, picnicking in gleeful abandon. I had no troubles. The bills were all paid, and a surplus of money was rolling in on me. The future ever-widened before me. And right there, in the kitchen, delicious things bubbled in the chafing-dish, our laughter bubbled, and my stomach was keen with a most delicious edge of appetite.

I felt so good, that somehow, somewhere, in me arose an insatiable greed to feel better. I was so happy that I wanted to pitch my happiness even higher. And I knew the way. Ten thousand contacts with John Barleycorn had taught me. Several times I wandered out of the kitchen to the cocktail bottle, and each time I left it diminished by one man's-size cocktail. The result was splendid, I wasn't jingled, I wasn't lighted up; but I was warmed, I glowed, my happiness was pyramided. Munificent as life was to me, I added to that munificence. It was a great hour—one of my greatest. But I paid for it, long afterwards, as you will see. One does not forget such experiences, and, in human stupidity, cannot be brought to realize that there is no immutable law which decrees that same things shall produce some results. For they don't, else would the thousandth pipe of opium be provocative of similar delights to the first, else would one cocktail instead of several, produce an equivalent glow after a year of cocktails.

One day, just before I ate midday dinner, after my morning's writing was done, when I had no guest, I took a cocktail by myself. Thereafter, when there were no guests, I took this daily pre-dinner cocktail. And right there John Barleycorn had me. I was beginning to drink regularly. I was beginning to drink alone. And I was beginning to drink, not for hospitality's sake, not for the sake of the taste, but for the effect of the drink.

I *wanted* that daily pre-dinner cocktail. And it never crossed my mind that there was any reason I should not have it. I paid for it. I could pay for a thousand cocktails each day if I wanted. And what was a cocktail—one cocktail— to me who on so many occasions for so many years had drunk inordinate quantities of stiffer stuff and been unharmed?

The program of my ranch life was as follows: Each morning, at eight-thirty, having been reading or correcting proofs in bed since four or five, I went to my desk. Odds and ends of correspondence and notes occupied me till nine, and at nine sharp, invariably, I began my writing. By eleven, sometimes a few minutes earlier or later, my thousand words were finished. Another half-hour at cleaning up my desk, and my day's work was done, so that at eleven-thirty I got into a hammock under the trees with my mailbag and the morning newspaper. At twelve-thirty I ate dinner and in the afternoon I swam and rode.

One morning, at eleven-thirty, before I got into the hammock, I took a cocktail. I repeated this on subsequent mornings of course, taking another cocktail just before I ate at twelve-thirty. Soon I found myself, seated at my desk in the midst of my thousand words, looking forward to that eleven-thirty cocktail.

At last, now, I was thoroughly conscious that I desired alcohol. But what of it? I wasn't afraid of John Barleycorn. I had associated with him too long. I was wise in the matter of drink. I was discreet. Never again would I drink to excess. I knew the dangers and the pitfalls of John Barleycorn, the various ways by which he had tried to kill me in the past. But all that was past, long past. Never again would I drink myself into stupefaction. Never again would I get drunk. All I wanted, and all I would take, was just enough to glow and warm me, to kick geniality alive in me and put laughter in my throat and stir the maggots of imagination slightly in the brain. Oh, I was thoroughly master of myself, and of John Barleycorn.

* * *

But the same stimulus to the human organism will not continue to produce the same response. By and by I discovered that there was no kick at all in one cocktail. One cocktail left me dead. There was no glow, no laughter tickle. Two or three cocktails were required to produce the original effect of one. And I wanted that effect. I drank my first cocktail at eleven-thirty when I took the morning's mail into the hammock, and I drank my second cocktail an hour later just before I ate. I got into the habit of crawling out of the hammock ten minutes earlier so as to find time and decency for two more cocktails ere I ate. This became schedule—three cocktails in the hour that intervened between my desk and dinner. And these are two of the deadliest drinking habits: regular drinking and solitary drinking.

I was always willing to drink when anyone was around. I drank by myself when no one was around. Then I made another step. When I had for guest a man of limited drinking caliber, I took two drinks to his one—one drink with him, the other without him and of which he did not know. I *stole* that other drink, and, worse than that, I began the habit of drinking alone when there was a guest, a man, a comrade, with whom I could have drunk. But John Barleycorn furnished the extenuation. It was a wrong thing to trip a guest up with excess of hospitality and get him drunk. If I persuaded him, with his limited caliber, into drinking up with me, I'd surely get him drunk. What could I do but steal that every second drink, or else deny myself the kick equivalent to what he got out of half the number?

Please remember, as I recite this development of my drinking, that I am no fool, no weakling. As the world measures such things, I am a success—I dare to say a success more conspicuous than the success of the average successful man, and a success that required a pretty fair amount of brains and will power. My body is a strong body. It has survived where weaklings died like flies. And yet these things which I am relating happened to my body and to me. I am a fact. My drinking is a fact. My drinking is a thing that has happened, and is no theory nor speculation; and, as I see it, it but lays the emphasis on the power of John Barleycorn—a savagery that we still permit to exist, a deadly institution that lingers from the mad old brutal days and that takes its heavy toll of youth and strength, and high spirit, and of very much of all the best we breed.

To return. After a boisterous afternoon in the swimming pool, followed by a glorious ride on horseback over the mountains or up or down the Valley of the Moon, I found myself so keyed up and splendid that I desired to be more highly keyed, to feel more splendid. I knew the way. A cocktail before supper was not the way. Two or three, at the very least, was what was needed. I took them. Why not? It was living. I had always dearly loved to live. This also became part of the daily schedule.

Then, too, I was perpetually finding excuses for extra cocktails. It might be the assembling of a particularly jolly crowd; a touch of anger against my architect or against a thieving stonemason working on my barn; the death of my favorite horse in a barbed wire fence; or news of good fortune in the morning mail from my dealings with editors and publishers. It was immaterial what the excuse might be, once the desire had germinated in me. The thing was: I *wanted* alcohol. At last, after a score and more of years of dallying and of not wanting, now I wanted it. And my strength was my weakness. I required two, three, or four drinks to get an effect commensurate with the effect the average man got out of one drink.

* * *

. . . The more I drank the more I was required to drink to get an equivalent effect. When I left the Valley of the Moon, and went to the city, and dined out, a cocktail served at the table was a wan and worthless thing. There was no predinner kick in it. On my way to dinner I was compelled to accumulate the kick—two cocktails, three, and if I met some fellows, four or five, or six, it didn't matter within several. Once, I was in a rush. I had no time decently to accumulate the several drinks. A brilliant idea came to me. I told the barkeeper to mix me a double cocktail. Thereafter, whenever I was in a hurry, I ordered double cocktails. It saved time.

One result of this regular heavy drinking was to jade me. My mind grew so accustomed to spring and liven by artificial means that without artificial means it refused to spring and liven. Alcohol became more and more imperative in order to meet people, in order to become sociably fit. I had to get the kick and the hit of the stuff, the crawl of the maggots, the genial brain glow, the laughter tickle, the touch of devilishness and sting, the smile over the face of things, ere I could join my fellows and make one with them.

Another result was that John Barleycorn was beginning to trip me up. He was thrusting my long sickness back upon me, inveigling me into again pursuing Truth and snatching her veils away from her, tricking me into looking reality stark in the face. But this came on gradually. My thoughts were growing harsh again, though they grew harsh slowly.

Sometimes warning thoughts crossed my mind. Where was this steady drinking leading? But trust John Barleycorn to silence such questions. "Come on and have a drink and I'll tell you all about it," is his way. And it works. For instance, the following is a case in point, and one which John Barleycorn never wearied of reminding me:

I had suffered an accident which required a ticklish operation. One morning, a week after I had come off the table, I lay on my hospital bed, weak and weary. The sunburn of my face, what little of it could be seen through a scraggly growth of beard, had faded to a sickly yellow. My doctor stood at my bedside on the verge of departure. He glared disapprovingly at the cigarette I was smoking.

"That's what you ought to quit," he lectured. "It will get you in the end. Look at me."

I looked. He was about my own age, broad-shouldered, deep-chested, eyes sparkling, and ruddy-cheeked with health. A finer specimen of manhood one would not ask.

"I used to smoke," he went on. "Cigars. But I gave even them up. And look at me."

The man was arrogant, and rightly arrogant, with conscious well-being. And within a month he was dead. It was no accident. Half a dozen different bugs of long scientific names had attacked and destroyed him. The complications were astonishing and painful, and for days before he died the screams of agony of that splendid manhood could be heard for a block around. He died screaming.

"You see," said John Barleycorn. "He took care of himself. He even stopped smoking cigars. And that's what he got for it. Pretty rotten, eh? But the bugs will jump. There's no forefending them. Your magnificent doctor took every precaution, yet they got him. When the bug jumps you can't tell where it will land. It may be you. Look what he missed. Will you miss all I can give you, only to have a bug jump on you and drag you down? There is no equity in life. It's all a lottery. But I put the lying smile on the face of life and laugh at the facts. Smile with me and laugh. You'll get yours in the end, but in the meantime laugh. It's a pretty dark world. I illuminate it for you. It's a rotten world, when things can happen such as happened to your doctor. There's only one thing to do: take another drink and forget it."

And of course, I took another drink for the inhibition that accompanied it. I took another drink every time John Barleycorn reminded me of what had happened. Yet I drank rationally, intelligently. I saw to it that the quality of the stuff was of the best. I sought the kick and the inhibition, and avoided the penalties of poor quality and of drunkenness. It is to be remarked, in passing, that when a man begins to drink rationally and intelligently that he betrays a grave symptom of how far along the road he has traveled.

But I continued to observe my rule of never taking my first drink of the day until the last word of my thousand words was written. On occasion, however, I took a day's vacation from my writing. At such times, since it was no violation of my rule, I didn't mind how early in the day I took that first drink. And persons who have never been through the drinking game wonder how the drinking habit grows!

* * *

. . . I achieved a condition in which my body was never free from alcohol. Nor did I permit myself to be away from alcohol. If I traveled to out-of-the-way places, I declined to run the risk of finding them dry. I took a quart, or several quarts, along in my grip. In the past I had been amazed by other men guilty of this practice. Now I did it myself unblushingly. And when I got out with the fellows, I cast all rules by the board. I drank when they drank, what they drank, and in the same way they drank.

I was carrying a beautiful alcoholic configuration around with me. The thing fed on its own heat and flamed the fiercer. There was no time, in all my waking time, that I didn't want a drink. I began to anticipate the completion of my daily thousand words by taking a drink when only five hundred words were written. It was not long until I prefaced the beginning of the thousand words with a drink.

The gravity of this I realized too well. I made new rules. Resolutely I would refrain from drinking until my work was done. But a new and most diabolical complication arose. The work refused to be done without drinking. It just couldn't be done. I had to drink in order to do it. I was beginning to fight now. I had the craving at last, and it was mastering me. I would sit at my desk and daily with pad and pen, but words refused to flow. My brain could not think the proper thoughts because continually it was obsessed with the one thought that across the room in the liquor cabinet stood John Barleycorn. When, in despair, I took my drink, at once my brain loosened up and began to roll off the thousand words.

In my town house, in Oakland, I finished the stock of liquor and willfully refused to purchase more. It was no use, because, unfortunately, there remained in the bottom of the liquor cabinet a case of beer. In vain I tried to write. Now beer is a poor substitute for stronger waters; besides, I didn't like beer, yet all I could think of was that beer so singularly accessible in the bottom of the cabinet. Not until I had drunk a pint of it did the words begin to reel off, and the thousand were reeled off to the tune of numerous pints. The worst of it was that the beer caused me severe heart-burn; but despite the discomfort I soon finished off the case.

Edwin Arlington Robinson (1869–1935)

Edwin Arlington Robinson was reared in Gardiner, Maine. Educated at Harvard, Robinson wrote about people, particularly New England characters remembered from his youth. He found considerable material for his stories and poems close to home in the troubled lives of his own family members and acquaintances. Many of his most famous poems, including the selection utilized here, "Miniver Cheevy," feature individuals with alcohol problems and depression.

Robinson's work was recognized with three Pulitzer Prizes (1921, 1924, and 1927). The model for Miniver Cheevy, with his naive Romanticism and selfish, drunken indulgence, was Robinson's brother Herman.

"Miniver Cheevy"

Miniver Cheevy, child of scorn,
Grew lean when he assailed the seasons;
He wept that he was ever born,
And he had reasons.

Miniver loved the days of old
When swords were bright and steeds were prancing;
The vision of a warrior bold
Would set him dancing.

Miniver sighed for what was not,
And dreamed, and rested from his labors;
He dreamed of Thebes and Camelot,
And Priam's neighbors.

Miniver mourned the ripe renown
That made so many a name so fragrant;
He mourned Romance, now on the town,
And Art, a vagrant.

Miniver loved the Medici,
Albeit he had never seen one;
He would have sinned incessantly
Could he have been one.

Minniver cursed the commonplace
And eyed a khaki suit with loathing;
He missed the mediaeval grace
Of iron clothing.

Miniver scorned the gold he sought,
But sore annoyed was he without it;
Miniver thought, and thought, and thought,
And thought about it.

Miniver Cheevy, born too late,
Scratched his head and kept on thinking:
Miniver coughed, and called it fate,
And kept on drinking.

Samuel Butler (1835–1902)

Samuel Butler was the son and grandson of eminent clergymen. He refused to be ordained and went to New Zealand, where he established a sheep farm and made a modest fortune. He returned to England in 1864 and pursued interests in art, music, biology, and literature. In 1872 he published *Erewhon*, a satire on English social and economic injustices. *Erewhon* established Butler's literary fame. His only novel, the autobiographical *The Way Of All Flesh*, was published after his death in 1902. In it Butler does an excellent job of describing the ability of an alcoholic to deceive even those closest to them. *The Way Of All Flesh* is considered among the great English novels.

The Way of All Flesh

. . . The great change in Ellen's life consequent upon her meeting Ernest and getting married had for a time actually sobered her by shaking her out of her old ways. Drunkenness is so much a matter of habit, and habit so much a matter of surroundings, that if you completely change the surroundings you will sometimes get rid of the drunkenness altogether. Ellen had intended remaining always sober henceforward, and never having had so long a steady fit before, believed she was now cured. So she perhaps would have been if she had seen none of her old acquaintances. When, however, her new life was beginning to lose its newness, and when her old acquaintances came to see her, her present surroundings became more like her past, and on this she herself began to get like her past too. At first she only got a little tipsy and struggled against a relapse; but it was no use, she soon lost the heart to fight, and now her object was not to try to keep sober, but to get gin without her husband's finding it out.

So the hysterics continued, and she managed to make her husband still think that they were due to her being about to become a mother. The worse her attacks were, the more devoted he became in his attention to her. At last he insisted that a doctor should see her. The doctor of course took in the situation at a glance, but said nothing to Ernest except in such a guarded way that he did not understand the hints that were thrown out to him. He was much too down-right and matter-of-fact to be quick at taking hints of this sort. He hoped that as soon as his wife's confinement was over she would regain her health and had no thought save how to spare her as far as possible till that happy time should come.

In the mornings she was generally better, as long that is to say as Ernest remained at home; but he had to go out buying, and on his return would generally find that she had had another attack as soon as he left the house. At times she would laugh and cry for half an hour together, at others she would lie in a semi-comatose state upon the bed, and when he came back he would find that the shop had been neglected and all the work of the household left undone. Still he took it for granted that this was all part of the usual course when women were going to become mothers, and when Ellen's share of the work settled down more and more upon his own shoulders he did it all and drudged away without a murmur. Nevertheless, he began to feel in a vague way more as he had felt in Ashpit Place, at Roughborough, or at Battersby, and to lose the buoyancy of spirits which had made another man of him during the first six months of married life.

It was not only that he had to do so much household work, for even the cooking, cleaning up slops, bed-making and fire-lighting ere long devolved upon him, but his business no longer prospered. He could buy as hitherto, but Ellen seemed unable to sell as she had sold at first. The fact was that she sold as well as ever, but kept back part of the proceeds in order to buy gin, and she did this more and more till even the unsuspecting Ernest ought to have seen that she was not telling the truth. When she sold better—that is to say when she did not think it safe to keep back more than a certain amount, she got money out of him on the plea that she had a longing for this or that, and that it would perhaps irreparably damage the baby if her longing was denied her. All seemed right, reasonable, and unavoidable, nevertheless Ernest saw that until the confinement was over he was likely to have a hard time of it. All, however, would then come right again.

*   *   *

. . . In the month of September, 1860, a girl was born, and Ernest was proud and happy. The birth of the child, and a rather alarming talk which the doctor had given to Ellen sobered her for a few weeks, and it really seemed as though his hopes were about to be fulfilled. The expenses of his wife's confinement were heavy, and he was obliged to trench upon his savings, but he had no doubt about soon recouping this, now that Ellen was herself again; for a time indeed his business did revive a little, nevertheless it seemed as though the interruption to his prosperity had in some way broken the spell of good luck which had attended him in the outset; he was still sanguine, however, and worked night and day with a will, but there was no more music, or reading, or writing now. His Sunday outings were put a stop to, and but for the first floor being let to myself, he would have lost his citadel there too, but he seldom used it, for Ellen had to wait more and more upon the baby, and, as a consequence, Ernest had to wait more and more upon Ellen.

One afternoon, about a couple of months after the baby had been born, and just as my unhappy hero was beginning to feel more hopeful and therefore better able to bear his burdens, he returned from a sale, and found Ellen in the same hysterical condition that he had found her in in the spring. She said she was again with child, and Ernest still believed her.

All the troubles of the preceding six months began again then and there, and grew worse and worse continually. Money did not come in quickly, for Ellen cheated him by keeping it back, and dealing improperly with the goods he bought. When it did come in she got it out of him as before on pretexts which it seemed inhuman to inquire into. It was always the same story. By and by a new feature began to show itself. Ernest had inherited his father's punctuality and exactness as regards money; he liked to know the worst of what he had to pay at once; he hated having expenses sprung upon him which if not foreseen might and ought to have been so, but now bills began to be brought to him for things ordered by Ellen without his knowledge, or for which he had already given her the money. This was awful, and even Ernest turned. When he remonstrated with her—not for having bought the things, but for having said nothing to him about the moneys being owing—Ellen met him with hysteria and there was a scene. She had now pretty well forgotten the hard times she had known when she had been on her own resources and reproached him downright with having married her—on that moment the scales fell from Ernest's eyes as they had fallen when Towneley had said, "No, no, no." He said nothing, but he woke up once for all to the fact that he had made a mistake in marrying. A touch had again come which had revealed him to himself.

He went upstairs to the disused citadel, flung himself into the armchair, and covered his face with his hands.

He still did not know that his wife drank, but he could no longer trust her, and his dream of happiness was over. He had been saved from the Church—so as by fire, but still saved—but what could now save him from his marriage? He had made the same mistake that he had made in wedding himself to the church, but with a hundred times worse results. He had learnt nothing by experience: he was as Esau—one of those wretches whose hearts the Lord had hardened, who, having ears, heard not, having eyes saw not, and who should find no place for repentance though they sought it even with tears.

Yet had he not on the whole tried to find out what the ways of God were, and to follow them in singleness of heart? To a certain extent, yes; but he had not been thorough; he had not given up all for God. He knew that very well; he had done little as compared with what he might and ought to have done, but still if he was being punished for this, God was a hard taskmaster, and one, too, who was continually pouncing out upon his unhappy creatures from ambuscades. In marrying Ellen he had meant to avoid a life of sin, and to take the course he believed to be moral and right. With his antecedents and surroundings it was the most natural thing in the world for him to have done, yet in what a frightful position had not his morality landed him. Could any amount of immorality have placed him in a much worse one? What was morality worth if it was not that which on the whole brought a man peace at the last, and could anyone have reasonable certainty that marriage would do this? It seemed to him that in his attempt to be moral he had been following a devil which had disguised itself as an angel of light. But if so, what ground was there on which a man might rest the sole of his foot and tread in reasonable safety?

He was still too young to reach the answer, "On common sense"—an answer which he would have felt to be unworthy of anyone who had an ideal standard.

However this might be, it was plain that he had now done for himself. It had been thus with him all his life. If there had come at any time a gleam of sunshine and hope, it was to be obscured immediately—why, prison was happier than this! There, at any rate, he had had no money anxieties, and these were beginning to weigh upon him now with all their horrors. He was happier even now than he had been at Battersby or at Roughborough, and he would not go back, even if he could, to his Cambridge life, but for all that the outlook was so gloomy, in fact so hopeless, that he felt as if he could have only too gladly gone to sleep and died in his armchair once for all.

As he was musing thus and looking upon the wreck of his hopes—for he saw well enough that as long as he was linked to Ellen he should never rise as he had dreamed of doing—he heard a noise below, and presently a neighbor ran upstairs and entered his room hurriedly.

"Good gracious, Mr. Pontifex," she exclaimed, "for goodness' sake come down quickly and help. Mrs. Pontifex is took with the horrors—and she's orkard."

The unhappy man came down as he was bid and found his wife mad with *delirium tremens.*

He knew all now. The neighbors thought he must have known that his wife drank all along, but Ellen had been so artful, and he so simple, that, as I have said, he had had no suspicion. "Why," said the woman who had summoned him, "she'll drink anything she can stand up and pay her money for." Ernest could hardly believe his ears, but when the doctor had seen his wife and she had become more quiet, he went over to the public house hard by and made enquiries, the result of which rendered further doubt impossible. The publican took the opportunity to present my hero with a bill of several pounds for bottles of spirits supplied to his wife, and what with his wife's confinement and the way business had fallen off, he had not the money to pay with, for the sum exceeded the remnant of his savings.

He came to me—not for money, but to tell me his miserable story. I had seen for some time that there was something wrong, and had suspected pretty shrewdly what the matter was, but of course I said nothing. Ernest and I had been growing apart for some time. I was vexed at his having married, and he knew I was vexed, though I did my best to hide it.

A man's friendships are, like his will, invalidated by marriage—but they are also no less invalidated by the marriage of friends. The rift in friendship which invariably makes its appearance on the marriage of either of the parties to it was fast widening, as it no less invariably does, into the great gulf which is fixed between the married and the unmarried, and I was beginning to leave my *protégé* to a fate with which I had neither right nor power to meddle. In fact I had begun to feel him rather a burden; I did not so much mind this when I could be of use, but I grudged it when I could be of none. He had made his bed and he must lie upon it. Ernest had felt all this and had seldom come near me till now, one evening late in 1860, he called on me, and with a very woe-begone face told me his troubles.

As soon as I found that he no longer liked his wife I forgave him at once, and was as much interested in him as ever. There is nothing an old bachelor likes better than to find a young married man who wishes he had not got married—especially when the case is such an extreme one that he need not pretend to hope that matters will come all right again, or encourage his young friend to make the best of it.

I was myself in favor of a separation, and said I would make Ellen an allowance myself—of course intending that it should come out of Ernest's money; but he would not hear of this. He had married Ellen, he said, and he must try to reform her. He hated it, but he must try; and finding him as usual very obstinate I was obliged to acquiesce, though with little confidence as to the result. I was vexed at seeing him waste himself upon such a barren task, and, again began to feel him burdensome. I am afraid I showed this, for he again avoided me for some time, and, indeed, for many months I hardly saw him at all.

Ellen remained very ill for some days, and then gradually recovered. Ernest hardly left her till she was out of danger. When she had recovered he got the doctor to tell her that if she had such another attack she would certainly die; this so frightened her that she took the pledge.

Then he became more hopeful again. When she was sober she was just what she was during the first days of her married life, and so quick was he to forget pain, that after a few days he was as fond of her as ever. But Ellen could not forgive him for knowing what he did. She knew that he was on the watch to shield her from temptation, and though he did his best to make her think that he had no further uneasiness about her, she found the burden of her union with respectability grow more and more heavy upon her, and looked back more and more longingly upon the lawless freedom of the life she had led before she met her husband.

I will dwell no longer on this part of my story. During the spring months of 1861 she kept straight—she had had her fling of dissipation, and this, together with the impression made upon her by having taken the pledge, tamed her for a while. The shop went fairly well, and enabled Ernest to make the two ends meet. In the spring and summer of 1861 he even put by a little money again. In the autumn his wife was confined of a boy—a very fine one, so everyone said. She soon recovered, and Ernest was beginning to breathe freely and be almost sanguine when, without a word of warning, the storm broke again. He returned one afternoon about two years after his marriage, and found his wife lying upon the floor insensible.

From this time he became hopeless, and began to go visibly down hill. He had been knocked about too much, and the luck had gone too long against him. The wear and tear of the last three years had told on him, and though not actually ill he was overworked, below par, and unfit for any further burden.

He struggled for a while to prevent himself from finding this out, but facts were too strong for him. Again he called on me and told me what had happened. I was glad the crisis had come; I was sorry for Ellen, but a complete separation from her was the only chance for her husband. Even after this last outbreak he was unwilling to consent to this, and talked nonsense about dying at his post, till I got tired of him. Each time I saw him the old gloom had settled more and more deeply upon his face, and I had about made up my mind to put an end to the situation by a *coup de main,* such as bribing Ellen to run away with somebody else, or something of that kind, when matters settled themselves as usual in a way which I had not anticipated.

Drug Dependence

Drug dependence, the problem of drug addiction, is associated with the misuse of both prescription drugs and illegal street drugs. Included in this category are such drugs as cocaine, heroin, amphetamines, cannabis, phencyclidine (PCP), hallucinogens, and many others.

Thomas de Quincey (1785–1859)

Thomas de Quincey was the son of a wealthy merchant in Manchester, England. After spending his formative years in private grammar schools, at the age of seventeen he decided to leave school and go traveling around Wales. After a period of poverty in London he ended up at Worcester College in Oxford. It was there that he acquired the lifelong habit of using opium. He first used opium to treat his chronic neuralgia but later became a recreational user.

In his *Confessions of an English Opium Eater,* de Quincey outlines the effects of the drug on himself and emphatically tells us why he likes the drug. In addition he also tells us of the horrific aftereffects he experienced as a result of long-term use.

De Quincey's *Confessions* was his first and most important book, and it established his reputation as a great leader of the Romantic movement. Such works as "Murder Considered as One of the Fine Arts" (1827), "The Revolt of the Tartars" (1837), and "The English Mail Coach" (1849) enhanced his fame. With a large family dependent on him, and generally in debt, de Quincey produced thousands of pages of writings in an effort to escape his creditors and avoid arrest.

This work provides insight into the efforts of a highly intelligent, drug-dependent person, who attempts to intellectualize his addiction and to justify his dependent behaviors. It is excerpted here and serves as a prime example of the lunacy and lucidity of drug addiction.

Confessions of an English Opium Eater

It is so long since I first took opium, that if it had been a trifling incident in my life, I might have forgotten its date: but cardinal events are not to be forgotten; and from circumstances connected with it, I remember that it must be referred to the autumn of 1804. During that season I was in London, having come thither for the first time since my entrance at college. And my introduction to opium arose in the following way. From an early age I had been accustomed to wash my head in cold water at least once a day: being suddenly seized with toothache, I attributed it to some relaxation caused by an accidental intermission of that practice; jumped out of bed; plunged my head into a bason of cold water; and with hair thus wetted went to sleep. The next morning, as I need hardly say, I awoke with excruciating rheumatic pains of the head and face, from which I had hardly any respite for about twenty days. On the twenty-first day, I think it was, and on a Sunday, that I went out into the streets; rather to run away, if possible, from my torments, than with any distinct purpose. By accident I met a college acquaintance who recommended opium. Opium! dread agent of unimaginable pleasure and pain! I had heard of it as I had of manna or of Ambrosia, but no further: how unmeaning a sound was it at that time! what solemn chords does it now strike upon my heart! what heart-quaking vibrations of sad and happy remembrances! Reverting for a moment to these, I feel a mystic importance attached to the minutest circumstances connected with the place and the time, and the man (if man he was) that first laid open to me the Paradise of Opium-eaters. It was a Sunday afternoon, wet and cheerless: and a duller spectacle this earth of ours has not to show than a rainy Sunday in London. My road homewards lay through Oxford-street; and near "the *stately* Pantheon," (as Mr. Wordsworth has obligingly called it) I saw a druggist's shop. The druggist—unconscious minister of celestial pleasures!—as if in sympathy with the rainy Sunday, looked dull and stupid, just as any mortal druggist might be expected to look on a Sunday; and, when I asked for the tincture of opium, he gave it to me as any other man might do: and furthermore, out of my shilling, returned me what seemed to be real copper halfpence, taken out of a real wooden drawer. Nevertheless, in spite of such indications of humanity, he has ever since existed in my mind as the beatific vision of an immortal druggist, sent down to earth on a special mission to myself. And it confirms me in this way of considering him, that, when I next came up to London, I sought him near the stately Pantheon, and found him not: and thus to me, who knew not his name (if indeed he had one) he seemed rather to have vanished from Oxford-street than to have removed in any bodily fashion. The reader may choose to think of him as, possibly, no more than a sublunary druggist: it may be so: but my faith is better: I believe him to have evanesced, or evaporated. So unwillingly would I connect any mortal remembrances with that hour, and place, and creature, that first brought me acquainted with the celestial drug.

Arrived at my lodgings, it may be supposed that I lost not a moment in taking the quantity prescribed. I was necessarily ignorant of the whole art and mystery of opium-taking: and, what I took, I took under every disadvantage. But I took it:—and in an hour, oh! Heavens! what a revulsion! what an upheaving, from its lowest depths, of the inner spirit! what an apocalypse of the world within me! That my pains had vanished, was now a trifle in my eyes:— this negative effect was swallowed up in the immensity of those positive effects which had opened before me—in the abyss of divine enjoyment thus suddenly revealed. Here was a panacea . . . for all human woes: here was the secret of happiness, about which philosophers had disputed for so many ages, at once discovered: happiness might now be bought for a penny, and carried in the waist-coat pocket: portable ecstasies might be had corked up in a pint bottle: and peace of mind could be sent down in gallons by the mail coach. But, if I talk in this way, the reader will think I am laughing: and I can assure him, that nobody will laugh long who deals much with opium: its pleasures even are of a grave and solemn complexion; and in his happiest state, the opium-eater cannot present himself in the character of *l'Allegro:* even then, he speaks and thinks as becomes *Il Penseroso.* Nevertheless, I have a very reprehensible way of jesting at times in the midst of my own misery: and, unless when I am checked by some more powerful feelings, I am afraid I shall be guilty of this indecent practice even in these annals of suffering or enjoyment. The reader must allow a little to my infirm nature in this respect: and with a few indulgences of that sort, I shall endeavour to be as grave, if not drowsy, as fits a theme like opium, so anti-mercurial as it really is, and so drowsy as it is falsely reputed.

And, first, one word with respect to its bodily effects: for upon all that has been hitherto written on the subject of opium, whether by travellers to Turkey (who may plead their privilege of lying as an old immemorial right), or by professors of medicine, writing *ex cathedra,*—I have but one emphatic criticism to pronounce—Lies! lies! lies! I remember once, in passing a book-stall, to have caught these words from a page of some satiric author:—"By this time I became convinced that the London newspapers spoke truth at least twice a week, viz. on Tuesday and Saturday, and might safely be depended upon for— the list of bankrupts." In like manner, I do by no means deny that some truths have been delivered to the world in regard to opium: thus it has been repeatedly affirmed by the learned, that opium is a dusky brown in colour; and this, take notice, I grant: secondly, that it is rather dear; which also I grant: for in my time, East-India opium has been three guineas a pound, and Turkey eight: and, thirdly, that if you eat a good deal of it, most probably you must—do what is particularly disagreeable to any man of regular habits, viz. die. These weighty propositions are, all and singular, true: I cannot gainsay them: and truth ever was, and will be, commendable. But in these three theorems, I believe we have exhausted the stock of knowledge as yet accumulated by man on the subject of opium. And therefore, worthy doctors, as there seems to be room for further discoveries, stand aside, and allow me to come forward and lecture on this matter.

First, then, it is not so much affirmed as taken for granted, by all who ever mention opium, formally or incidentally, that it does, or can, produce intoxication. Now, reader, assure yourself, *meo periculo,* that no quantity of opium ever did, or could intoxicate. As to the tincture of opium (commonly called laudanum) *that* might certainly intoxicate if a man could bear to take enough of it; but why? because it contains so much proof spirit, and not because it contains so much opium. But crude opium, I affirm peremptorily, is incapable of producing any state of body at all resembling that which is produced by alcohol; and not in *degree* only incapable, but even in *kind:* it is not in the quantity of its effects merely, but in the quality, that it differs altogether. The pleasure given by wine is always mounting, and tending to a crisis, after which it declines: that from opium, when once generated, is stationary for eight or ten hours: the first, to borrow a technical distinction from medicine, is a case of acute—the second of chronic pleasure: the one is a flame, the other a steady and equable glow. But the main distinction lies in this, that whereas wine disorders the mental faculties, opium, on the contrary (if taken in a proper manner), introduces amongst them the most exquisite order, legislation, and harmony. Wine robs a man of his self-possession: opium greatly invigorates it. Wine unsettles and clouds the judgment, and gives a preternatural brightness, and a vivid exaltation to the contempts and the admirations, the loves and hatreds, of the drinker: opium, on the contrary, communicates serenity and equipoise to all the faculties, active or passive: and with respect to the temper and moral feelings in general, it gives simply that sort of vital warmth which is approved by the judgment, and which would probably always accompany a bodily constitution of primeval antediluvian health. Thus, for instance, opium, like wine, gives an expansion to the heart and the benevolent affections: but then, with this remarkable difference, that in the sudden development of kind-heartedness which accompanies inebriation, there is always more or less of a maudlin character, which exposes it to the contempt of the by-stander. Men shake hands, swear eternal friendship, and shed tears— no mortal knows why: and the sensual creature is clearly uppermost. But the expansion of the benigner feelings, incident to opium, is no febrile access, but a healthy restoration to that state which the mind would naturally recover upon the removal of any deep-seated irritation of pain that had disturbed and quarreled with the impulses of a heart originally just and good. True it is, that even wine, up to a certain point, and with certain men, rather tends to exalt and to steady the intellect: I myself, who have never been a great wine-drinker, used to find that half a dozen glasses of wine advantageously affected the faculties— brightened and intensified the consciousness—and gave to the mind a feeling of being "ponderibus librata suis:" and certainly it is most absurdly said, in popular language, of any man, that he is *disguised* in liquor: for, on the contrary, most men are disguised by sobriety; and it is when they are drinking (as some old gentleman says in Athenaeus), that men. . . .—display themselves in their true complexion of character; which surely is not disguising themselves. But still, wine constantly leads a man to the brink of absurdity and extravagance; and, beyond a certain point, it is sure to volatilize and to disperse the intellectual energies: whereas opium always seems to compose what had been agitated, and to concentrate what had been distracted. In short, to sum up all in one word, a man who is inebriated, or tending to inebriation, is, and feels that he is, in a condition which calls up into supremacy the merely human, too often the brutal, part of his nature: but the opium-eater (I speak of him who is not suffering from any disease, or other remote effects of opium) feels that the diviner part of his nature is paramount; that is, the mortal affections are in a state of cloudless serenity; and over all is the great light of the majestic intellect.

This is the doctrine of the true church on the subject of opium: of which church I acknowledge myself to be the only member—the alpha and the omega: but then it is to be recollected, that I speak from the ground of a large and profound personal experience: whereas most of the unscientific authors who have at all treated of opium, and even of those who have written expressly on the materia medica, make it evident, from the horror they express of it, that their experimental knowledge of its action is none at all. I will, however, candidly acknowledge that I have met with one person who bore evidence to its intoxicating power, such as staggered my own incredulity: for he was a surgeon, and had himself taken opium largely. I happened to say to him, that his enemies (as I had heard) charged him with talking nonsense on politics, and that his friends apologized for him, by suggesting that he was constantly in a state of intoxication from opium. Now the accusation, said I, is not *prima facie*, and of necessity, an absurd one: but the defence *is*. To my surprise, however, he insisted that both his enemies and his friends were in the right: "I will maintain," said he, "that I *do* talk nonsense; and secondly, I will maintain that I do not talk nonsense upon principle, or with any view to profit, but solely and simply, said he, solely and simply,—solely and simply (repeating it three times over), because I am drunk with opium: and *that* daily." I replied that, as to the allegation of his enemies, as it seemed to be established upon such respectable testimony, seeing that the three parties concerned all agreed in it, it did not become me to question it; but the defense set up I must demur to. He proceeded to discuss the matter, and to lay down his reasons: but it seemed to me so impolite to pursue an argument which must have presumed a man mistaken in a point belonging to his own profession, that I did not press him even when his course of argument seemed open to objection: not to mention that a man who talks nonsense, even though "with no view to profit," is not altogether the most agreeable partner in a dispute, whether as opponent or respondent. I confess, however, that the authority of a surgeon, and one who was reputed a good one, may seem a weighty one to my prejudice: but still I must plead my experience, which was greater than his greatest by 7000 drops a day; and, though it was not possible to suppose a medical man unacquainted with the characteristic symptoms of vinous intoxication, it yet struck me that he might proceed on a logical error of using the word intoxication with too great latitude, and extending it generically to all modes of nervous excitement, instead of restricting it as the expression for a specific sort of excitement, connected with certain diagnostics. Some people have maintained, in my hearing, that they had been drunk upon green tea: and a medical student in London, for whose knowledge in his profession I have reason to feel great respect, assured me, the other day, that a patient, in recovering from an illness, had got drunk on beef-steak.

Having dwelt so much on this first and leading error, in respect to opium, I shall notice very briefly a second and a third: which are, that the elevation of spirits produced by opium is necessarily followed by a proportionate depression, and that the natural and even immediate consequence of opium is torpor and stagnation, animal and mental. The first of these errors I shall content myself with simply denying; assuring my reader, that for ten years, during which I took opium at intervals, the day succeeding to that on which I allowed myself this luxury was always a day of unusually good spirits.

With respect to the torpor supposed to follow, or rather (if we were to credit the numerous pictures of Turkish opium-eaters) to accompany the practice of opium-eating, I deny that also. Certainly, opium is classified under the head of narcotics; and some such effect it may produce in the end: but the primary effects of opium are always, and in the highest degree, to excite and stimulate the system: this first stage of its action always lasted with me, during my noviciate, for upwards of eight hours: so that it must be the fault of the opium-eater himself if he does not so time his exhibition of the dose (to speak medically) as that the whole weight of its narcotic influence may descend upon his sleep. Turkish opium-eaters, it seems, are absurd enough to sit, like so many equestrian statues, on logs of wood as stupid as themselves. But that the reader may judge of the degree in which opium is likely to stupify the faculties of an Englishman, I shall (by way of treating the question illustratively, rather than argumentatively) describe the way in which I myself often passed an opium evening in London, during the period between 1804–1812. It will be seen, that at least opium did not move me to seek solitude, and much less to seek inactivity, or the torpid state of self-involution ascribed to the Turks. I give this account at the risk of being pronounced a crazy enthusiast or visionary: but I regard *that* little: I must desire my reader to bear in mind, that I was a hard student, and at severe studies for all the rest of my time: and certainly I had a right occasionally to relaxations as well as other people: these, however, I allowed myself but seldom.

The late Duke of [Norfolk] used to say, "Next Friday, by the blessing of Heaven, I propose to be drunk:" and in like manner I used to fix beforehand how often, within a given time, and when, I would commit a debauch of opium. This was seldom more than once in three weeks: for at that time I could not have ventured to call every day (as I did afterwards) for *"a glass of laudanum negus, warm, and without sugar."* No: as I have said, I seldom drank laudanum, at that time, more than once in three weeks: this was usually on a Tuesday or a Saturday night; my reason for which was this. In those days Grassini sang at the Opera: and her voice was delightful to me beyond all that I had ever heard. I know not what may be the state of the Opera-house now, having never been within its walls for seven or eight years, but at that time it was by much the most pleasant place of public resort in London for passing an evening. Five shillings admitted one to the gallery, which was subject to far less annoyance than the pit of the theatres: the orchestra was distinguished by its sweet and melodious grandeur from all English orchestras, the composition of which, I confess, is not acceptable to my ear, from the predominance of the clangorous instruments, and the absolute tyranny of the violin. The choruses were divine to hear: and when Grassini appeared in some interlude, as she often did, and poured forth her passionate soul as Andromache, at the tomb of Hector, &c. I question whether any Turk, of all that ever entered the Paradise of opium-eaters, can have had half the pleasure I had. But, indeed, I honour the Barbarians too much by supposing them capable of any pleasures approaching to the intellectual ones of an Englishman. For music is an intellectual or a sensual pleasure, according to the temperament of him who hears it. And, by the bye, with the exception of the fine extravaganza on that subject in Twelfth Night, I do not recollect more than one thing said adequately on the subject of music in all literature: it is a passage in the *Religio Medici* of Sir T. Brown; and, though chiefly remarkable for its sublimity, has also a philosophic value, inasmuch as it points to the true theory of musical effects. The mistake of most people is to suppose that it is by the ear they communicate with music, and, therefore, that they are purely passive to its effects. But this is not so: it is by the re-action of the mind upon the notices of the ear, (the *matter* coming by the senses, the *form* from the mind) that the pleasure is constructed: and therefore it is that people of equally good ear differ so much in this point from one another. Now opium, by greatly increasing the activity of the mind generally, increases, of necessity, that particular mode of its activity by which we are able to construct out of the raw material of organic sound an elaborate intellectual pleasure. But, says a friend, a succession of musical sounds is to me like a collection of Arabic characters: I can attach no ideas to them. Ideas! my good sir? there is no occasion for them: all that class of ideas, which can be available in such a case, has a language of representative feelings. But this is a subject foreign to my present purposes: it is sufficient to say, that a chorus, &c. of elaborate harmony, displayed before me, as in a piece of arras work, the whole of my past life—not, as if recalled by an act of memory, but as if present and incarnated in the music: no longer painful to dwell upon: but the detail of its incidents removed, or blended in some hazy abstraction; and its passions exalted, spiritualized, and sublimed. All this was to be had for five shillings. And over and above the music of the stage and the orchestra, I had all around me, in the intervals of the performance, the music of the Italian language talked by Italian women: for the gallery was usually crowded with Italians: and I listened with a pleasure such as with which Weld the traveler lay and listened, in Canada, to the sweet laughter of Indian women; for the less you understand of a language, the more sensible you are to the melody or harshness of its sounds: for such a purpose, therefore, it was an advantage to me that I was a poor Italian scholar, reading it but little, and not speaking it at all, nor understanding a tenth part of what I heard spoken.

These were my Opera pleasures: but another pleasure I had which, as it could be had only on a Saturday night, occasionally struggled with my love of the Opera; for, at that time, Tuesday and Saturday were the regular Opera nights. On this subject I am afraid I shall be rather obscure, but, I can assure the reader, not at all more so than Marinus in his life of Proclus, or many other biographers and auto-biographers of fair reputation. This pleasure, I have said, was to be had only on a Saturday night. What then was Saturday night to me more than any other night? I had no labours that I rested from; no wages to receive: what needed I to care for Saturday night, more than as it was a summons to hear Grassini? True, most logical reader: what you say is unanswerable. And yet so it was and is, that, whereas different men throw their feelings into different channels, and most are apt to show their interest in the concerns of the poor, chiefly by sympathy, expressed in some shape or other, with their distresses and sorrows, I, at that time, was disposed to express my interest by sympathising with their pleasures. The pains of poverty I had lately seen too much of; more than I wished to remember: but the pleasures of the poor, their consolations of spirit, and their reposes from bodily toil, can never become oppressive to contemplate. Now Saturday night is the season for the chief, regular, and periodic return of rest to the poor: in this point the most hostile sects unite, and acknowledge a common link of brotherhood: almost all Christendom rests from its labours. It is a rest introductory to another rest: and divided by a whole day and two nights from the renewal of toil. On this account I feel always, on a Saturday night, as though I also were released from some yoke of labour, had some wages to receive, and some luxury of repose to enjoy. For the sake, therefore, of witnessing, upon as large a scale as possible, a spectacle with which my sympathy was so entire, I used often, on Saturday nights, after I had taken opium, to wander forth, without much regarding the direction or the distance, to all the markets, and other parts of London, to which the poor resort on a Saturday night, for laying out their wages. Many a family party, consisting of a man, his wife, and sometimes one or two of his children, have I listened to, as they stood consulting on their ways and means, or the strength of their exchequer, or the price of household articles. Gradually I became familiar with their wishes, their difficulties, and their opinions. Sometimes there might be heard murmurs of discontent: but far oftener expressions on the countenance, or uttered in words, of patience, hope, and tranquility. And taken generally, I must say, that, in this point at least, the poor are far more philosophic than the rich—that they show a more ready and cheerful submission to what they consider as irremediable evils, or irreparable losses. Whenever I saw occasion, or could do it without appearing to be intrusive, I joined their parties; and gave my opinion upon the matter in discussion, which, if not always judicious, was always received indulgently. If wages were a little higher, or expected to be so, or the quartern loaf a little lower, or it was reported that onions and butter were expected to fall, I was glad: yet, if the contrary were true, I drew from opium some means of consoling myself. For opium (like the bee, that extracts its materials indiscriminately from roses and from the soot of chimneys) can over-rule all feelings into a compliance with the master key. Some of these rambles led me to great distances: for an opium-eater is too happy to observe the motion of time. And sometimes in my attempts to steer homewards, upon nautical principles, by fixing my eye on the pole-star, and seeking ambitiously for a north-west passage, instead of circumnavigating all the capes and head-lands I had doubled in my outward voyage, I came suddenly upon such knotty problems of alleys, such enigmatical entries, and such sphynx's riddles of streets without thoroughfares, as must, I conceive, baffle the audacity of porters, and confound the intellects of hackney-coachmen. I could almost have believed, at times, that I must be the first discoverer of some of these *terra incognita,* and doubted, whether they had yet been laid down in the modern charts of London. For all this, however, I paid a heavy price in distant years, when the human face tyrannized over my dreams, and the perplexities of my steps in London came back and haunted my sleep, with the feeling of perplexities moral or intellectual, that brought confusion to the reason, or anguish and remorse to the conscience.

Thus I have shown that opium does not, of necessity, produce inactivity or torpor; but that, on the contrary, it often led me into markets and theatres. Yet, in candor, I will admit that markets and theatres are not the appropriate haunts of the opium-eater, when in the divinest state incident to his enjoyment. In that state, crowds become an oppression to him; music even, too sensual and gross. He naturally seeks solitude and silence, as indispensable conditions of those trances, or profoundest reveries, which are the crown and consummation of what opium can do for human nature. I, whose disease it was to meditate too much, and to observe too little, and who, upon my first entrance at college, was nearly falling into a deep melancholy, from brooding too much on the sufferings which I had witnessed in London, was sufficiently aware of the tendencies of my own thoughts to do all I could to counteract them.—I was, indeed, like a person who, according to the old legend, had entered the cave of Trophonius; and the remedies I sought were to force myself into society, and to keep my understanding in continual activity upon matters of science. But for these remedies, I should certainly have become hypochondriacally melancholy. In after years, however, when my cheerfulness was more fully re-established, I yielded to my natural inclination for a solitary life. And, at that time, I often fell into these reveries upon taking opium; and more than once it has happened to me, on a summer-night, when I have been at an open window, in a room from which I could overlook the sea at a mile below me, and could command a view of the great town of L[iverpool], at about the same distance, that I have sate, from sun-set to sun-rise, motionless, and without wishing to move.

I shall be charged with mysticism, Behmenism, quietism, &c. but *that* shall not alarm me. Sir H. Vane, the younger, was one of our wisest men: and let my readers see if he, in his philosophical works, be half as unmystical as I am—I say, then, that it has often struck me that the scene itself was somewhat typical of what took place in such a reverie. The town of L[iverpool] represented the earth, with its sorrows and its graves left behind, yet not out of sight, nor wholly forgotten. The ocean, in everlasting but gentle agitation, and brooded over by a dove-like calm, might not unfitly typify the mind and the mood which then swayed it. For it seemed to me as if then first I stood at a distance, and aloof from the uproar of life; as if the tumult, the fever, and the strife, were suspended; a respite granted from the secret burthens of the heart; a sabbath of repose; a resting from human labours. Here were the hopes which blossom in the paths of life, reconciled with the peace which is in the grave; motions of the intellect as unwearied as the heavens, yet for all anxieties a halcyon calm: a tranquillity that seemed no product of inertia, but as if resulting from mighty and equal antagonisms; infinite activities, infinite repose.

Oh! Just, subtle, and mighty opium! that to the hearts of poor and rich alike, for the wounds that will never heal, and for "the pangs that tempt the spirit to rebel," bringest an assuaging balm; eloquent opium! that with thy potent rhetoric stealest away the purposes of wrath; and to the guilty man, for one night givest back the hopes of his youth, and hands washed pure from blood; and to the proud man, a brief oblivion for

Wrongs unredress'd, and insults unavenged;

that summonest to the chancery of dreams, for the triumphs of suffering innocence, false witnesses; and confoundest perjury; and dost reverse the sentences of unrighteous judges:—thou buildest upon the bosom of darkness, out of the fantastic imagery of the brain, cities and temples, beyond the art of Phidias and a Praxiteles—beyond the splendour of Babylon and Hekatompylos: and "from the anarchy of dreaming sleep," callest into sunny light the faces of long-buried beauties, and the blessed household countenances, cleansed from the "dishonours of the grave." Thou only givest these gifts to man; and thou has the keys of Paradise, oh, just, subtle, and mighty opium!

Discussion Questions

1.   Often the level of alcohol or drug addiction is hidden from those closest to the addicted person. Is there any evidence in the selection from *The Way of All Flesh* that Ellen had a severe drinking problem that might have assisted Ernest in getting her help? There are several specific problems experienced by individuals diagnosed with substance dependence, and they include: problems in living, physical effects, psychological and behavioral effects, financial problems, legal problems, occupational problems, social problems, and health problems. List the specific problems that Ellen was experiencing.

2.　Thomas de Quincey presents numerous intellectual arguments and rationalizations to justify his drug use. List several of his justifications and rationalizations and comment on each of them.

3.　Jack London describes numerous signs of alcohol dependence in *John Barleycorn*. List as many signs and symptoms of alcohol dependence as you can from this selection. How would you begin to work with someone who had all of these signs and symptoms of alcohol dependence yet denied that their drinking was a problem?

4.　Some people might argue that Miniver Cheevy was simply an eccentric person and that his overall attitude and behavior were not indicative of alcoholism. Others would interpret his attitudes and behavior as the results of his drinking. Write an argument for each of these positions. Which position do you think is the stronger? Why?

5.　One of the basic methods of treatment utilized with substance abusers is group therapy. Do you believe that group therapy is an effective method of treating these individuals? List three reasons that group treatment might be effective with this group of literary characters.

Chapter 4

Schizophrenia and Other Psychotic Disorders

Schizophrenia is considered the most devastating of the mental illnesses. Symptoms can be very destructive to the individual and to family and friends. In schizophrenia the individual exhibits a marked discrepancy between thinking, feeling, and action. The two major symptoms in schizophrenia are

- Hallucinations: false sensory perceptions not associated with real external stimuli

- Delusions: false beliefs, based on incorrect inferences about external reality, not consistent with the individual's intelligence and cultural background, that cannot be corrected by reasoning

Paranoid Schizophrenia

These individuals are preoccupied with persecutory or grandiose delusions. They are tense, suspicious, guarded, and mistrustful of others. Some paranoid schizophrenic individuals may be prone to violence and hostility. The paranoid type of schizophrenia often manifests itself later in life and interferes less with social functioning than other types of schizophrenia. Paranoid schizophrenia has a better prognosis than other types of the illness.

Edgar Allan Poe (1809–1849)

In "The Tell-Tale Heart" we have another of Poe's stories in the "madman" narrative style. The narrator of this selection demonstrates many of the characteristics of the paranoid schizophrenic, including anger, anxiety, and mistrust of others.

This selection is most memorable for Poe's ability to capture the vivid hallucinations and delusions of this disorder.

(Refer to chapter 1 for biographical information on Poe.)

"The Tell-Tale Heart"

True!—Nervous—Very, very, dreadfully nervous I had been and am; but why *will* you say that I am mad? The disease had sharpened my senses—not destroyed—not dulled them. Above all was the sense of hearing acute. I heard all things in the heaven and in the earth. I heard many things in hell. How, then am I mad? Harken! and observe how healthily—how calmly I can tell you the whole story.

It is impossible to tell how first the idea entered my brain; but once conceived, it haunted me day and night. Object there was none. Passion there was none. I loved the old man. He had never wronged me. He had never given me insult. For his gold I had no desire. I think it was his eye! yes it was this! One of his eyes resembled that of a vulture—a pale blue eye, with a film over it. Whenever it fell upon me, my blood ran cold; and so by degrees—very gradually—I made up my mind to take the life of the old man, and thus rid myself of the eye for ever.

Now this is the point. You fancy me mad. Madmen know nothing. But you should have seen *me*. You should have seen how wisely I proceeded—with what caution—with what foresight—with what dissimulation I went to work! I was never kinder to the old man than during the whole week before I killed him. And every night, about midnight, I turned the latch of his door and opened it—oh, so gently! And then, when I had made an opening sufficient for my head, I put in a dark lantern, all closed, closed, so that no light shone out, and then I thrust in my head. Oh, you would have laughed to see how cunningly I thrust it in! I moved it slowly—very, very slowly, so that I might not disturb the old man's sleep. It took me an hour to place my whole head within the opening so far that I could see him as he lay upon his bed. Ha!—would a madman have been so wise as this? And then, when my head was well in the room, I undid the lantern cautiously—oh, so cautiously—cautiously (for the hinges creaked)—I undid it just so much that a single thin ray fell upon the vulture eye. And this I did for seven long nights—every night just at midnight—but I found the eye always closed; and so it was impossible to do the work; for it was not the old man who vexed me, but his Evil Eye. And every morning, when the day broke, I went boldly into the chamber, and spoke courageously to him, calling him by name in a hearty tone, and inquiring how he had passed the night. So you see he would have been a very profound old man, indeed, to suspect that every night, just at twelve, I looked in upon him while he slept.

Upon the eighth night I was more than usually cautious in opening the door. A watch's minute hand moves more quickly than did mine. Never before that night had I *felt* the extent of my own powers—of my sagacity. I could scarcely contain my feelings of triumph. To think that there I was, opening the door, little by little, and he not even to dream of my secret deeds or thoughts. I fairly chuckled at the idea; and perhaps he heard me; for he moved on the bed suddenly, as if startled. Now you may think that I drew back—but no. His room was as black as pitch with the thick darkness (for the shutters were close fastened, through fear of robbers), and so I knew that he could not see the opening of the door, and I kept pushing it on steadily, steadily.

I had my head in, and was about to open the lantern, when my thumb slipped upon the tin fastening, and the old man sprang up in bed, crying out— "Who's there?"

I kept quite still and said nothing. For a whole hour I did not move a muscle, and in the meantime I did not hear him lie down. He was still sitting up in the bed listening;—just as I have done, night after night, hearkening to the death watches in the wall.

Presently I heard a slight groan, and I knew it was the groan of mortal terror. It was not a groan of pain or grief—oh no!—it was the low stifled sound that arises from the bottom of the soul when overcharged with awe. I knew the sound well. Many a night, just at midnight, when all the world slept, it has welled up from my own bosom, deepening, with its dreadful echo, the terrors that distracted me. I say I knew it well. I knew what the old man felt, and pitied him, although I chuckled at heart. I knew that he had been lying awake ever since the first slight noise, when he had turned in the bed. His fears had been ever since growing upon him. He had been trying to fancy them causeless, but could not. He had been saying to himself—"It is nothing but the wind in the chimney—it is only a mouse crossing the floor." or "it is merely a cricket which has made a single chirp." Yes, he had been trying to comfort himself with these suppositions; but he had found all of them in vain. *All in vain*; because Death, in approaching him, had stalked with his black shadow before him, and enveloped the victim. And it was the mournful influence of the unperceived shadow that caused him to feel—although he neither saw nor heard—to *feel* the presence of my head within the room.

When I had waited a long time, very patiently, without hearing him lie down, I resolved to open a little—a very, very little crevice in the lantern. So I opened it—you cannot imagine how stealthily, stealthily—until, at length, a single dim ray, like the thread of the spider, shot from out the crevice and fell upon the vulture eye.

It was open—wide, wide open—and I grew furious as I gazed upon it. I saw it with perfect distinctness—all a dull blue, with a hideous veil over it that chilled the very marrow in my bones; but I could see nothing else of the old man's face or person: for I had directed the ray as if by instinct, precisely upon the damned spot.

And now have I not told you that what you mistake for madness is but over-acuteness of the senses?—now, I say, there came to my ears a low, dull, quick sound, such as a watch makes when enveloped in cotton. I knew *that* sound well too. It was the beating of the old man's heart. It increased my fury, as the beating of a drum stimulates the soldier into courage.

But even yet I refrained and kept still. I scarcely breathed. I held the lantern motionless. I tried how steadily I could maintain the ray upon the eye.

Meantime the hellish tattoo of the heart increased. It grew quicker and quicker, and louder and louder every instant. The old man's terror *must* have been extreme! It grew louder, I say, louder every moment!—do you mark me well? I have told you that I am nervous: so I am. And now at the dead hour of night, amid the dreadful silence of that old house, so strange a noise as this excited me to uncontrollable terror. Yet, for some minutes longer I refrained and stood still. But the beating grew louder, louder! I thought the heart must burst. And now a new anxiety seized me—the sound would be heard by a neighbor! The old man's hour had come! With a loud yell, I threw open the lantern and lept into the room. He shrieked once—once only. In an instant I dragged him to the floor, and pulled the heavy bed over him. I then smiled gaily, to find the deed so far done. But, for many minutes, the heart beat on with a muffled sound. This, however, did not vex me; it would not be heard through the wall. At length it ceased. The old man was dead. I removed the bed and examined the corpse. Yes, he was stone, stone dead. I placed my hand upon the heart and held it there many minutes. There was no pulsation. He was stone dead. His eye would trouble me no more.

If still you think me mad, you will think so no longer when I describe the wise precautions I took for the concealment of the body. The night waned, and I worked hastily, but in silence. First of all I dismembered the corpse. I cut off the head and the arms and the legs.

I then took up three planks from the flooring of the chamber, and deposited all between the scantlings. I then replaced the boards so cleverly, so cunningly, that no human eye—not even *his*—could have detected anything wrong. There was nothing to wash out—no stain of any kind—no blood-spot whatever. I had been too wary for that. A tub had caught all—ha! ha!

When I had made an end of these labors, it was four o'clock—still dark as midnight. As the bell sounded the hour, there came a knocking at the street door. I went down to open it with a light heart,—for what had I *now* to fear? There entered three men, who introduced themselves, with perfect suavity, as officers of the police. A shriek had been heard by a neighbor during the night; suspicion of foul play had been aroused; information had been loged at the police office, and they (the officers) had been deputed to search the premises.

I smiled—for *what* had I to fear? I bade the gentlemen welcome. The shriek, I said, was my own in a dream. The old man, I mentioned, was absent in the country. I took my visitors all over the house. I bade them search—search *well*. I led them, at length, to *his* chamber. I showed them his treasures, secure, undisturbed. In the enthusiasm of my confidence, I brought chairs into the room, and desired them *here* to rest from their fatigues, while I myself, in the wild audacity of my perfect triumph, placed my own seat upon the very spot beneath which reposed the corpse of the victim.

The officers were satisfied. My *manner* had convinced them. I was singularly at ease. They sat, and while I answered cheerily, they chatted familiar things. But ere long, I felt myself getting pale and wished them gone. My head ached, and I fancied a ringing in my ears: but still they sat and still chatted. The ringing became more distinct—it continued and became more distinct: I talked more freely to get rid of the feeling: but it continued and gained definitiveness—until, at length, I found that the noise was *not* within my ears.

No doubt I now grew *very* pale;—but I talked more fluently, and with a heightened voice. Yet the sound increased—and what could I do? It was *a low dull, quick sound—much such a sound as a watch makes when enveloped in cotton.* I gasped for breath—and yet the officers heard it not. I talked more quickly—more vehemently; but the noise steadily increased. I arose and argued about trifles, in a high key and with violent gesticulations, but the noise steadily increased. Why *would* they not be gone? I paced the floor to and fro with heavy strides, as if excited to fury by the observation of the men—but the noise steadily increased. Oh, God! what *could* I do? I foamed—I raved—I swore! I swung the chair upon which I had been sitting, and grated it upon the boards, but the noise arose over all and continually increased. It grew louder—louder—*louder!* And still the men chatted pleasantly, and smiled. Was it possible they heard not? Almighty God!—no, no! They heard!—they suspected—they *knew!*—they were making a *mockery* of my horror!—this I thought, and this I think. But anything was better than this agony! Any thing was more tolerable than this derision! I could bear those hypocritical smiles no longer! I felt that I must scream or die!—and now again!—hark! louder! louder! *Louder*—

"Villains!" I shrieked, "dissemble no more! I admit the deed!—tear up the planks!—here, here!—it is the beating of his hideous heart!"

Disorganized Schizophrenia

A prominent feature of this type is marked incoherence, regression to primitive behavior, or unorganized behavior, along with silly or inappropriate affect. Affected people often burst into laughter for no apparent reason. These people experience an early and gradual onset of symptoms. Their overall functioning prior to the illness is poor, their social impairment is usually severe, and the illness has a chronic course.

William Shakespeare (1564–1616)

William Shakespeare was born in Stratford-upon-Avon, England in 1564. He was the third of eight children. Shakespeare probably attended the Stratford grammar school, which provided him with his only formal education. He married Anne Hathaway when he was only eighteen years old, and they had three children.

Little is known about Shakespeare's life from the years 1585 through 1592. There is no record of his departure from Stratford to London or the beginnings of his theatrical career. His first recognition came in 1592 in the form of criticism by jealous dramatist, Robert Green, who had written a letter criticizing actors and writers. By 1594

Shakespeare had written at least six plays, the first being *The Comedy of Errors*. He was involved in the London theater from 1594 to 1608.

By the late 1590s Shakespeare and his associates became owners of a new theater, the Globe. This became the home of Shakespeare's acting company, the King's Men. During his career William Shakespeare wrote thirty-seven plays, and he is considered the world's greatest playwright.

Shakespeare provides us with an outstanding portrait of disorganized schizophrenia in the character of Ophelia, from his classic *Hamlet*.

Hamlet

Enter Ophelia *distracted.*

Ophelia. Where is the beauteous majesty of Denmark?

Queen. How now, Ophelia?

Ophelia *(sings).*　　　*How should I your true-love know*
　　　　　　　　　　　From another one?
　　　　　　　　　　　By his cockle hat and staff
　　　　　　　　　　　And his sandal shoon.

Queen. Alas, sweet lady, what imports this song?

Ophelia. Say you? Nay, pray you mark.

[Sings]　　　　　　　　*He is dead and gone, lady,*
　　　　　　　　　　　He is dead and gone;
　　　　　　　　　　At his head a grass-green turf,
　　　　　　　　　　　At his heels a stone.
　　　　　　　　　　　　O, ho!

Queen. Nay, but Ophelia—

Ophelia. Pray you mark.

[Sings]　　　　*White his shroud as the mountain snow—*

Enter King.

Queen. Alas, look here, my lord!

Ohpelia *(sings).*　　　*Larded all with sweet flowers;*
　　　　　　　　　Which bewept to the grave did not go
　　　　　　　　　　With true-love showers.

King. How do you, pretty lady?

Ophelia. Well, God dild you! They say the owl was a baker's daughter. Lord, we know what we are, but know not what we may be. God be at your table!

King. Conceit upon her father.

Ophelia. Pray let's have no words of this; but when they ask you what it means, say you this:

[*Sings*]
    To-morrow is Saint Valentine's *day,*
     All in the morning betime,
     And I a maid at your window,
      To be your Valentine.

    Then up he rose and donn'd his clo'es
     And dupp'd the chamber door,
    Let in the maid, that out a maid
     Never departed more.

King. Pretty Ophelia!

Ophelia. Indeed, la, without an oath, I'll make an end on't!

[*Sings*]
    By Gis and by Saint Charity,
     Alack, and fie for shame!
    Young men will do't if they come to't.
     By Cock, they are to blame.

    Quoth she, "Before you tumbled me,
     You promis'd me to wed."

He answers:

    'So would I 'a' done, by yonder sun,
    an thou hadst not come to my bed.'

King. How long hath she been thus?

Ophelia. I hope all will be well. We must be patient; but I cannot choose but weep to think they would lay him i' th' cold ground. My brother shall know of it; and so I thank you for your good counsel. Come, my coach! Good night, ladies. Good night, sweet ladies. Good night, good night.

King. Follow her close; give her good watch, I pray you.

                [*Exit* Horatio.]

O, this is the poison of deep grief; it springs
All from her father's death. O Gertrude, Gertrude,
When sorrows come, they come not single spies,
But in battalions! First, her father slain;
Next, your son gone, and he most violent author
Of his own just remove; the people muddied,
Thick and unwholesome in their thoughts and whispers
For good Polonius' death, and we have done but greenly
In hugger-mugger to inter him; poor Ophelia
Divided from herself and her fair judgment,
Without which we are pictures or mere beasts.

*   *   *

A noise within: "Let her come in."

Laertes. How now? What noise is that?

Enter Ophelia.

O heat, dry up my brains! Tears seven times salt
Burn out the sense and virtue of mine eye!
By heaven, thy madness shall be paid by weight
Till our scale turn the beam. O rose of May!
Dear maid, kind sister, sweet Ophelia!
O heavens! Is't possible a young maid's wits
Should be as mortal as an old man's life?
Nature is fine in love, and where 'tis fine,
It sends some precious instance of itself
After the thing it loves.

Ophelia *(sings)*

> They bore him barefac'd on the bier
> *(Hey non nony, nony, hey nony)*
> And in his grave rain'd many a tear.

Fare you well, my dove!

Laertes. Hadst thou thy wits, and didst persuade revenge,
It could not move thus.

Ophelia. You must sing "A-down a'down," and you call him a down'a.
O, how the wheel becomes it! It is the false steward, that stole his master's
daughter.

Laertes. This nothing's more than matter.

Ophelia. There's rosemary, that's for remembrance. Pray you, love,
remember: And there is pansies, that's for thoughts.

Laertes. A document in madness! Thoughts and remembrance fitted.

Ophelia. There's fennel for you, and columbines. There's rue for you and
here's some for me. We may call it herb of grace o' Sundays. O, you must wear
your rue with a difference! There's a daisy. I would give you some violets, but
they wither'd all when my father died. They say he made a good end.

[Sings]   *For bonny sweet Robin is all my joy.*

Laertes. Thought and affliction, passion, hell itself,
She turns to favour and to prettiness.

Ophelia *(sings)*.

And will he not come again?
And will he not come again?
No, no, he is dead;
Go to thy deathbed;
He never will come again.

His beard was as white as snow,
All flaxen was his poll.
He is gone, he is gone,
And we cast away moan,
God 'a' mercy on his soul!

And of all Christian souls, I pray God. God b' wi' you.

* * *

Enter Queen.

King. How now, sweet queen?

Queen. One woe doth tread upon another's heel,
So fast they follow. Your sister's drown'd, Laertes.

Laertes. Drown'd! O, where?

Queen. There is a willow grows aslant a brook,
That shows his hoar leaves in the glassy stream.
There with fantastic garlands did she come
Of crowflowers, nettles, daisies, and long purples,
That liberal shepherds give a grosser name,
But our cold maids do dead men's fingers call them.
There on the pendent boughs her coronet weeds
Clamb'ring to hand, an envious sliver broke,
When down her weedy trophies and herself
Fell in the weeping brook. Her clothes spread wide
And, mermaid-like, awhile they bore her up;
Which time she chaunted snatches of old tunes,
As one incapable of her own distress,
Or like a creature native and indued
Unto that element; but long it could not be
Till that her garments, heavy with their drink,
Pull'd the poor wretch from her melodious lay
To muddy death.

Undifferentiated Schizophrenia

These individuals meet the basic criteria for schizophrenia but not criteria for a specific type.

Charlotte Perkins Gilman (1860–1935)

Charlotte Perkins Gilman was born in Hartford, Connecticut in 1860. Her father deserted the family when she was very young, leaving her mother to raise two children on her own.

Gilman dropped out of college, married an artist, and gave birth to her first child. After the birth of her daughter, she suffered from serious bouts of depression. As a result of her depression she relocated to California, got a divorce, and left her daughter in the care of her ex-husband.

Gilman is best known for her 1882 short story, "The Yellow Wallpaper" utilized as our example in this section. In "The Yellow Wallpaper," Gilman calls attention to the physical, psychological, and intellectual repression of women in late-nineteenth- and early twentieth-century America.

Gilman was very active in political and reform movements. After divorcing her husband, she traveled widely, strongly advocating and speaking on issues of women's rights. In 1898 she published the book *Women and Economics*, which is considered a classic feminist text.

In 1900, Gilman married her first cousin and continued her writing. In 1915 Gilman, along with Jane Adams, founded the Women's Peace Party. She was diagnosed with inoperable breast cancer in 1932 and committed suicide in 1935. Her autobiography, *The Living of Charlotte Perkins Gilman*, was published posthumously in 1935.

Gilman beautifully describes the characteristic signs and symptoms of the undifferentiated type of schizophrenia in "The Yellow Wallpaper."

"The Yellow Wallpaper"

It is very seldom that mere ordinary people like John and myself secure ancestral halls for the summer.

A colonial mansion, a hereditary estate, I would say a haunted house, and reach the height of romantic felicity—but that would be asking too much of fate!

Still I will proudly declare that there is something queer it.

Else, why should it be let so cheaply? And why have stood so long untenanted?

John laughs at me, of course, but one expects that in marriage.

John is practical in the extreme. He has no patience with faith, an intense horror of superstition, and he scoffs openly at any talk of things not to be felt and seen and put down in figures.

John is a physician, and *perhaps*—(I would not say it to a living soul, of course, but this is a dead paper and a great relief to my mind—) *perhaps* that is one reason I do not get well faster.

You see he does not believe I am sick!

And what can one do?

If a physician of high standing, and one's own husband, assures friends and relatives that there is really nothing the matter with one but temporary nervous depression—a slight hysterical tendency—what is one to do?

My brother is also a physician, and also of high standing, and says the same thing.

So I take phosphates or phosphites—whichever it is, and tonics, and journeys, and air, and exercise, and am absolutely forbidden to "work" until I am well again.

Personally, I disagree with their ideas.

Personally, I believe that congenial work, with excitement and change, would do me good.

But what is one to do?

I did write for a while in spite of them; but it *does* exhaust me a good deal—having to be so sly about it, or else meet with heavy opposition.

I sometimes fancy that in my condition if I had less opposition and more society and stimulus—but John says the very worst thing I can do is to think about my condition, and I confess it always makes me feel bad.

So I will let it alone and talk about the house.

The most beautiful place! It is quite alone, standing well back from the road, quite three miles from the village. It makes me think of English places that you read about, for there are hedges and walls and gates that lock, and lots of separate little houses for the gardeners and people.

There is a *delicious* garden! I never saw such a garden—large and shady, full of box-bordered paths, and lined with long grape-covered arbors with seats under them.

There were greenhouses, too, but they are all broken now.

There was some legal trouble, I believe, something about the heirs and co-heirs; anyhow, the place has been empty for years.

That spoils my ghostliness, I am afraid, but I don't care—there is something strange about the house—I can feel it.

I even said so to John one moonlight evening, but he said what I felt was a *draught,* and shut the window.

I get unreasonably angry with John sometimes. I'm sure I never used to be so sensitive. I think it is due to this nervous condition.

But John says if I feel so, I shall neglect proper self-control; so I take pains to control myself—before him, at least, and that makes me very tired.

I don't like our room a bit. I wanted one downstairs that opened on the piazza and had roses all over the window, and such pretty old-fashioned chintz hangings! but John would not hear of it.

He said there was only one window and not room for two beds, and no near room for him if he took another.

He is very careful and loving, and hardly lets me stir without special direction.

I have a schedule prescription for each hour in the day; he takes all care from me, and so I feel basely ungrateful not to value it more.

He said we came here solely on my account, that I was to have perfect rest and all the air I could get. "Your exercise depends on your strength, my dear," said he, "and your food somewhat on your appetite; but air you can absorb all the time." So we took the nursery at the top of the house.

It is a big, airy room, the whole floor nearly, with windows that look all ways, and air and sunshine galore. It was nursery first and then playroom and gymnasium, I should judge; for the windows are barred for little children, and there are rings and things in the walls.

The paint and paper look as if a boys' school had used it. It is stripped off— the paper—in great patches all around the head of my bed, about as far as I can reach, and in a great place on the other side of the room low down. I never saw a worse paper in my life.

One of those sprawling flamboyant patterns committing every artistic sin.

It is dull enough to confuse the eye in following, pronounced enough to constantly irritate and provoke study, and when you follow the lame uncertain curves for a little distance they suddenly commit suicide—plunge off at outrageous angles, destroy themselves in unheard of contradictions.

The color is repellent, almost revolting; a smoldering unclean yellow, strangely faded by the slow-turning sunlight.

It is a dull yet lurid orange in some places, a sickly sulphur tint in others.

No wonder the children hated it! I should hate it myself if I had to live in this room long.

There comes John, and I must put this away,—he hates to have me write a word.

* * *

We have been here two weeks, and I haven't felt like writing before, since that first day.

I am sitting by the window now, up in this atrocious nursery, and there is nothing to hinder my writing as much as I please, save lack of strength.

John is away all day, and even some nights when his cases are serious.

I am glad my case is not serious!

But these nervous troubles are dreadfully depressing.

John does not know how much I really suffer. He knows there is no *reason* to suffer, and that satisfies him.

Of course it is only nervousness. It does weigh on me so not to do my duty in any way!

I meant to be such a help to John, such a real rest and comfort, and here I am a comparative burden already!

Nobody would believe what an effort it is to do what little I am able,—to dress and entertain, and order things.

It is fortunate Mary is so good with the baby. Such a dear baby!

And yet I *cannot* be with him, it makes me so nervous.

I suppose John never was nervous in his life. He laughs at me so about this wall-paper!

At first he meant to repaper the room, but afterwards he said that I was letting it get the better of me, and that nothing was worse for a nervous patient than to give way to such fancies.

He said that after the wall-paper was changed it would be the heavy bedstead, and then the barred windows, and then that gate at the head of the stairs, and so on.

"You know the place is doing you good," he said, "and really, dear, I don't care to renovate the house just for a three months' rental."

"Then do let us go downstairs," I said, "there are such pretty rooms there."

Then he took me in his arms and called me a blessed little goose, and said he would go down cellar, if I wished, and have it white-washed in the bargain.

But he is right enough about the beds and windows and things.

It is an airy and comfortable room as any one need wish, and, of course, I would not be so silly as to make him uncomfortable just for a whim.

I'm really getting quite fond of the big room, all but that horrid paper.

Out of one window I can see the garden, those mysterious deep shaded arbors, the riotous old-fashioned flowers, and bushes and gnarly trees.

Out of another I get a lovely view of the bay and a little private wharf belonging to the estate. There is a beautiful shaded lane that runs down there from the house. I always fancy I see people walking in these numerous paths and arbors, but John has cautioned me not to give way to fancy in the least. He says that with my imaginative power and habit of story-making, a nervous weakness like mine is sure to lead to all manner of excited fancies, and that I ought to use my will and good sense to check the tendency. So I try.

I think sometimes that if I were only well enough to write a little it would relieve the press of ideas and rest me.

But I find I get pretty tired when I try.

It is so discouraging not to have any advice and companionship about my work. When I get really well, John says we will ask cousin Henry and Julia down for a long visit; but he says he would as soon put fireworks in my pillow-case as to let me have those stimulating people about now.

I wish I could get well faster.

But I must not think about that. This paper looks to me as if it *knew* what a vicious influence it had!

There is a recurrent spot where the pattern lolls like a broken neck and two bulbous eyes stare at you upside down.

I get positively angry with the impertinence of it and the everlastingness. Up and down and sideways they crawl, and those absurd, unblinking eyes are everywhere. There is one place where two breadths didn't match, and the eyes go all up and down the line, one a little higher than the other.

I never saw so much expression in an inanimate thing before, and we all know how much expression they have! I used to lie awake as a child and get more entertainment and terror out of blank walls and plain furniture than most children could find in a toy-store.

I remember what a kindly wink the knobs of our big, old bureau used to have, and there was one chair that always seemed like a strong friend.

I used to feel that if any of the other things looked too fierce I could always hop into that chair and be safe.

The furniture in this room is no worse than inharmonious, however, for we had to bring it all from downstairs. I suppose when this was used as a playroom they had to take the nursery things out, and no wonder! I never saw such ravages as the children have made here.

The wall-paper, as I said before, is torn off in spots, and it sticketh closer than a brother—they must have had perseverance as well as hatred.

Then the floor is scratched and gouged and splintered, the plaster itself is dug out here and there, and this great heavy bed which is all we found in the room, looks as if it had been through the wars.

But I don't mind it a bit—only the paper.

There comes John's sister. Such a dear girl as she is, and so careful of me! I must not let her find me writing.

She is a perfect and enthusiastic housekeeper, and hopes for no better profession. I verily believe she thinks it is the writing which makes me sick!

But I can write when she is out, and see her a long way off from these windows.

There is one that commands the road, a lovely shaded winding road, and one that just looks off over the country. A lovely country, too, full of great elms and velvet meadows.

This wall-paper has a kind of sub-pattern in a different shade, a particularly irritating one, for you can only see it in certain lights, and not clearly then.

But in places where it isn't faded and where the sun is just so—I can see a strange, provoking, formless sort of figure, that seems to skulk about behind that silly and conspicuous front design.

There's sister on the stairs!

*   *   *

Well, the Fourth of July is over! The people are all gone and I am tired out. John thought it might do me good to see a little company, so we just had mother and Nellie and the children down for a week.

Of course I didn't do a thing. Jennie sees to everything now.

But it tired me all the same.

John says if I don't pick up faster he shall send me to Weir Mitchell in the fall.

But I don't want to go there at all. I had a friend who was in his hands once, and she says he is just like John and my brother, only more so!

Besides, it is such an undertaking to go so far.

I don't feel as if it was worth while to turn my hand over for anything, and I'm getting dreadfully fretful and querulous.

I cry at nothing, and cry most of the time.

Of course I don't when John is here, or anybody else, but when I am alone.

And I am alone a good deal just now. John is kept in town very often by serious cases, and Jennie is good and lets me alone when I want her to.

So I walk a little in the garden or down that lovely lane, sit on the porch under the roses, and lie down up here a good deal.

I'm getting really fond of the room in spite of the wall-paper. Perhaps *because* of the wall-paper.

It dwells in my mind so!

I lie here on this great immovable bed—it is nailed down, I believe—and follow that pattern about by the hour. It is as good as gymnastics, I assure you. I start, we'll say, at the bottom down in the corner over there where it has not been touched, and I determine for the thousandth time that I *will* follow that pointless pattern to some sort of a conclusion.

I know a little of the principle of design, and I know this thing was not arranged on any laws of radiation, or alteration, or repetition, or symmetry, or anything else that I ever heard of.

It is repeated, of course, by the breadths, but not otherwise.

Looked at in one way each breadth stands alone, the bloated curves and flourishes—a kind of "debased Romanesque" with *delirium tremens*—go waddling up and down in isolated columns of fatuity.

But, on the other hand, they connect diagonally, and the sprawling outlines run off in great slanting waves of optic horror, like a lot of wallowing seaweeds in full chase.

The whole thing goes horizontally, too, at least it seems so, and I exhaust myself in trying to distinguish the order of its going in that direction.

They have used a horizontal breadth for a frieze, and that adds wonderfully to the confusion.

There is one end of the room where it is almost intact, and there, when the crosslights fade and the low sun shines directly upon it, I can almost fancy radiation after all,—the interminable grotesques seem to form around a common centre and rush off in headlong plunges of equal distraction.

It makes me tired to follow it. I will take a nap I guess.

* * *

I don't know why I should write this.

I don't want to.

I don't feel able.

And I know John would think it absurd. But I *must* say what I feel and think in some way—it is such a relief!

But the effort is getting to be greater than the relief.

Half the time now I am awfully lazy, and lie down ever so much.

John says I mustn't lose my strength, and has me take cod liver oil and lots of tonics and things, to say nothing of ale and wine and rare meat.

Dear John! He loves me very dearly, and hates to have me sick. I tried to have a real earnest reasonable talk with him the other day, and tell him how I wish he would let me go and make a visit to Cousin Henry and Julia.

But he said I wasn't able to go, nor able to stand it after I got there; and I did not make out a very good case for myself, for I was crying before I had finished.

It is getting to be a great effort for me to think straight. Just this nervous weakness I suppose.

And dear John gathered me up in his arms, and just carried me upstairs and laid me on the bed, and sat by me and read to me till it tired my head.

He said I was his darling and his comfort and all he had, and that I must take care of myself for his sake, and keep well.

He says no one but myself can help me out of it, that I must use my will and self-control and not let any silly fancies run away with me.

There's one comfort, the baby is well and happy, and does not have to occupy this nursery with the horrid wall-paper.

If we had not used it, that blessed child would have! What a fortunate escape! Why, I wouldn't have a child of mine, an impressionable little thing, live in such a room for worlds.

I never thought of it before, but it is lucky that John kept me here after all, I can stand it so much easier than a baby, you see.

Of course I never mention it to them any more—I am too wise,—but I keep watch of it all the same.

There are things in that paper that nobody knows but me, or ever will.

Behind that outside pattern the dim shapes get clearer every day.

It is always the same shape, only very numerous.

And it is like a woman stooping down and creeping about behind that pattern. I don't like it a bit. I wonder—I begin to think—I wish John would take me away from here!

* * *

It is so hard to talk with John about my case, because he is so wise, and because he loves me so.

But I tried it last night.

It was moonlight. The moon shines in all around just as the sun does.

I hate to see it sometimes, it creeps so slowly, and always comes in by one window or another.

John was asleep and I hated to waken him, so I kept still and watched the moonlight on that undulating wall-paper till I felt creepy.

The faint figure behind seemed to shake the pattern, just as if she wanted to get out.

I got up softly and went to feel and see if the paper *did* move, and when I came back John was awake.

"What is it, little girl?" he said. "Don't go walking about like that—you'll get cold."

I thought it was a good time to talk, so I told him that I really was not gaining here, and that I wished he would take me away.

"Why, darling!" said he, "our lease will be up in three weeks, and I can't see how to leave before.

"The repairs are not done at home, and I cannot possibly leave town just now. Of course if you were in any danger, I could and would, but you really are better, dear, whether you can see it or not. I am a doctor, dear, and I know. You are gaining flesh and color, your appetite is better, I feel really much easier about you."

"I don't weigh a bit more," said I, "nor as much; and my appetite may be better in the evening when you are here, but it is worse in the morning when you are away!"

"Bless her little heart!" said he with a big hug, "she shall be as sick as she pleases! But now let's improve the shining hours by going to sleep, and talk about it in the morning!"

"And you won't go away?" I asked gloomily.

"Why, how can I, dear? It is only three weeks more and then we will take a nice little trip of a few days while Jennie is getting the house ready. Really dear you are better!"

"Better in body perhaps—" I began, and stopped short, for he sat up straight and looked at me with such a stern, reproachful look that I could not say another word.

"My darling," said he, "I beg of you, for my sake and for our child's sake, as well as for your own, that you will never for one instant let that idea enter your mind! There is nothing so dangerous, so fascinating, to a temperament like yours. It is a false and foolish fancy. Can you not trust me as a physician when I tell you so?"

So of course I said no more on that score, and we went to sleep before long. He thought I was asleep first, but I wasn't, and lay there for hours trying to decide whether that front pattern and the back pattern really did move together or separately.

* * *

On a pattern like this, by daylight, there is a lack of sequence, a defiance of law, that is a constant irritant to a normal mind.

The color is hideous enough, and unreliable enough, and infuriating enough, but the pattern is torturing.

You might have mastered it, but just as you get well underway in following, it turns a back-somersault and there you are. It slaps you in the face, knocks you down, and tramples upon you. It is like a bad dream.

The outside pattern is a florid arabesque, reminding one of a fungus. If you can imagine a toadstool in joints, an interminable string of toadstools, budding and sprouting in endless convolutions—why, that is something like it.

That is, sometimes!

There is one marked peculiarity about this paper, a thing nobody seems to notice but myself, and that is that it changes as the light changes.

When the sun shoots in through the east window—I always watch for that first long, straight ray—it changes so quickly that I never can quite believe it.

That is why I watch it always.

By moonlight—the moon shines in all night when there is a moon—I wouldn't know it was the same paper.

At night in any kind of light, in twilight, candlelight, lamplight, and worst of all by moonlight, it becomes bars! The outside pattern I mean, and the woman behind it is as plain as can be.

I didn't realize for a long time what the thing was that showed behind, that dim sub-pattern, but now I am quite sure it is a woman.

By daylight she is subdued, quiet. I fancy it is the pattern that keeps her so still. It is so puzzling. It keeps me quiet by the hour.

I lie down ever so much now. John says it is good for me, and to sleep all I can.

Indeed he started the habit by making me lie down for an hour after each meal.

It is a very bad habit I am convinced, for you see I don't sleep.

And that cultivates deceit, for I don't tell them I'm awake—O no!

The fact is I am getting a little afraid of John.

He seems very queer sometimes, and even Jennie has an inexplicable look.

It strikes me occasionally, just as a scientific hypothesis, —that perhaps it is the paper!

I have watched John when he did not know I was looking, and come into the room suddenly on the most innocent excuses, and I've caught him several times *looking at the paper!* And Jennie too. I caught Jennie with her hand on it once.

She didn't know I was in the room, and when I asked in a quiet, a very quiet voice, with the most restrained manner possible, what she was doing with the paper—she turned around as if she had been caught stealing, and looked quite angry—asked me why I should frighten her so!

Then she said that the paper stained everything it touched, that she had found yellow smooches on all my clothes and John's, and she wished we would be more careful!

Did not that sound innocent? But I know she was studying that pattern, and I am determined that nobody shall find it out but myself!

*   *   *

Life is very much more exciting now than it used to be. You see I have something more to expect, to look forward to, to watch. I really do eat better, and am more quiet than I was.

John is so pleased to see me improve! He laughed a little the other day, and said I seemed to be flourishing in spite of my wall-paper.

I turned it off with a laugh. I had no intention of telling him it was *because* of the wall-paper—he would make fun of me. He might even want to take me away.

I don't want to leave now until I have found it out. There is a week more, and I think that will be enough.

*   *   *

I'm feeling ever so much better! I don't sleep much at night, for it is so interesting to watch developments; but I sleep a good deal in the daytime.

In the daytime it is tiresome and perplexing.

There are always new shoots on the fungus, and new shades of yellow all over it. I cannot keep count of them, though I have tried conscientiously.

It is the strangest yellow, that wall-paper! It makes me think of all the yellow things I ever saw—not beautiful ones like buttercups, but old foul, bad yellow things.

But there is something else about that paper—the smell! I noticed it the moment we came into the room, but with so much air and sun it was not bad. Now we have had a week of fog and rain, and whether the windows are open or not, the smell is here.

It creeps all over the house.

I find it hovering in the dining-room, skulking in the parlor, hiding in the hall, lying in wait for me on the stairs.

It gets into my hair.

Even when I go to ride, if I turn my head suddenly and surprise it—there is that smell!

Such a peculiar odor, too! I have spent hours in trying to analyze it, to find what it smelled like.

It is not bad—at first, and very gentle, but quite the subtlest, most enduring odor I ever met.

In this damp weather it is awful, I wake up in the night and find it hanging over me.

It used to disturb me at first. I thought seriously of burning the house—to reach the smell.

But now I am used to it. The only thing I can think of that it is like is the *color* of the paper! A yellow smell.

There is a very funny mark on this wall, low down, near the mopboard. A streak that runs round the room. It goes behind every piece of furniture, except the bed, a long, straight, even *smooch*, as if it had been rubbed over and over.

I wonder how it was done and who did it, and what they did it for. Round and round and round—round and round and round—it makes me dizzy!

* * *

I really discovered something at last.

Through watching so much at night, when it changes so, I have finally found out.

The front pattern *does* move—and no wonder! The woman behind shakes it!

Sometimes I think there are a great many women behind, and sometimes only one, and she crawls around fast, and her crawling shakes it all over.

Then in the very bright spots she keeps still, and in the very shady spots she just takes hold of the bars and shakes them hard.

And she is all the time trying to climb through. But nobody could climb through that pattern—it strangles so; I think that is why it has so many heads.

They get through, and then the pattern strangles them off and turns them upside down, and makes their eyes white!

If those heads were covered or taken off it would not be half so bad.

* * *

I think that woman gets out in the daytime!

And I'll tell you why—privately—I've seen her!

I can see her out of every one of my windows!

It is the same woman, I know for she is always creeping, and most women do not creep by daylight.

I see her in that long shaded lane, creeping up and down. I see her in those dark grape arbors, creeping all around the garden.

I see her on that long road under the trees, creeping along, and when a carriage comes she hides under the blackberry vines.

I don't blame her a bit. It must be very humiliating to be caught creeping by daylight!

I always lock the door when I creep by daylight. I can't do it at night, for I know John would suspect something at once.

And John is so queer now, that I don't want to irritate him. I wish he would take another room! Besides, I don't want anybody to get that woman out at night but myself.

I often wonder if I could see her out of all the windows at once.

But, turn as fast as I can, I can only see out of one at one time.

And though I always see her, she *may* be able to creep faster than I can turn!

I have watched her sometimes away off in the open country, creeping as fast as a cloud shadow in a high wind.

* * *

If only that top pattern could be gotten off from the under one! I mean to try it, little by little.

I have found out another funny thing, but I shan't tell it this time! It does not do to trust people too much.

There are only two more days to get this paper off, and I believe John is beginning to notice. I don't like the look in his eyes.

And I heard him ask Jennie a lot of professional questions about me. She had a very good report to give.

She said I slept a good deal in the daytime.

John knows I don't sleep very well at night, for all I'm so quiet!

He asked me all sorts of questions, too, and pretended to be very loving and kind.

As if I couldn't see through him!

Still, I don't wonder he acts so, sleeping under this paper for three months.

It only interests me, but I feel sure John and Jennie are secretly affected by it.

* * *

Hurrah! This is the last day, but it is enough. John is to stay in town over night, and won't be out until this evening.

Jennie wanted to sleep with me—the sly thing! but I told her I should undoubtedly rest better for a night all alone.

That was clever, for really I wasn't alone a bit! As soon as it was moonlight and that poor thing began to crawl and shake the pattern, I got up and ran to help her.

I pulled and shook, I shook and she pulled, and before morning we had peeled off yards of that paper.

A strip about as high as my head and half around the room.

And then when the sun came and that awful pattern began to laugh at me, I declared I would finish it to-day!

We go away to-morrow, and they are moving all my furniture down again to leave things as they were before.

Jennie looked at the wall in amazement, but I told her merrily that I did it out of pure spite at the vicious thing.

She laughed and said she wouldn't mind doing it herself, but I must not get tired.

How she betrayed herself that time!

But I am here, and no person touches this paper but me,—not *alive!*

She tried to get me out of the room—it was too patent! But I said it was so quiet and empty and clean now that I believed I would lie down again and sleep all I could; and not to wake me even for dinner—I would call when I woke.

So now she is gone, and the servants are gone, and the things are gone, and there is nothing left but that great bedstead nailed down, with the canvas mattress we found on it.

We shall sleep downstairs to-night, and take the boat home to-morrow.

I quite enjoy the room, now it is bare again.

How those children did tear about here!

This bedstead is fairly gnawed!

But I must get to work.

I have locked the door and thrown the key down into the front path.

I don't want to go out, and I don't want to have anybody come in, till John comes.

I want to astonish him.

I've got a rope up here that even Jennie did not find. If that woman does get out, and tries to get away, I can tie her!

But I forgot I could not reach far without anything to stand on!

This bed will *not* move!

I tried to lift and push it until I was lame, and then I got so angry I bit off a little piece at one corner—but it hurt my teeth.

Then I peeled off all the paper I could reach standing on the floor. It sticks horribly and the pattern just enjoys it! All those strangled heads and bulbous eyes and waddling fungus growths just shriek with derision!

I am getting angry enough to do something desperate. To jump out of the window would be admirable exercise, but the bars are too strong even to try.

Besides I wouldn't do it. Of course not. I know well enough that a step like that is improper and might be misconstrued.

I don't like to *look* out of the windows even—there are so many of those creeping women, and they creep so fast.

I wonder if they all come out of that wall-paper as I did?

But I am securely fastened now by my well-hidden rope—you don't get *me* out in the road there!

I suppose I shall have to get back behind the pattern when it comes night, and that is hard!

It is so pleasant to be out in this great room and creep around as I please!

I don't want to go outside. I won't, even if Jennie asks me to.

For outside you have to creep on the ground, and everything is green instead of yellow.

But here I can creep smoothly on the floor, and my shoulder just fits in that long smooch around the wall, so I cannot lose my way.

Why there's John at the door!

It is no use, young man, you can't open it!

How he does call and pound!

Now he's crying for an axe.

It would be a shame to break down that beautiful door!

"John dear!" said I in the gentlest voice, "the key is down by the front steps, under a plantain leaf!"

That silenced him for a few moments.

Then he said—very quietly indeed, "Open the door, my darling!"

"I can't," said I. "The key is down by the front door under a plantain leaf!"

And then I said it again, several times, very gently and slowly, and said it so often that he had to go and see, and he got it of course, and came in. He stopped short by the door.

"What is the matter?" he cried. "For God's sake, what are you doing!"

I kept on creeping just the same, but I looked at him over my shoulder.

"I've got out at last," said I, "in spite of you and Jane. And I've pulled off most of the paper, so you can't put me back!"

Now why should that man have fainted? But he did, and right across my path by the wall, so that I had to creep over him every time!

Schizoaffective Disorder

Individuals with schizoaffective disorder have symptoms of both schizophrenia and a major mood disorder. They must continuously meet the criteria for schizophrenia and also experience a major depressive episode, manic episode, or mixed episode. In order for this disorder to be differentiated from mood disorders with psychotic features the person must experience the schizophrenic symptoms of delusions or hallucinations for at least two weeks in the absence of the mood disorder symptoms.

Anton Chekhov (1860–1904)

Anton Chekhov was born in Taganrog, Russia. His father, who was a controlling religious fanatic, dominated his childhood. His father owned his own grocery business, and when the business went bankrupt the family was thrown into financial ruin. In later life, Chekhov recalled his childhood as a very unpleasant time.

In 1879 Chekhov entered the Moscow University Medical School. While in medical school he started to publish short stories to support his family. Chekhov graduated from medical school in 1884, and he practiced medicine and continued to write until 1892. After 1892 he devoted all of his efforts toward his literary career.

As a writer Chekhov combined the objectivity of a scientist and doctor with a strong sensitivity for people and deep understanding of human nature. Many of his characters are portrayed as victims of circumstances and filled with feelings of hopelessness.

Chekhov died of tuberculosis in 1904 at the age of forty-four. Since his death he has come to be considered one of the greatest Russian storytellers and dramatists. During his career he produced several hundred short stories.

The selection utilized here, "Ward No. 6," was written in 1892, and in it Chekhov provides us with an excellent example of the schizo-affective disorder. The schizophrenic symptoms in this story have a decided paranoid character. Note the symptoms of major depression, which include depressed mood, markedly diminished interest or pleasure in activities, insomnia, psychomotor agitation, feelings of worthlessness and guilt, and diminished ability to think or concentrate. These symptoms of major depression occur along with symptoms of schizophrenia. While the story does not clearly describe a period of schizophrenia in the absence of these mood disorder symptoms, it is utilized here to demonstrate schizoaffective disorder because both disorders appear in the same individual.

"Ward No. 6"

. . . Ivan Dmitritch Gromof is a man of thirty-three years of age. He is a noble by birth, and has been an usher in the law courts, and a government secretary; but now he suffers from the mania of persecution. He lies upon his bed twisted into a lump resembling a roll of bread, or marches from corner to corner for the sake of motion. He is always in a state of excitement and agitation; and seems strained by some dull, indefinable expectation. It needs but the slightest rustle in the hall, the slightest noise in the yard, to make him raise his head and listen intently. Is it for him they are coming? Are they searching for him? And his face immediately takes on an expression of restlessness and repulsion.

There is something attractive about his broad, high cheek-boned face, which reflects, as a mirror, the tortured wrestlings and eternal terror of his mind. His grimaces are strange and sickly; but the delicate lines engraven on his face by sincere suffering express reason and intelligence, and his eyes burn with a healthy and passionate glow. There is something attractive also in his character, in his politeness, his attentiveness, and in the singular delicacy of his bearing toward everyone except Nikita. If his neighbor drops a spoon or a button he jumps immediately out of bed and picks it up. When he wakes he invariably says, "Good morning!" to his companions; and every evening on going to bed wishes them "good night!"

But madness shows itself in other things besides his grimaces and continual mental tension. In the evening he wraps himself in his dressing-gown, and, trembling all over, and chattering his teeth, he walks from corner to corner, and in between the beds. He seems to be in a state of fever. From his sudden stoppages and strange looks at his fellow-prisoners it is plain that he has something very serious to say; but, no doubt, remembering that they will neither listen nor understand, he says nothing, shakes his head impatiently, and continues his walk. But at last the desire to speak conquers all other considerations, and he gives way, and speaks passionately. His words are incoherent, gusty, and delirious; he cannot always be understood; but the sound of his voice expresses some exceptional goodness. In every word you hear the madman and the man. He speaks of human baseness, of violence trampling over truth, of the beautiful life on earth that is to come, and of the barred windows which remind him every moment of the folly and cruelty of the strong. And he hums medleys of old but forgotten songs.

II

Fifteen years before, in his own house, in the best street in the town, lived an official named Gromof—a solid and prosperous man. Gromof had two sons, Sergei and Ivan. Sergei, when a student in the fourth class, was seized with consumption and died; and his death was the first of a series of misfortunes which overtook the Gromofs. A week after Sergei's death his old father was tried for forgery and misappropriation of public moneys, and soon afterwards died of typhus in the prison infirmary. His house and all his belongings were sold by auction, and Ivan Dmitritch and his mother remained without a penny.

When his father was alive, Ivan Dmitritch studied at St. Petersburg University, received an allowance of sixty or seventy rubles a month, and had no idea of the meaning of poverty. Now he had to change his whole life. From early morning till late at night he gave cheap lessons to students and copied documents, yet starved, for all his earnings went to support his mother. The life was impossible, and Ivan Dmitritch ruined his health and spirits, threw up his university studies, and returned home. Through interest he obtained an appointment as usher in the district school; but he was disliked by his colleagues, failed to get on with the pupils, and gave up the post. His mother died. For six months he lived without resources, eating black bread and drinking water, until at last he obtained an appointment as Usher of the Court. This duty he fulfilled until he was discharged due to illness.

Never, even in his student days, had he had the appearance of a strong man. He was pale, thin, and sensitive to cold; he ate little and slept badly. A single glass of wine made him giddy and sent him into hysterics. His disposition impelled him to seek companionship, but thanks to his irritable and suspicious character he never became intimate with anyone, and had no friends. Of his fellow-citizens he always spoke with contempt, condemning as disgusting and repulsive their gross ignorance and torpid, animal life. He spoke in a tenor voice, loudly and passionately, and always seemed to be in a sincere state of indignation, excitement, or rapture. However he began a conversation, it ended always in one way—in a lament that the town was stifling and tiresome, that its people had no high interests, but led a dull, unmeaning life, varied only by violence, coarse debauchery and hypocrisy; that scoundrels were fed and clothed while honest men ate crusts; that the town was crying out for schools, honest newspapers, a theatre, public lectures, a union of intellectual forces; and that the time had come for the townspeople to awaken to, and be shocked at, the state of affairs. In his judgments of men he laid on his colours thickly, using only white and black, and recognizing no gradations; for him humanity was divided into two sections, honest men and rogues—there was nothing between. Of woman and woman's love he spoke passionately and with rapture. But he had never been in love.

In the town, notwithstanding his nervous character and censorious temper, he was loved, and called caressingly "Vanya." His innate delicacy, his attentiveness, his neatness, his moral purity, his worn coat, his sickly appearance, the misfortunes of his family, inspired in all feelings of warmth, and compassion. Besides, he was educated and well-read; in the opinion of the townsmen he knew everything; and occupied among them the place of a walking reference-book. He read much. He would sit for hours at the club, pluck nervously at his beard, and turn over the pages of books and magazines—by his face it might be seen that he was not reading but devouring. Yet reading was apparently merely one of his nervous habits, for with equal avidity he read everything that fell into his hands, even old newspapers and calendars. At home he always read, lying down.

III

One Autumn morning, Ivan Dmitritch, with the collar of his coat turned up, trudged through the mud to the house of a certain tradesman to receive money due on a writ of execution. As always in the morning, he was in a gloomy mood. Passing through a lane, he met two convicts in chains and with them four wardens armed with rifles. Ivan Dmitritch had often met convicts before, and they had awakened in him a feeling of sympathy and confusion. But this meeting produced upon him an unusual impression. It suddenly occurred to him that he too might be shackled and driven through the mud to prison. Having finished his work, he was returning home when he met a police-inspector, an acquaintance, who greeted him and walked with him a few yards down the street. This seemed to him for some reason suspicious. At home visions of convicts and of soldiers armed with rifles haunted him all day, and an inexplicable spiritual dread prevented him from reading or concentrating his mind. In the evening he sat without a fire, and lay awake all night thinking how he also might be arrested, manacled, and flung into prison. He knew that he had committed no crime, and was quite confident that he would never commit murder, arson, or robbery; but then, he remembered, how easy it was to commit a crime by accident or involuntarily, and how common were convictions on false evidence and owing to judicial errors! And in the present state of human affairs how probable, how little to be wondered at, were judicial errors! Men who witness the sufferings of others only from a professional standpoint; for instance, judges, policemen, doctors, became hardened to such a degree that even if they wished otherwise they could not resist the habit of treating accused persons formally; they got to resemble those peasants who kill sheep and calves in their back-yards without even noticing the blood. In view of the soulless relationship to human personality which everywhere obtains, all that a judge thinks of is the observance of certain formalities, and then all is over, and an innocent man perhaps deprived of his civil rights or sent to the galleys. Who indeed would expect justice or intercession in this dirty, sleepy little town, two hundred versts from the nearest railway? And indeed was it not ridiculous to expect justice when society regards every form of violence as rational, expedient, and necessary; and when an act of common mercy such as the acquittal of an accused man calls forth an explosion of unsatisfied vindictiveness!

Next morning Ivan Dmitritch awoke in terror with drops of cold sweat on his forehead. He felt convinced that he might be arrested at any moment. That the evening's gloomy thoughts had haunted him so persistently, he concluded, must mean that there was some ground for his apprehensions. Could such thoughts come into his head without cause?

A policeman walked slowly past the window; that must mean something. Two men in plain clothes stopped outside the gate, and stood without saying a word. Why were they silent?

For a time, Ivan Dmitritch spent his days and nights in torture. Every man who passed the window or entered the yard was a spy or detective. Every day at twelve o'clock the Chief Constable drove through the street on his way from his suburban house to the Department of Police, and every day it seemed to Ivan Dmitritch that the Constable was driving with unaccustomed haste, and that there was a peculiar expression on his face; he was going, in short, to announce that a great criminal had appeared in the town. Ivan Dmitritch shuddered at every sound, trembled at every knock at the yard-gate, and was in torment when any strange man visited his landlady. When he met a gendarme in the street, he smiled, whistled, and tried to assume an indifferent air. For whole nights, expecting arrest, he never closed his eyes, but snored carefully so that his landlady might think he was asleep; for if a man did not sleep at night it meant that he was tormented by gnawings of conscience, and that might be taken as a clue. Reality and healthy reasoning convinced him that his fears were absurd and psychopathic, and that, regarded from a broad standpoint, there was nothing very terrible in arrest and imprisonment for a man whose conscience was clean. But the more consistently and logically he reasoned the stronger grew his spiritual torture; his efforts reminded him of the efforts of a pioneer to hack a path through virgin forest, the harder he worked with the hatchet the thicker and stronger became the undergrowth. So in the end, seeing that his efforts were useless, he ceased to struggle, and gave himself up to terror and despair.

He avoided others and became more and more solitary in his habits. His duties had always been detestable, now they became intolerable. He imagined that someone would hide money in his pockets and then denounce him for taking bribes, that he would make mistakes in official documents which were equivalent to forgery, or that he would lose the money entrusted to him. Never was his mind so supple and ingenious as when engaged in inventing various reasons for fearing for his freedom and honour. On the other hand, his interest in the outside world decreased correspondingly, he lost his passion for books, and his memory daily betrayed him.

Next spring when the snow had melted, the semidecomposed corpses of an old woman and a boy, marked with indications of violence, were found in a ravine beside the graveyard. The townspeople talked of nothing but the discovery and the problem: who were the unknown murderers? In order to avert suspicion, Ivan Dmititritch walked about the streets and smiled; and when he met his acquaintances, first grew pale and then blushed, and declared vehemently that there was no more detestable crime than the killing of the weak and defenseless. But this pretense soon exhausted him, and after consideration he decided that the best thing he could do was to hide in his landlady's cellar. In the cellar therefore, chilled to the bone, he remained all day, all next night, and yet another day, after which, waiting until it was dark, he crept secretly back to his room. Till daylight he stood motionless in the middle of the room, and listened. At sunrise a number of artisans rang at the gate. Ivan Dmitritch knew very well that they had come to put up a new stove in the kitchen; but his terror suggested that they were constables in disguise. He crept quietly out of his room, and overcome by panic, without cap or coat, fled down the street. Behind him ran barking dogs, a woman called after him, in his ears the wind whistled, and it seemed to him that the scattered violences of the whole world had united and were chasing him through the town.

He was captured and brought home. His landlady sent for a doctor. Doctor Andrei Yefimitch Ragin, of whom we shall hear again, prescribed cold compresses for his head, ordered him to take drops of bay rum, and went away saying that he would come no more, as it was not right to prevent people going out of their minds. So, as there were no means of treating him at home, Ivan Dmitritch was sent to hospital, and put into the ward for sick men. He did not sleep at night, was unruly, and disturbed his neighbors, so that soon, by arrangement with Doctor Andrei Yefimitch, Ragin was transferred to Ward No. 6.

Before a year had passed, the townspeople had quite forgotten Ivan Dmitritch; and his books, piled up in a sledge by his landlady and covered with a curtain, were torn to pieces by children.

Delusional Disorder

Individuals with delusional disorder experience nonbizarre delusions (delusions regarding situations that can reasonably occur in everyday life) for at least one month that are not attributable to another psychotic condition. They must also have never met the criteria for schizophrenia. These individuals function reasonably well aside from the impact or ramifications of their delusions.

Guy de Maupassant (1850–1893)

Guy de Maupassant was born of noble French ancestors. His parents separated when he was eleven years old, and he grew up in Normandy. His grandfather was Gustave Flaubert's godfather. In his early twenties, Maupassant joined the literary circle of Flaubert in Paris. As a member of Flaubert's group he learned much about writing and also met many of the leading writers of his day including Ivan Turgenev and Henry James.

De Maupassant contracted syphilis in his twenties and as he grew older the disease produced increasing symptoms of mental disorder. He is well known for his stories filled with characters suffering from mental illness. Critics have attributed his interest in seriously disturbed individuals and ability to capture their thoughts and feelings to his own developing illness. However, the theme of mental disorder is seen in de Maupassant's early works as well. In de Maupassant's stories related to mental problems there is a recurring theme of madness and suicide.

In 1892 de Maupassant tried to commit suicide by cutting his throat. He was committed to the famous private asylum of Dr. Esprit Blanche at Passay in Paris, where he died the next year.

De Maupassant wrote 300 short stories, six novels, three travel books, and one volume of verse. He is considered by many to be the greatest French story writer.

De Maupassant brilliantly captured the essence of the delusional disorder in his short story "A Madman." In this story the judge functions extremely well in most areas of his life, but when it comes to "murder and bloodshed" his thoughts and actions become delusional.

"A Madman"

He died judge of a high tribunal—an upright magistrate whose irreproachability of life was cited in all the courts of France. Attorneys, young barristers, and even judges had been wont to bow very low as a special mark of profound respect, whenever they saluted his great white thin face, illuminated by two brilliant and deep-set eyes. He had spent his whole life in the prosecution of crime and the protection of the weak. Thieves and murderers had no enemy more terrible than he; for he seemed to read their secret thoughts in the very depths of their souls; and to unravel, with a single look, all the mysteries of their plots.

So he died at the age of eighty-two, an object of universal homage, followed to his grave by the regrets of an entire people. Soldiers in red trousers escorted him to the tomb; and men in white cravats had poured out upon his coffin many phrases of grief and many tears that appeared to be sincere.

Now, this is the extraordinary document which an astonished notary discovered in the Judge's writing desk— the same desk in which he was accustomed to preserve all the papers relating to important criminal cases.

It bore this simple title:

WHY?

June 20, 1851.—I have just left the courtroom. I sentenced Blondel to death! Why on earth did that man kill his five children? Why? . . . People are often to be met with who find a delight in destroying life. Yes, yes, it must be a pleasure—the greatest of all pleasures, perhaps; for killing is the nearest thing to creating, is it not? To make, to destroy! These two words include the history of the universe, all the history of all worlds, all that exists—all! Why is it intoxicating to kill?

June 25.—To think that a creature is there—a creature that lives, that walks, that runs. . . . A creature? What is a creature? A being? That animated thing, having within it the principle of movement and a will governing that movement! That thing depends on nothing. Its feet do not communicate with the soil. It is an atom of life that moves upon the earth; and that atom of life, come from I know not whence, can be destroyed at will. Then nothing, absolutely nothing. The thing rots; that is the end of it.

June 26.—Why is it a crime to kill?—Yes, why is it? On the contrary to kill is a law of nature. The mission of every being is to kill; he kills in order to live, and he also kills for the sake of killing. . . . To kill is a part of our nature; killing is absolutely necessary. The animal kills unceasingly, all day long, at every instant of its existence. Man kills unceasingly for the sake of food; but as he is under the necessity of also killing for sport, he invented hunting! The child kills any insects he happens to find, little birds, any little animals that happen to fall into his hands. But even all this does not satisfy the irresistible necessity of massacre that is born within us. It is not enough to kill dumb brutes; we need also to kill men. In ancient times this need was satisfied by human sacrifices. Today the necessities of social existence have made murder a crime. The assassin is condemned and punished! But as we cannot live without yielding to this natural and imperious instinct of slaughter, we find relief occasionally in wars, during which one whole nation slaughters another whole nation. Then we have an orgy of blood—a debauch that maddens armies and intoxicates even the *bourgeois*, and the women, and the children who read the exciting recital of massacres by light of the evening lamp.

And it might be supposed that those destined to execute such human butcheries are despised! No: Honors are lavished upon them! They are garbed in gold and brilliantly colored cloth; their heads are bedecked with plumes, their breasts with decorations; and they receive crosses, rewards, titles of every description. They are proud, respected, beloved by women, cheered by crowds—simply because it is their mission to shed human blood. They drag through all our streets their implements of death, which the black-clad passers-by look at with envy. For to kill is the great law implanted by nature in the heart of every being! There is nothing so fine, so honorable, as to kill!

June 30.—To kill is the law, because Nature loves eternal youth. She seems to cry out through all her unconscious acts; *'Quick! Quick! Quick!'* The more she destroys, the more she renews herself.

July 2.— The human being—what is the human being? Everything and nothing. By thought he is the reflection of all things. By memory and science he is an epitome of that world whereof he hears the history within him. A mirror of objects—a mirror of facts—each human being becomes a miniature universe in the midst of the universe.

But travel; look upon the swarming of races; and man is no longer anything! He is nothing, absolutely nothing! Go on board a ship, and sail away from that shore which is so thronged with people, and you will soon be able to perceive nothing but the shore itself. So little, so insignificant is the individual, the imperceptible being, that he disappears utterly. Traverse Europe by rail, and look out of the coach-window as you travel. Men, men, always men—innumerable, unknown—swarming in the fields, swarming in the streets; stupid peasants with barely enough sense to enable them to till the ground, hideous women, knowing just enough to be able to make soup for the males and to bear children. Go to India, go to China; and again you will see the movement of thousands of millions of beings that are born, that live, and that finally die without leaving any more trace of their existence on the face of the world than the ant that is crushed upon some highroad. Go to the country of the blacks, huddling in their huts of mud; or go to the land of the whiter Arabs, sheltered by some brown tent flapping in the wind—and you will see that the individual, the single being, considered apart, is nothing, nothing at all. The race is everything. What is one being? What is one member of one wandering tribe of the desert? Among those men of the desert, who are wise, death is never a subject of anxiety. The man is not taken into consideration. One kills one's enemy: that is war. Long ago the same things were done among our people—it was war between house and house, between province and province.

July 3.— It must be a strange and savory pleasure to kill; to have right before you some living, thinking being—to make a little hole in that being, just one little hole—to see the flowing of that red thing called blood, which makes life—and then to find you have nothing before you but a mass of soft, cold, inert flesh, empty of thought!

August 5.— I who have spent all my life in judging people, in sentencing them, in killing by mere word of mouth, in killing with the guillotine those who have killed with the knife—I!—I!— were I to do as the assassins I have sentenced—I!—I!—who could ever know it?

August 10.—Who could ever find it out? Could anyone suspect me—me!—me!—especially if I should select an individual whose existence I would have no personal motive in suppressing?

August 15.—The temptation! Temptation has entered into me like a crawling worm. It crawls; it advances; it creeps through my whole body—through my whole mind also, my mind which now dwells only upon this one idea, *kill:* it has entered my eyes which want to see blood, to see the act of dying; it has entered my ears which perpetually ring with an unfamiliar, hideous, agonizing, maddening sound, like the last outcry of a creature; it has entered into my feet, which tremble with the desire to go, to go to the spot where the act shall be done; it is in my hands which quiver with the longing to slay. How agreeable it must be! How refined! How well worthy of a free man, superior to other men, master of his own heart, and ever thirsting for new and exquisite sensations!

Yes; wander over the world and watch the swarming of men—innumerable, unknown men. *Unknown?* Ah! there is the key to the whole enigma. To kill is criminal because we have counted the number of creatures! When one of them is born, the fact is registered; the creature is named, is baptized. The law claims possession of all these! There's the secret! But the being that is not registered does not count! Kill such a one wherever you find him, on the heath or in the desert, on the mountain or upon the plain—it matters not! Nature loves death! She never punishes the slayer!

What is particularly sacred, by the way, is the registry office! You understand! The individual is sacred because he is registered! Respect the registry office—the legal God! On your knees!

The government can kill, because it possesses the power to modify the census. When it causes two hundred thousand men to be slaughtered in war, it erases them all from its civil register, it suppresses them by the hand of its recorders. And that is the end of the matter. But the rest of us, we who have no power to change the records of municipalities, we are obliged to respect life. Registry office, glorious Divinity who reignest in the temples of municipalities, I bow before thee! Thou art stronger than Nature is. Ah! Ah!

August 22.—I could not resist any longer. I have just killed a little creature as an experiment—as a commencement.

My servant Jean had a goldfinch, which he used to keep in a cage hanging at the office window. I sent him out on an errand; and then I took the little bird in my hand—in my hand, against which I could feel his heart beat. He was quite warm. I went up to my room. From time to time I squeezed him a little harder—then his heart beat more quickly: it was a sensation at once atrocious and delicious. I was very nearly on the point of smothering him. But if I had smothered him, I would not have seen the blood.

Then I took a pair of scissors, short-bladed nail scissors; and I cut his throat with three nips—very slowly. He opened his beak, he tried to escape; but I held him—oh! I held him! I could have held an enraged mastiff! And I saw the blood come. How beautiful blood is—red, shining, bright! I wanted to drink it. I dipped the end of my tongue into it! It is good. But then he had so little of it—that poor atom of a bird! I did not have time enough to enjoy the sight as I would have liked to do. It must be simply superb to see a bull bleed.

And then I did just as murderers do—real murderers. I washed the scissors; I washed my hands; I threw the water away; and I took the body, the corpse, into the garden to bury it. I hid it under a strawberry plant. It will never be found there. Every day I intend to eat one strawberry off that plant. How one can really enjoy life . . . when he knows how!

My servant cried. He thought his bird had flown away. How could he ever suspect me! Ah! Ah!

August 25.—I must really kill a man! It must be done.

August 30.—It has to be done. How easy a thing to do!

I had gone out to the Bois de Vernes just for a walk. I was not thinking about anything in particular, not thinking about anything at all. A child came along the pathway—a little boy eating a slice of bread and butter.

He stopped to watch me pass by, and said: "Good day, your Honor!"

Then the thought came into my head: *Suppose I kill him?* . . .

I replied:

"Well, my boy, are you all by yourself?"

"Yes, sir."

"All by yourself in the woods, eh?"

"Yes, sir."

And the wish to kill him made me drunk like alcohol. I approached him very gently, being afraid that he might try to run away. And all of a sudden I seized him by the throat. . . . And I squeezed his throat; I squeezed it. I squeezed it with all my might. He looked at me with such a frightful look in his eyes! What eyes! Big, and all round—deep, limpid, terrible! Never did I experience an emotion so brutal . . . yet so brief! He tried to pull my wrists with his little hands; and his body twisted like a feather flung upon hot coals. Finally he ceased to move at all.

My heart beat so fast—ah! I thought of the heart of the bird! I threw the body into the ditch; and put some grass over it. . . .

I went home. I ate a hearty dinner. How easily the thing is done! I was very merry that evening—quite jovial; felt ever so much younger. I spent the evening at the house of the Prefect of Police. Everybody thought I was unusually witty.

August 30.—The corpse has been found. The police are looking for the murderer. Ah! Ah!

September 1.—Two tramps have been arrested. No proofs against them.

September 2.—The parents of the boy came to see me. They wept!—Oh! how they wept. Ah! Ah!

October 6.—No clue whatever has been found. It is supposed that some tramp must have done the deed. Ah! Ah! If I could only have had the pleasure of seeing the blood actually flow, I think I should now feel perfectly satisfied!

October 10.—The desire to kill thrills the very marrow of my bones. It is a desire comparable for intensity to nothing except the passion of love at twenty years.

October 20.—Still another. I was taking a walk on the river bank, after breakfast. And I saw a fisherman sleeping under a willow tree. It was midday. A spade seemed to have been left on purpose sticking in the clay of a neighboring potato field.

I took it; I came back; I lifted it like a club; and with the edge of it, I split the fisherman's head at one blow. Oh! but he bled—that one! Pink blood, full of brains. It trickled into the river very gently. And I walked away with a solemn step. Suppose anybody had seen me! . . . Ah! Ah! I would have made an excellent murderer.

October 25.—The murder of the fisherman has caused a great excitement. His nephew, who was fishing with him, is accused of the murder.

October 26.—The examining judge declares that the nephew is guilty. Everybody in town believes it. Ah! Ah!

October 27.—The nephew's defense is very poor indeed. He says that he went to the village to buy some bread and cheese. He swears that his uncle must have been killed while he was away! Who is going to believe him?

October 28.—The nephew has almost been forced to confess; they have confused him so! Ah! Ah! This is justice!

November 15.—The evidence against the nephew is overwhelming. It appears that he was to inherit his uncle's property. I am to try the case!

January 25.—To death! To death! To death! I have sentenced him to death! Ah! Ah! The prosecuting attorney argued like an angel! Ah! Ah! Still another. I will go to see the execution.

March 10.—It is all over. He is dead now, sure enough—dead as a door nail! I enjoyed it immensely! How beautiful it is to see a man's head chopped off! The blood gushed out like a stream—like a torrent! Oh! if I had been able, how I should have liked to bathe in it! What delight to lie down in it—to get the warm jet right in my face, and in my hair—and to get up all red, all red! Ah! if they only knew!

Now I shall wait. I can afford to wait. It would take so little to betray me . . .

The MS. contained many more pages, but no reference to any new crime.

The medical alienists to whom it was given declare that many unknown madmen exist in society—quite as adroit and quite as terrible as this demented monster.

Discussion Questions

1. In the story "Ward No. 6," identify the schizophrenic symptoms exhibited by Ivan. Looking now to affective disorder, symptoms of major depression include depressed mood, diminished interest or pleasure in activities, insomnia, psychomotor agitation, feelings of worthlesness and guilt, and diminished ability to think or concentrate. Identify as many of these symptoms as you can in the story. If you were going to work with a person with schizoaffective disorder which would you work on first, the schizophrenia or the affective disorder? Why? What would you do?

2. Is it possible to be as disturbed as the judge appears to be in "A Madman" and yet avoid detection? Were there any indications that the judge was suffering from delusional disorder and committing these crimes, which the authorities simply overlooked? Identify any indications you may discover.

3. Identify several points where the main character in "The Yellow Wallpaper" slips deeper into her psychotic illness.

4. There are some indications that individuals with paranoid schizophrenia may be dangerous. Discuss how you would go about determining if an individual with this disorder might be dangerous. What questions would you ask? What other people would you want to talk to about the individual's behavior?

5. You have been appointed to explain their loved one's disorder to the family of a recently diagnosed paranoid schizophrenic person. Write out what you would say to the family to explain the individual's illness. After your explanation the family asks you the following questions: Will she have to take medicine? Is she a danger to herself or to us? Will she be able to live at home, or will she have to be in a hospital? Will she ever get better? If she has children, will they be schizophrenic also? Answer each of their questions.

Chapter 5

Mood Disorders

The basic issue related to this group of disorders is the development of an abnormal mood characterized by depression, mania, or both symptoms in alternating fashion. The mood disorders are distinguished from normal moods by the intensity of the abnormal mood, the duration of the mood, and the impairment the mood produces.

Depression is distinguished by an unusually sad, gloomy, or dejected mood. These individuals experience a markedly diminished interest and pleasure in everyday activities. A depressed mood and loss of interest or pleasure are the key symptoms of depression. The possibility of suicide is a serious consideration when working with depressed individuals.

Mania is an unusually and persistently elevated, expansive, or irritable mood. Hypomania is a less severe variant of mania.

Major Depressive Disorder

Major depressive disorder is the most serious form of depression. Individuals with major depression often look lifeless or dull rather than crying and appearing sad. Additional symptoms of major depression include reduced energy, difficulty sleeping, decreased appetite, weight loss or weight gain, increased sleep, and anxiety. A significant number of depressed persons experience a diurnal variation in symptoms, with increased severity of symptoms in the morning and a lessening of symptoms by evening. Cognitive symptoms are common and include the inability to concentrate, impaired thinking, inability to make decisions, and negative thoughts about the past (guilt), the present (low self-esteem), and the future (hopelessness).

Sylvia Plath (1932–1963)

Sylvia Plath was born in Jamacia Plain, Massachusetts. Her father was a professor of German and entomology at Boston University, and her mother was a high school teacher.

Plath discovered her literary calling early in life. By the time she entered Smith College, she had published poetry in various newspapers and had written over fifty short stories. Her writing talent was recognized and led to her selection for the college board of *Mademoiselle* magazine in 1953. Plath suffered from depression and was treated with electroconvulsive shock treatments on an outpatient basis. In August 1953, she attempted suicide by overdosing on sleeping pills. She received six months of treatment in a private hospital, and after responding well to her treatment she returned to Smith.

Plath graduated from Smith in 1955 and went to Cambridge University on a Fulbright scholarship, where she met poet Ted Hughes. Plath and Hughes were married in London in 1956. The marriage was marked by personal jealousies, differing views of gender roles, and the return of Plath's depression. The couple divorced in 1962. After her divorce Plath entered a highly productive period during which she produced the forty poems that have been the major reason for her posthumous fame.

Beginning in January 1963, Plath again experienced a period of deep depression, and on February 11, 1963, she committed suicide. Plath's work reflects a unique openness and sincere honesty, and her willingness to look deeply into her own difficulties has given us a unique point of view regarding major depression.

One of Plath's most significant works is *The Bell Jar* (1961), from which the selection utilized here is taken. In this excerpt Plath paints a clear portrait of the loss of interest experienced in major depression.

The Bell Jar

Doctor Gordon's waiting room was hushed and beige.

The walls were beige, and the carpets were beige, and the upholstered chairs and sofas were beige. There were no mirrors or pictures, only certificates from different medical schools, with Doctor Gordon's name in Latin, hung about the walls. Pale green loopy ferns and spiked leaves of a much darker green filled the ceramic pots on the end table and the coffee table and the magazine table.

At first I wondered why the room felt so safe. Then I realized it was because there were no windows.

The air-conditioning made me shiver.

I was still wearing Betsy's white blouse and dirndl skirt. They drooped a bit now, as I hadn't washed them in my three weeks at home. The sweaty cotton gave off a sour but friendly smell.

I hadn't washed my hair for three weeks, either.

I hadn't slept for seven nights.

My mother told me I must have slept, it was impossible not to sleep in all that time, but if I slept, it was with my eyes wide open, for I had followed the green, luminous course of the second hand and the minute hand and the hour hand of the bedside clock through their circles and semi-circles, every night for seven nights, without missing a second, or a minute, or an hour.

The reason I hadn't washed my clothes or my hair was because it seemed so silly.

I saw the days of the year stretching ahead like a series of bright, white boxes, and separating one box from another was sleep, like a black shade. Only for me, the long perspective of shades that set off one box from the next had suddenly snapped up, and I could see day after day glaring ahead of me like a white, broad, infinitely desolate avenue.

It seemed so silly to wash one day when I would only have to wash again the next.

It made me tired just to think of it.

I wanted to do everything once and for all and be through with it.

Edward Arlington Robinson (1869–1935)

Edward Arlington Robinson's poem "Richard Corey" describes a man who seems to have everything going for him. His unexpected suicide reminds us of the potential of suicide with depressed individuals who may not appear in danger.

(Refer to chapter 3 for biographical information on Robinson.)

"Richard Corey"

Whenever Richard Cory went downtown
We people on the pavement looked at him,
He was a gentleman from sole to crown:
Clean-favored and imperially slim.

And he was always graciously arrayed
And he was always human when he talked
But still he fluttered pulses when he said
"Good morning"; and he glittered when he walked.

And he was rich, yes, richer than a king
And admirably schooled in every grace
In fine, we thought that he was everything
To make us wish that we were in his place.

So we all worked and waited for the light
And went without the meat and cursed the bread,
And Richard Cory one calm summer night
Went home and put a bullet in his head.

Kate Chopin (1850–1904)

Kate Chopin was born Katherine O'Flaherty in St. Louis, Missouri. By the time she was twenty-four years old her father, grandmother, best friend, and all of her brothers and sisters had died. When she graduated from the Academy of the Sacred Heart, she was known as a lonely student with a depressed manner who was a brilliant story-teller.

In 1870 she married Oscar Chopin, who died in 1883, leaving her with their six young children to raise alone. One year later her mother died. Her mother's death left Chopin emotionally drained from the numerous losses in her life. When she turned to her family doctor for help, he suggested that she begin to write as a way to express her anger and frustration about the losses in her life.

Chopin was quite successful in her writing efforts and became a very popular writer. Her finest work was *The Awakening,* published in 1899. The novel was widely condemned because of its openly sexual content. After *The Awakening* Kate Chopin was shunned by her publishers and her career faltered. Her work was rediscovered in the 1950s and has since been given its due respect. Chopin's work is remembered today for its depth of understanding and insight into human emotions and motivation.

Chopin's works are filled with memorable characters and lives full of tragedy and heartbreak. Her ability to describe the loneliness and hopelessness of life is clearly evident in this selection from *The Awakening.* The suicide of Edna Pontillier describes the despondency and anguish of major depression that results in the worst possible outcome.

The Awakening

He reproached his wife with her inattention, her habitual neglect of the children. If it was not a mother's place to look after children, whose on earth was it? He himself had his hands full with his brokerage business. He could not be in two places at once; making a living for his family on the street, and staying at home to see that no harm befell them. He talked in a monotonous, insistent way.

Mrs. Pontellier sprang out of bed and went into the next room. She soon came back and sat on the edge of the bed, leaning her head down on the pillow. She said nothing, and refused to answer her husband when he questioned her. When his cigar was smoked out he went to bed, and in half a minute he was fast asleep.

Mrs. Pontellier was by that time thoroughly awake. She began to cry a little, and wiped her eyes on the sleeve of her *peignoir*. Blowing out the candle, which her husband had left burning, she slipped her bare feet into a pair of satin mules at the foot of the bed and went out on the porch, where she sat down in the wicker chair and began to rock gently to and fro.

It was then past midnight. The cottages were all dark. A single faint light gleamed out from the hallway of the house. There was no sound abroad except the hooting of an old owl in the top of a water-oak, and the everlasting voice of the sea, that was not uplifted at that soft hour. It broke like a mournful lullaby upon the night.

The tears came so fast to Mrs. Pontellier's eyes that the damp sleeve of her *peignoir* no longer served to dry them. She was holding the back of her chair with one hand; her loose sleeve had slipped almost to the shoulder of her up-lifted arm. Turning, she thrust her face, steaming and wet, into the bend of her arm, and she went on crying there, not caring any longer to dry her face, her eyes, her arms. She could not have told why she was crying. Such experiences as the foregoing were not uncommon in her married life. They seemed never before to have weighed much against the abundance of her husband's kindness and a uniform devotion which had come to be tacit and self-understood.

An indescribable oppression, which seemed to generate in some unfamiliar part of her consciousness, filled her whole being with a vague anguish. It was like a shadow, like a mist passing across her soul's summer day. It was strange and unfamiliar; it was a mood. She did not sit there inwardly upbraiding her husband, lamenting at Fate, which had directed her footsteps to the path which they had taken. She was just having a good cry all to herself. The mosquitoes made merry over her, biting her firm, round arms and nipping at her bare insteps.

* * *

It was a large, beautiful room, rich and picturesque in the soft, dim light which the maid had turned low. She went and stood at an open window and looked out upon the deep tangle of the garden below. All the mystery and witchery of the night seemed to have gathered there amid the perfumes and the dusky and tortuous outlines of flowers and foliage. She was seeking herself and finding herself in just such sweet, half darkness which met her moods. But the voices were not soothing that came to her from the darkness and the sky above and the stars. They jeered and sounded mournful notes without promise, devoid even of hope. She turned back into the room and began to walk to and fro down its whole length, without stopping, without resting. She carried in her hands a thin handkerchief, which she tore into ribbons, rolled into a ball, and flung from her. Once she stopped, and taking off her wedding ring, flung it upon the carpet. When she saw it lying there, she stamped her heel upon it, striving to crush it. But her small boot heel did not make an indenture, not a mark upon the little glittering circlet.

In a sweeping passion she seized a glass vase from the table and flung it upon the tiles of the hearth. She wanted to destroy something. The crash and clatter were what she wanted to hear.

* * *

But as she sat there amid her guests, she felt the old ennui overtaking her, the hopelessness which so often assailed her, which came upon her like an ob-session, like something extraneous, independent of volition. It was something which announced itself; a chill breath that seemed to issue from some vast cavern wherein discords wailed. There came over her the acute longing which always summoned into her spiritual vision the presence of the beloved one, overpowering her at once with a sense of the unattainable.

* * *

Despondency had come upon her there in the wakeful night, and had never lifted. There was no one thing in the world that she desired. There was no human being whom she wanted near her except Robert; and she even realized that the day would come when he, too, and the thought of him would melt out of her existence, leaving her alone. The children appeared before her like an-tagonists who had overcome her; who had overpowered and sought to drag her into the soul's slavery for the rest of her days. But she knew a way to elude them. She was not thinking of these things when she walked down to the beach.

The water of the Gulf stretched out before her, gleaming with the million lights of the sun. The voice of the sea is seductive, never ceasing, whispering, clamoring, murmuring, inviting the soul to wander in abysses of solitude. All along the white beach, up and down, there was no living thing in sight. A bird with a broken wing was beating the air above, reeling, fluttering, circling dis-abled down, down to the water.

Edna had found her old bathing suite still hanging, faded, upon its accus-tomed peg.

She put it on, leaving her clothing in the bath-house. But when she was there beside the sea, absolutely alone, she cast the unpleasant, prickling gar-ments from her, and for the first time in her life she stood naked in the open air, at the mercy of the sun, the breeze that beat upon her, and the waves that invited her.

How strange and awful it seemed to stand naked under the sky! how deli-cious! She felt like some new-born creature, opening its eyes in a familiar world that it had never known.

The foamy wavelets curled up to her white feet, and coiled like serpents about her ankles. She walked out. The water was chill, but she walked on. The water was deep, but she lifted her white body and reached out with a long, sweeping stroke. The touch of the sea is sensuous, enfolding the body in its soft, close embrace.

She went on and on. She remembered the night she swam far out, and recalled the terror that seized her at the fear of being unable to regain the shore. She did not look back now, but went on and on, thinking of the blue-grass meadow that she had traversed when a little child, believing that it had no beginning and no end.

Her arms and legs were growing tired.

She thought of Leonce and the children. They were a part of her life. But they need not have thought that they could possess her, body and soul. How Mademoiselle Reisz would have laughed, perhaps sneered, if she knew! "And you call yourself an artist! What pretensions, Madame! The artist must posses the courageous soul that dares and defies."

Exhaustion was pressing upon and overpowering her.

"Good-bye—because, I love you." He did not know; he did not understand. He would never have understood if she had seen him— but it was too late; the shore was far behind her, and her strength was gone.

She looked into the distance, and the old terror flamed up for an instant, then sank again. Edna heard her father's voice and her sister Margaret's. She heard the barking of an old dog that was chained to the sycamore tree. The spurs of the cavalry officer clanged as he walked across the porch. There was the hum of bees, and the musky odor of pinks filled the air.

Dysthymic Disorder

Dysthymic disorder is considered a less intense form of depression. These individuals have a persistent depression lasting at least two years. Dysthymia means "ill-humored," and these individuals are often sarcastic, demanding, and complaining. They are rigid and resistant to therapy. Difficulties in social functioning sometimes lead these people to seek treatment. Such difficulties include marital problems, employment problems, and various somatic complaints. Addictions, particularly alcoholism, are prevalent among people with dysthymia. Dysthymia typically emerges in early adult life, although it may be diagnosed in children and adolescents, and its course is generally chronic.

Charles Dickens (1812–1870)

Charles Dickens provides us with a wonderful portrait of a dysthymic individual in the person of Mr. Nicodemus Dumps. Mr. Dumps, "The most unfortunate man in the world," cross, ill-natured, and miserable, personifies the disorder of dysthymia.

(Refer to chapter 2 for biographical information on Dickens.)

"The Bloomsbury Christening"

Mr. Nicodemus Dumps, or, as his acquaintance called him, "long Dumps," was a bachelor, six feet high, and fifty years old: cross, cadaverous, odd, and ill-natured. He was never happy but when he was miserable; and always miserable when he had the best reason to be happy. The only real comfort of his existence was to make everybody about him wretched—then he might be truly said to enjoy life. He was afflicted with a situation in the Bank worth five hundred a year, and he rented a "first-floor furnished," at Pentonville, which he originally took because it commanded a dismal prospect of an adjacent churchyard. He was familiar with the face of every tombstone, and the burial service seemed to excite his strongest sympathy. His friends said he was surly—he insisted he was nervous; they thought him a lucky dog, but he protested that he was "the most unfortunate man in the world." Cold as he was, and wretched as he declared himself to be, he was not wholly unsusceptible of attachments. He revered the memory of Hoyle, as he was himself an admirable and imperturbable whist player, and he chuckled with delight at a fretful and impatient adversary. He adored King Herod for his massacre of the innocents; and if he hated one thing more than another, it was a child. However, he could hardly be said to hate anything in particular, because he disliked everything in general; but perhaps his greatest antipathies were cabs, old women, doors that would not shut, musical amateurs, and omnibus cads. He subscribed to the "Society for the Suppression of Vice" for the pleasure of putting a stop to any harmless amusements; and he contributed largely towards the support of two itinerant Methodist parsons, in the amiable hope that if circumstances rendered any people happy in this world, they might perchance be rendered miserable by fears for the next.

Mr. Dumps had a nephew who had been married about a year, and who was somewhat of a favorite with his uncle, because he was an admirable subject to exercise his misery-creating powers upon. Mr. Charles Kitterbell was a small, sharp, spare man, with a very large head, and a broad, good-humored countenance. He looked like a faded giant, with the head and face partially restored; and he had a cast in his eye which rendered it quite impossible for any one with whom he conversed to know where he was looking. His eyes appeared fixed on the wall, and he was staring you out of countenance; in short, there was no catching his eye, and perhaps it is a merciful dispensation of Providence that such eyes are not catching. In addition to these characteristics, it may be added that Mr. Charles Kitterbell was one of the most credulous and matter-of-fact little personages that ever took *to* himself a wife, and *for* himself a house in Great Russell Street, Bedford Square. (Uncle Dumps always dropped the "Bedford Square," and inserted in lieu thereof the dreadful words "Tottenham Court Road.")

"No, but, uncle, 'pon my life you must—you must promise to be godfather," said Mr. Kitterbell, as he sat in conversation with this respected relative one morning.

"I cannot, indeed I cannot," returned Dumps.

"Well, but why not? Jemima will think it very unkind. It's very little trouble."

"As to the trouble," rejoined the most unhappy man in existence, "I don't mind that; but my nerves are in that state—I cannot go through the ceremony. You know I don't like going out. For God's sake, Charles, don't fidget with that stool so; you'll drive me mad." Mr. Kitterbell, quite regardless of his uncle's nerves, had occupied himself for some ten minutes in describing a circle on the floor with one leg of the office stool on which he was seated, keeping the other three up in the air, and holding fast on by the desk.

"I beg your pardon, uncle," said Kitterbell, quite abashed, suddenly releasing his hold of the desk, and bringing the three wandering legs back to the floor, with a force sufficient to drive them through it.

"But come, don't refuse. If it's a boy, you know, we must have two godfathers."

"If it's a boy!" said Dumps; "why can't you say at once whether it is a boy or not?"

"I should be very happy to tell you, but it's impossible I can undertake to say whether it's a girl or a boy, if the child isn't born yet."

"Not born yet!" echoed Dumps, with a gleam of hope lighting up his lugubrious visage. "Oh well, it *may* be a girl, and then you won't want me; or if it is a boy, it *may* die before it is christened."

"I hope not," said the father that expected to be, looking very grave.

"I hope not," acquiesced Dumps, evidently pleased with the subject. He was beginning to get happy. "I hope not, but distressing cases frequently occur during the first two or three days of a child's life; fits, I am told, are exceedingly common, and alarming convulsions are almost matters of course."

"Lord, uncle!" ejaculated little Kitterbell, gasping for breath.

"Yes; my landlady was confined—let me see—last Tuesday: an uncommonly fine boy. On the Thursday night the nurse was sitting with him upon her knee before the fire, and he was as well as possible. Suddenly he became black in the face, and alarmingly spasmodic. The medical man was instantly sent for, and every remedy was tried, but—"

"How frightful!" interrupted the horror-stricken Kitterbell.

"The child died, of course. However, your child *may* not die; and if it should be a boy, and should *live* to be christened, why I suppose I must be one of the sponsors." Dumps was evidently good natured on the faith of his anticipations.

"Thank you, uncle," said his agitated nephew, grasping his hand as warmly as if he had done him some essential service. "Perhaps I had better not tell Mrs. K. what you have mentioned."

"Why, if she's low-spirited, perhaps you had better not mention the melancholy case to her," returned Dumps, who of course had invented the whole story; "though perhaps it would be but doing your duty as a husband to prepare her for the *worst*."

A day or two afterward, as Dumps was perusing a morning paper at the chop-house which he regularly frequented, the following paragraph met his eyes:

"*Births,*—On Saturday, the 18th inst., in Great Russell Street, the lady of Charles Kitterbell, Esq., of a son."

"It *is* a boy!" he exclaimed, dashing down the paper, to the astonishment of the waiters. "It *is* a boy!" But he speedily regained his composure as his eye rested on a paragraph quoting the number of infant deaths from the bills of mortality.

Six weeks passed away, and as no communication had been received from Kitterbells, Dumps was beginning to flatter himself that the child was dead, when the following note painfully resolved his doubts:

"Great Russell Street,
"Monday morning:

"Dear Uncle—You will be delighted to hear that my dear Jemima has left her room, and that your future godson is getting on capitally. He was very thin at first, but he is getting much larger, and nurse says he is filling out every day. He cries a good deal, and is a very singular color, which made Jemima and me rather uncomfortable; but as nurse says it's natural, and as of course we know nothing about these things yet, we are quite satisfied with what nurse says. We think he will be a sharp child; and nurse says she's sure he will, because he never goes to sleep. You will readily believe that we are all very happy, only we're a little worn out for want of rest, as he keeps us awake all night; but this we expect, nurse says, for the first six or eight months. He has been vaccinated, but in consequence of the operation being rather awkwardly performed, some small particles of glass were introduced into the arm with the matter. Perhaps this may in some degree account for his being rather fractious; at least, so nurse says. We propose to have him christened at twelve o'clock on Friday, at Saint George's church, in Hart Street, by the name of Frederick Charles William. Pray don't be later than a quarter before twelve. We shall have a very few friends in the evening, when of course we shall see you. I am sorry to say that the dear boy appears rather restless and uneasy today: the cause, I fear, is fever.

"Believe me, dear Uncle,
"Yours affectionately,
"Charles Kitterbell

"P.S.—I open this note to say that we have just discovered the cause of little Frederick's restlessness. It is not fever, as I apprehended, but a small pin, which nurse accidentally stuck in his leg yesterday evening. We have taken it out, and he appears more composed, though he still sobs a good deal."

It is almost unnecessary to say that the perusal of the above interesting statement was no great relief to the mind of the hypochondriacal Dumps. It was impossible to recede, however, and so he put the best face—that is to say, an uncommonly miserable one—upon the matter; and purchased a handsome silver mug for the infant Kitterbell, upon which he ordered the initials "F. C. W. K.," with the customary untrained grape-vine-looking flourishes, and a large full stop, to be engraved forthwith.

Monday was a fine day, Tuesday was delightful, Wednesday was equal to either, and Thursday was finer than ever; four successive fine days in London! Hackney coachmen became revolutionary, and crossing-sweepers began to doubt the existence of a First Cause. The *Morning Herald* informed its readers that an old woman in Camden Town had been heard to say that the fineness of the season was "unprecedented in the memory of the oldest inhabitant"; and Islington clerks, with large families and small salaries, left off their black gaiters, disdained to carry their once green cotton umbrellas, and walked to town in the conscious pride of white stockings and cleanly brushed Bluchers. Dumps beheld all this with an eye of supreme contempt—his triumph was at hand. He knew that if it had been fine for four weeks instead of four days, it would rain when he went out; he was lugubriously happy in the conviction that Friday would be a wretched day—and so it was. "I knew how it would be," said Dumps, as he turned round opposite the Mansion House at half-past eleven o'clock on the Friday morning. "I knew how it would be. *I* am concerned, and that's enough"; and certainly the appearance of the day was sufficient to depress the spirits of a much more buoyant-hearted individual than himself. It had rained, without a moment's cessation, since eight o'clock; everybody that passed up Cheapside, and down Cheapside, looked wet, cold, and dirty. All sorts of forgotten and long-concealed umbrellas had been put into requisition. Cabs whisked about, with the "fare" as carefully boxed up behind two glazed calico curtains as any mysterious picture in any one of Mrs. Radcliffe's castles; omnibus horses smoked like steam-engines; nobody thought of "standing up" under doorways or arches; they were painfully convinced it was a hopeless case; and so everybody went hastily along, jumbling and jostling, and swearing and perspiring, and slipping about, like amateur skaters behind wooden chairs on the Serpentine on a frosty Sunday.

Dumps paused; he could not think of walking, being rather smart for the christening. If he took a cab he was sure to be split, and a hackney coach was too expensive for his economical ideas. An omnibus was waiting at the opposite corner—it was a desperate case—he had never heard of an omnibus upsetting or running away, and if the cad did knock him down, he could "pull him up" in return.

"Now, sir!" cried the young gentleman who officiated as "cad" to the "Lads of the Village," which was the name of the machine just noticed. Dumps crossed.

"This vay, sir!" shouted the driver of the "Hark-away," pulling up his vehicle immediately across the door of the opposition—"This vay, sir—he's full." Dumps hesitated, whereupon the "Lads of the Village" commenced pouring out a torrent of abuse against the "Hark-away"; but the conductor of the

"Admiral Napier" settled the contest in a most satisfactory manner for all parties by seizing Dumps round the waist, and thrusting him into the middle of his vehicle, which had just come up and only wanted the sixteenth inside.

"All right," said the "Admiral," and off the thing thundered, like a fire engine at full gallop, with the kidnapped customer inside, standing in the position of a half doubled-up bootjack, and falling about with every jerk of the machine, first on the one side, and then on the other, like a "Jack-in-the-green," on May day, setting to the lady with a brass ladle.

"For Heaven's sake, where am I to sit?" inquired the miserable man of an old gentleman, into whose stomach he had just fallen for the fourth time.

"Anywhere but on my *chest*, sir," replied the old gentleman in a surly tone.

"Perhaps the *box* would suit the gentleman better," suggested a very damp lawyer's clerk, in a pink shirt, and a smirking countenance.

After a great deal of struggling and falling about, Dumps at last managed to squeeze himself into a seat, which, in addition to the slight disadvantage of being between a window that would not shut, and a door that must be open, placed him in close contact with a passenger, who had been walking about all the morning without an umbrella, and who looked as if he had spent the day in a full water-butt—only wetter.

"Don't bang the door so," said Dumps to the conductor, as he shut it after letting out four of the passengers; "I am very nervous—it destroys me."

"Did any gen'lm'n say anythink?" replied the cad, thrusting in his head, and trying to look as if he didn't understand the request.

"I told you not to bang the door so!" repeated Dumps, with an expression of countenance like the knave of clubs, in convulsions.

"Oh! vy, it's rather a sing'ler circumstance about this here door, sir, that it von't shut without banging," replied the conductor; and he opened the door very wide, and shut it again with a terrific bang, in proof of the assertion.

"I beg your pardon, sir," said a little prim, wheezing old gentleman, sitting opposite Dumps, "I beg your pardon; but have you ever observed, when you have been in an omnibus on a wet day, that four people out of five always come in with large cotton umbrellas, without a handle at the top, or the brass spike at the bottom?"

"Why, sir," returned Dumps, as he heard the clock strike twelve, "it never struck me before; but now you mention it, I—Hollo! hollo!" shouted the persecuted individual, as the omnibus dashed past Drury Lane, where he had directed to be set down—"Where is the cad?"

"I think he's on the box, sir," said the young gentleman before noticed in the pink shirt, which looked like a white one ruled with red ink.

"I want to be set down!" said Dumps in a faint voice, overcome by his previous efforts.

"I think these cads want to be *set down*," returned the attorney's clerk, chuckling at his sally.

"Hollo!" cried Dumps again.

"Hollo!" echoed the passengers. The omnibus passed St. Giles's church.

"Hold hard!" said the conductor; "I'm blowed if we ha'n't forgot the gen'lm'n as vas to be set down at Doory Lane.—Now, sir, make haste, if you please," he added, opening the door, and assisting Dumps out with as much coolness as if it was "all right." Dumps's indignation was for once getting the better of his cynical equanimity. "Drury Lane!" he gasped, with the voice of a boy in a cold bath for the first time.

"Doory Lane, sir?—yes, sir—third turning on the right-hand side, sir."

Dumps's passion was paramount: he clutched his umbrella, and was striding off with the firm determination of not paying the fare. The cad, by a remarkable coincidence, happened to entertain a different contrary opinion, and Heaven knows how far the altercation would have proceeded, if it had not been most ably and satisfactorily brought to a close by the driver.

"Hollo!" said that respectable person, standing up on the box, and leaning with one hand on the roof of the omnibus. "Hollo, Tom! tell the gentleman if so be as he feel aggrieved, we will take him up to the Edge-er (Edgeware) Road for nothing, and set him down at Doory Lane when we comes back. He can't reject that, anyhow."

The argument was irresistible: Dumps paid the disputed sixpence, and in a quarter of an hour was on the staircase of No. 14, Great Russell Street.

Everything indicated that preparations were making for the reception of "a few friends" in the evening. Two dozen extra tumblers, and four ditto wine glasses—looking anything but transparent, with little bits of straw in them—were on the slab in the passage, just arrived. There was a great smell of nutmeg, port wine, and almonds, on the staircase; the covers were taken off the stair carpet, and the figure of Venus on the first landing looked as if she were ashamed of the composition candle in her right hand, which contrasted beautifully with the lamp-blacked drapery of the goddess of love. The female servant (who looked very warm and bustling) ushered Dumps into a front drawing-room, very prettily furnished, with a plentiful sprinkling of little baskets, paper table mats, china watchmen, pink and gold albums, and rainbow-bound little books on different tables.

"Ah, Uncle!" said Mr. Kitterbell, "how d'ye do? Allow me—Jemima, my dear—my uncle. I think you've seen Jemima before, sir?"

"Have had the *pleasure*," returned big Dumps, his tone and look making it doubtful whether in his life he had ever experienced the sensation.

"I'm sure," said Mrs. Kitterbell, with a languid smile, and a slight cough. "I'm sure—hem—any friend—of Charles's—hem—much less a relation, is—"

"I knew you'd say so, my love," said little Kitterbell, who, while he appeared to be gazing on the opposite houses, was looking at his wife with a most affectionate air: "Bless you!" The last two words were accompanied with a simper, and a squeeze of the hand, which stirred up all Uncle Dumps's bile.

"Jane, tell nurse to bring down baby," said Mrs. Kitterbell, addressing the servant. Mrs. Kitterbell was a tall, thin young lady, with very light hair, and a particularly white face—one of those young women who almost invariably, though one hardly knows why, recall to one's mind the idea of a cold fillet of veal. Out went the servant, and in came the nurse, with a remarkably small parcel in her arms, packed up in a blue mantle trimmed with white fur.—This was the baby.

"Now, uncle," said Mr. Kitterbell, lifting up that part of the mantle which covered the infant's face, with an air of great triumph, "*who* do you think he's like?"

"He! he! Yes, who?" said Mrs. K., putting her arm through her husband's, and looking up into Dumps's face with an expression of as much interest as she was capable of displaying.

"Good God, how small he is!" cried the amiable uncle, starting back with well-feigned surprise; "*remarkably* small indeed."

"Do you think so?" inquired poor little Kitterbell, rather alarmed. "He's a monster to what he was—ain't he, nurse?"

"He's a dear," said the nurse, squeezing the child, and evading the question—not because she scrupled to disguise the fact, but because she couldn't afford to throw away the chance of Dumps's half-crown.

"Well, but who is he like?" inquired little Kitterbell.

Dumps looked at the little pink heap before him, and only thought at the moment of the best mode of mortifying the youthful parents.

"I really don't know *who* he's like," he answered, very well knowing the reply expected of him.

"Don't you think he's like *me*?" inquired his nephew with a knowing air.

"Oh, *decidedly* not!" returned Dumps, with an emphasis not to be misunderstood. "Decidedly not like you.—Oh, certainly not."

"Like Jemima?" asked Kitterbell, faintly.

"Oh, dear no; not in the least. I'm no judge, of course, in such cases; but I really think he's more like one of those little carved representations that one sometimes sees blowing a trumpet on a tombstone!" The nurse stooped down over the child, and with great difficulty prevented an explosion of mirth. Pa and ma looked almost as miserable as their amiable uncle.

"Well!" said the disappointed little father, "you'll be better able to tell what he's like by-and-by. You shall see him this evening with his mantle off."

"Thank you," said Dumps, feeling particularly grateful.

"Now, my love," said Kitterbell to his wife, "it's time we were off. We're to meet the other godfather and the godmother at the church, uncle—Mr. and Mrs. Wilson from over the way—uncommonly nice people. My love, are you well wrapped up?"

"Yes, dear."

"Are you sure you won't have another shawl?" inquired the anxious husband.

"No, sweet," returned the charming mother, accepting Dumps's proffered arm; and the little party entered the hackney coach that was to take them to the church; Dumps amusing Mrs. Kitterbell by expatiating largely on the danger of measles, thrush, teeth-cutting, and other interesting diseases to which children are subject.

The ceremony (which occupied about five minutes) passed off without anything particular occurring. The clergyman had to dine some distance from town, and had two churchings, three christenings, and a funeral to perform in something less than an hour. The godfathers and godmother, therefore, promised to renounce the devil and all his works—"and all that sort of thing"—as little Kitterbell said—"in less than no time"; and with the exception of Dumps nearly letting the child fall into the font when he handed it to the clergyman, the whole affair went off in the usual business like and matter-of-course manner, and Dumps reentered the Bank gates at two o'clock with a heavy heart, and the painful conviction that he was regularly booked for an evening party.

Evening came—and so did Dumps's pumps, black silk stockings, and white cravat which he had ordered to be forwarded, per boy, from Pentonville. The depressed godfather dressed himself at a friend's counting house, from whence, with his spirits fifty degrees below proof, he sallied forth—as the weather had cleared up, and the evening was tolerably fine—to walk to Great Russell Street. Slowly he paced up Cheapside, Newgate Street, down Snow Hill, and up Holborn ditto, looking as grim as the figurehead of a man-of-war, and finding out fresh causes of misery at every step. As he was crossing the corner of Hatton Garden, a man, apparently intoxicated, rushed against him, and would have knocked him down, had he not been providentially caught by a very genteel young man, who happened to be close to him at the time. The shock so disarranged Dumps's nerves, as well as his dress, that he could hardly stand. The gentleman took his arm, and in the kindest manner walked with him as far as Furnival's Inn. Dumps, for about the first time in his life, felt grateful and polite; and he and the gentlemanly-looking young man parted with mutual expressions of goodwill.

"There are at least some well-disposed men in the world," ruminated the misanthropical Dumps, as he proceeded towards his destination.

Rat—tat—ta-ra-ra-ra-ra-rat—knocked a hackney-coachman at Kitterbell's door, in imitation of a gentleman's servant, just as Dumps reached it; and out came an old lady in a large toque, and an old gentleman in a blue coat, and three female copies of the old lady in pink dresses, and shoes to match.

"It's a large party," sighed the unhappy godfather, wiping the perspiration from his forehead, and leaning against the area-railings. It was some time before the miserable man could muster up courage to knock at the door, and when he did, the smart appearance of a neighboring greengrocer (who had been hired to wait for seven and sixpence, and whose calves alone were worth double the money), the lamp in the passage, and the Venus on the landing, added to the hum of many voices, and the sound of a harp and two violins, painfully convinced him that his surmises were but too well founded.

"How are you?" said little Kitterbell, in a greater bustle than ever, bolting out of the little back parlor with a corkscrew in his hand, and various particles of sawdust, looking like so many inverted commas, on his inexpressibles.

"Good God!" said Dumps, turning into the aforesaid parlor to put his shoes on, which he had brought in his coat-pocket, and still more appalled by the sight of seven fresh-drawn corks, and a corresponding number of decanters. "How many people are there upstairs?"

"Oh, not above thirty-five. We've had the carpet taken up in the back drawing-room, and the piano and the card-tables are in the front. Jemima thought we'd better have a regular sit-down supper in the front parlor, because of the speechifying, and all that. But, Lord! uncle, what's the matter?" continued the excited little man, as Dumps stood with one shoe on, rummaging his pockets with the most frightful distortion of visage. "What have you lost? Your pocketbook?"

"No," returned Dumps, diving first into one pocket and then into the other, and speaking in a voice like Desdemona with the pillow over her mouth.

"Your card-case? snuff-box? the key of your lodgings?" continued Kitterbell, pouring question on question with the rapidity of lightning.

"No! no!" ejaculated Dumps, still diving eagerly into his empty pockets.

"Not—not—the *mug* you spoke of this morning?"

"Yes, the *mug!*" replied Dumps, sinking into a chair.

"How *could* you have done it?" inquired Kitterbell. "Are you sure you brought it out?"

"Yes! yes! I see it all!" said Dumps, starting up as the idea flashed across his mind; "miserable dog that I am—I was born to suffer. I see it all; it was the gentlemanly-looking young man!"

"Mr. Dumps!" shouted the greengrocer in a stentorian voice, as he ushered the somewhat recovered godfather into the drawing room half an hour after the above declaration. "Mr. Dumps!"—everybody looked at the door, and in came Dumps, feeling about as much out of place as a salmon might be supposed to be on a gravel-walk.

"Happy to see you again," said Mrs. Kitterbell, quite unconscious of the unfortunate man's confusion and misery; "you must allow me to introduce you to a few of our friends: my mamma, Mr. Dumps—my papa and sisters." Dumps seized the hand of the mother as warmly as if she was his own parent, bowed *to* the young ladies, and *against* a gentleman behind him, and took no notice whatever of the father, who had been bowing incessantly for three minutes and a quarter.

"Uncle," said little Kitterbell, after Dumps had been introduced to a select dozen or two, "you must let me lead you to the other end of the room, to introduce you to my friend Danton. Such a splendid fellow!—I'm sure you'll like him—this way."—Dumps followed as tractably as a tame bear.

Mr. Danton was a young man of about five-and-twenty, with a considerable stock of impudence, and a very small share of ideas: he was a great favorite, especially with young ladies of from sixteen to twenty-six years of age, both inclusive. He could imitate the French horn to admiration, sang comic songs most inimitably, and had the most insinuating way of saying impertinent nothings to his doting female admirers. He had acquired, somehow or other, the reputation of being a great wit, and, accordingly, whenever he opened his mouth, everybody who knew him laughed very heartily.

The introduction took place in due form. Mr. Danton bowed, and twirled a lady's handkerchief, which he held in his hand, in a most comic way. Everybody smiled.

"Very warm," said Dumps, feeling it necessary to say something.

"Yes. It was warmer yesterday," returned the brilliant Mr. Danton.—A general laugh.

"I have great pleasure in congratulating you on your first appearance in the character of a father, sir," he continued, addressing Dumps—"godfather, I mean."—The young ladies were convulsed, and the gentlemen in ecstasies.

A general hum of admiration interrupted the conversation and announced the entrance of nurse with the baby. An universal rush of the young ladies immediately took place. (Girls are always *so* fond of babies in company.)

"Oh, you dear!" said one.

"How sweet!" cried another, in a low tone of the most enthusiastic admiration.

"Heavenly!" added a third.

"Oh! what dear little arms!" said a fourth, holding up an arm and fist about the size and shape of the leg of a fowl cleanly picked.

"Did you ever!"—said a little coquette with a large bustle, who looked like a French lithograph, appealing to a gentleman in three waistcoats—Did you ever!"

"Never, in my life," returned her admirer, pulling up his collar.

"Oh! *do* let me take it, nurse!" cried another young lady. "The love."

"Can it open its eyes, nurse?" inquired another, affecting the utmost innocence. Suffice it to say, that the single ladies unanimously voted him an angel, and that the married ones, *nem. con,* agreed that he was decidedly the finest baby they had ever beheld—except their own.

The quadrilles were resumed with great spirit. Mr. Danton was universally admitted to be beyond himself; several young ladies enchanted the company and gained admirers by singing "We met"—"I saw her at the Fancy Fair"—and other equally sentimental and interesting ballads. "The young men," as Mrs. Kitterbell said, "made themselves very agreeable"; the girls did not lose their opportunity; and the evening promised to go off excellently. Dumps didn't mind it: he had devised a plan for himself—a little bit of fun in his own way—and he was almost happy! He played a rubber and lost every point. Mr. Danton said he could not have lost every point, because he made a point of losing: everybody laughed tremendously. Dumps retorted with a better joke, and nobody smiled, with the exception of the host, who seemed to consider it his duty to laugh till he was black in the face, at everything. There was only one drawback—the musicians did not play with quite as much spirit as could have been wished. The cause, however, was satisfactorily explained; for it appeared, on the testimony of a gentleman who had come up from Gravesend in the afternoon, that they had been engaged on board a steamer all day, and had played almost without cessation all the way to Gravesend, and all the way back again.

The "sit-down supper" was excellent; there were four barley-sugar temples on the table, which would have looked beautiful if they had not melted away when the supper began; and a water-mill, whose only fault was that instead of going round, it ran over the tablecloth. Then there were fowls, and tongue, and trifle, and sweets, and lobster salad, and potted beef—and everything. And little Kitterbell kept calling out for clean plates, and the clean plates did not come: and then the gentlemen who wanted the plates said they didn't mind, they'd take a lady's; and then Mrs. Kitterbell applauded their gallantry, and the greengrocer ran about till he thought his seven and sixpence very hardly earned; and the young ladies didn't eat much for fear it shouldn't look romantic, and the married ladies ate as much as possible, for fear they shouldn't have enough; and a great deal of wine was drunk, and everybody talked and laughed considerably.

"Hush! hush!" said Mr. Kitterbell, rising and looking very important. "My love (this was addressed to his wife at the other end of the table), take care of Mrs. Maxwell, and your mamma, and the rest of the married ladies; the gentlemen will persuade the young ladies to fill their glasses, I am sure."

"Ladies and gentlemen," said long Dumps, in a very sepulchral voice and rueful accent, rising from his chair like the ghost in Don Juan, "will you have the kindness to charge your glasses? I am desirous of proposing a toast."

A dead silence ensued, and the glasses were filled—everybody looked serious.

"Ladies and gentlemen," slowly continued the ominous Dumps. "I"— (here Mr. Danton imitated two notes from the French horn, in a very loud key, which electrified the nervous toast-proposer, and convulsed his audience).

"Order! order!" said little Kitterbell, endeavoring to suppress his laughter.

"Order!" said the gentlemen.

"Danton, be quiet," said a particular friend on the opposite side of the table.

"Ladies and gentlemen," resumed Dumps, somewhat recovered, and not much disconcerted, for he was always a pretty good hand at a speech—"In accordance with what is, I believe, the established usage on these occasions, I, as one of the godfathers of Master Frederick Charles William Kitterbell—(here the speaker's voice faltered, for he remembered the mug)—venture to rise to propose a toast. I need hardly say that it is the health and prosperity of that young gentlemen, the particular event of whose early life we are here met to celebrate—(applause). Ladies and gentlemen, it is impossible to suppose that our friends here, whose sincere well-wishers we all are, can pass through life without some trials, considerable suffering, severe affliction, and heavy losses!"—Here the arch-traitor paused, and slowly drew forth a long, white pocket-handkerchief—his example was followed by several ladies. "That these trials may be long spared them is my most earnest prayer, my most fervent wish (a distinct sob from the grandmother). I hope and trust, ladies and gentlemen, that the infant whose christening we have this evening met to celebrate, may not be removed from the arms of his parents by premature decay (several cambrics were in requisition): that his young and now *apparently* healthy form may not be wasted by lingering disease. (Here Dumps cast a sardonic glance around, for a great sensation was manifest among the married ladies.) You, I am sure, will concur with me in wishing that he may live to be a comfort and a blessing to his parents. ('Hear, hear!' and an audible sob from Mr. Kitterbell.) But should he not be what we could wish—should he forget in after times the duty which he owes them—should they unhappily experience that distracting truth, 'how sharper than a serpent's tooth it is to have a thankless child'"— Here Mrs. Kitterbell, with her handkerchief to her eyes, and accompanied by several ladies, rushed from the room, and went into violent hysterics in the passage, leaving her better half in almost as bad a condition, and a general impression in Dumps's favor; for people like sentiment, after all.

It need hardly be added, that this occurrence quite put a stop to the harmony of the evening. Vinegar, hartshorn, and cold water, were now as much in request as negus, rout-cakes, and *bon-bons* had been a short time before. Mrs. Kitterbell was immediately conveyed to her apartment, the musicians were silenced, flirting ceased, and the company slowly departed. Dumps left the house at the commencement of the bustle, and walked home with a light step, and (for him) a cheerful heart. His landlady, who slept in the next room, has offered to make oath that she heard him laugh, in his peculiar manner, after he had locked his door. The assertion, however, is so improbable, and bears on the face of it such strong evidence of untruth, that it has never obtained credence to this hour.

The family of Mr. Kitterbell has considerably increased since the period to which we have referred; he has now two sons and a daughter; and as he expects, at no distant period, to have another addition to his blooming progeny, he is anxious to secure an eligible godfather for the occasion. He is determined, however, to impose upon him two conditions. He must bind himself, by a solemn obligation, not to make any speech after supper; and it is indispensable that he should be in no way connected with "the most miserable man in the world."

Bipolar Disorder

The major symptom of bipolar disorder is mood swings. These individuals display either mania or hypomania. They are often hyperactive, highly distractible, and grandiose. Common characteristics include flight of ideas, pressured speech, tangentiality, and a diminished need for sleep. Individuals experiencing bipolar illness have few inhibitions and are often described as very unpredictable. Bipolar illness is generally considered a more severe illness than major depression. Individuals with bipolar depression may stay depressed longer, relapse more frequently, display more depressive symptoms, show more severe symptoms, have more delusions and hallucinations, commit more suicides, require more hospitalizations, and experience more incapacitation than individuals who experience major depression alone.

Kay Redfield Jamison (b. 1946)

Kay Redfield Jamison completed her undergraduate and doctoral degrees in psychology at the University of California, Los Angeles. She joined the faculty of the medical school at UCLA in 1974, where she founded the Affective Disorders Clinic.

In 1995 she published *An Unquiet Mind*, a reflection of her personal struggles with manic-depressive illness (currently known as "bipolar disorder"). Jamison's descriptions of her illness are utilized here to demonstrate bipolar disorder.

Jamison is currently professor of psychiatry at the Johns Hopkins University School of Medicine. She is the author or coauthor of five books and more than 100 scientific articles about mood disorders, suicide, psychotherapy, and lithium.

In this selection she shares her struggles with bipolar disorder. Her excellent work provides us with remarkable insight and clarity in regard to this disorder.

An Unquiet Mind

I was a senior in high school when I had my first attack of manic-depressive illness; once the siege began, I lost my mind rather rapidly. At first, everything seemed so easy. I raced about like a crazed weasel, bubbling with plans and enthusiasms, immersed in sports, and staying up all night, night after night, out with friends, reading everything that wasn't nailed down, filling manuscript books with poems and fragments of plays, and making expansive, completely unrealistic, plans for my future. The world was filled with pleasure and promise; I felt great. Not just great, I felt *really* great. I felt I could do anything, that no task was too difficult. My mind seemed clear, fabulously focused, and able to make intuitive mathematical leaps that had up to that point entirely eluded me. Indeed, they elude me still. At the time, however, not only did everything make perfect sense, but it all began to fit into a marvelous kind of cosmic relatedness. My sense of enchantment with the laws of the natural world caused me to fizz over, and I found myself buttonholing my friends to tell them how beautiful it all was. They were less than transfixed by my insights into the webbings and beauties of the universe, although considerably impressed by how exhausting it was to be around my enthusiastic ramblings: You're talking too fast, Kay. Slow down, Kay. You're wearing me out, Kay. Slow down, Kay. And those times when they didn't actually come out and say it, I still could see it in their eyes: For God's sake, Kay, slow down.

I did, finally, slow down. In fact, I came to a grinding halt. Unlike the very severe manic episodes that came a few years later and escalated wildly and psychotically out of control, this first sustained wave of mild mania was a light, lovely tincture of true mania; like hundreds of subsequent periods of high enthusiasms it was short-lived and quickly burned itself out: tiresome to my friends, perhaps; exhausting and exhilarating to me, definitely; but not disturbingly over the top. Then the bottom began to fall out of my life and mind. My thinking, far from being clearer than a crystal, was tortuous. I would read the same passage over and over again only to realize that I had no memory at all for what I had just read. Each book or poem I picked up was the same way. Incomprehensible. Nothing made sense. I could not begin to follow the material presented in my classes, and I would find myself staring out the window with no idea what was going on around me. It was very frightening.

I was used to my mind being my best friend; of carrying on endless conversations within my head; of having a built-in source of laughter or analytic thought to rescue me from boring or painful surroundings. I counted upon my mind's acuity, interest, and loyalty as a matter of course. Now, all of a sudden, my mind had turned on me: it mocked me for my vapid enthusiasms; it laughed at all of my foolish plans; it no longer found anything interesting or enjoyable or worthwhile. It was incapable of concentrated thought and turned time and again to the subject of death: I was going to die, what difference did anything make? Life's run was only a short and meaningless one, why live? I was totally exhausted and could scarcely pull myself out of bed in the mornings. It took me twice as long to walk anywhere as it ordinarily did, and I wore the same clothes over and over again, as it was otherwise too much of an effort to make a decision about what to put on. I dreaded having to talk with people, avoided my friends whenever possible, and sat in the school library in the early mornings and late afternoons, virtually inert, with a dead heart and a brain as cold as clay.

Each day I awoke deeply tired, a feeling as foreign to my natural self as being bored or indifferent to life. Those were next. Then a gray, bleak preoccupation with death, dying, decaying, that everything was born but to die, best to die now and save the pain while waiting. I dragged exhausted mind and body around a local cemetery, ruminating about how long each of its inhabitants had lived before the final moment. I sat on the graves writing long, dreary, morbid poems, convinced that my brain and body were rotting, that everyone knew and no one would say. Laced into the exhaustion were periods of frenetic and horrible restlessness; no amount of running brought relief. For several weeks, I drank vodka in my orange juice before setting off for school in the mornings, and I thought obsessively about killing myself. It was a tribute to my ability to present an image so at variance with what I felt that few noticed I was in any way different. Certainly no one in my family did. Two friends were concerned, but I swore them to secrecy when they asked to talk with my parents. One teacher noticed, and the parent of a friend called me aside to ask if something was wrong. I lied readily: I'm fine, but thank you for asking.

I have no idea how I managed to pass as normal in school, except that other people are generally caught up in their own lives and seldom notice despair in others if those despairing make an effort to disguise the pain. I made not just an effort, but an enormous effort not to be noticed. I knew something was dreadfully wrong, but I had no idea what, and I had been brought up to believe that you kept your problems to yourself. Given that, it turned out to be unnervingly easy to keep my friends and family at psychological bay: "To be sure," wrote Hugo Wolf, "I appear at times merry and in good heart, talk, too, before others quite reasonably, and it looks as if I felt, too, God knows how well within my skin. Yet the soul maintains its deathly sleep and the heart bleeds from a thousand wounds."

It was impossible to avoid quite terrible wounds to both my mind and heart—the shock of having been so unable to understand what had been going on around me, the knowledge that my thoughts had been so completely out of my control, and the realization that I had been so depressed that I wanted only to die—and it was several months before the wounds could even begin to heal. Looking back I am amazed I survived, that I survived on my own, and that high school contained such complicated life and palpable death. I aged rapidly during those months, as one must with such loss of one's self, with such proximity to death, and such distance from shelter.

*　*　*

There is a particular kind of pain, elation, loneliness, and terror involved in this kind of madness. When you're high it's tremendous. The ideas and feelings are fast and frequent like shooting stars, and you follow them until you find better and brighter ones. Shyness goes, the right words and gestures are suddenly there, the power to captivate others a felt certainty. There are interests found in uninteresting people. Sensuality is pervasive and the desire to seduce and be seduced irresistible. Feelings of ease, intensity, power, well-being, financial omnipotence, and euphoria pervade one's marrow. But, somewhere, this changes. The fast ideas are far too fast, and there are far too many; overwhelming confusion replaces clarity. Memory goes. Humor and absorption on friends' faces are replaced by fear and concern. Everything previously moving with the grain is now against—you are irritable, angry, frightened, uncontrollable, and enmeshed totally in the blackest caves of the mind. You never knew those caves were there. It will never end, for madness carves its own reality.

It goes on and on, and finally there are only others' recollections of your behavior—your bizarre, frenetic, aimless behaviors—for mania has at least some grace in partially obliterating memories. What then, after the medications, psychiatrist, despair, depression, and overdose? All those incredible feelings to sort through. Who is being too polite to say what? Who knows what? What did I do? Why? And most hauntingly, when will it happen again? Then, too, are the bitter reminders—medicine to take, resent, forget, take, resent, and forget, but always to take. Credit cards revoked, bounced checks to cover, explanations due at work, apologies to make, intermittent memories (what did I do?), friendships gone or drained, a ruined marriage. And always, when will it happen again? Which of my feelings are real? Which of the me's is me? The wild, impulsive, chaotic, energetic, and crazy one? Or the shy, withdrawn, desperate, suicidal, doomed, and tired one? Probably a bit of both, hopefully much that is neither. Virginia Wolf, in her dives and climbs, said it all: "How far do our feelings take their colour from the dive underground? I mean, what is the reality of any feeling?"

* * *

When I am high I couldn't worry about money if I tried. So I don't. The money will come from somewhere; I am entitled; God will provide. Credit cards are disastrous, personal checks worse. Unfortunately, for manics anyway, mania is a natural extension of the economy. What with credit cards and bank accounts there is little beyond reach. So I bought twelve snakebite kits, with a sense of urgency and importance. I bought precious stones, elegant and unnecessary furniture, three watches within an hour of one another (in the Rolex rather than Timex class: champagne tastes bubble to the surface, are the surface, in mania), and totally inappropriate sirenlike clothes. During one spree in London I spent several hundred pounds on books having titles or covers that somehow caught my fancy: books on the natural history of the mole, twenty sundry Penguin books because I thought it could be nice if penguins could form a colony. Once I think I shoplifted a blouse because I could not wait a minute longer for the woman-with-molasses feet in front of me in line. Or maybe I just thought about shoplifting, I don't remember, I was totally confused. I imagine I must have spent far more than thirty thousand dollars during my two major manic episodes, and God knows how much more during my frequent milder manias.

But then back on lithium and rotating on the planet at the same pace as everyone else, you find your credit is decimated, your mortification complete: mania is not a luxury one can easily afford. It is devastating to have the illness and aggravating to have to pay for medications, blood tests, and psychotherapy. They, at least, are partially deductible. But money spent while manic doesn't fit into the Internal Revenue Service concept of medical expense or business loss. So after mania, when most depressed, you're given excellent reason to be even more so.

* * *

Slowly the darkness began to weave its way into my mind, and before long I was hopelessly out of control. I could not follow the path of my own thoughts.

Sentences flew around in my head and fragmented first into phrases and then words; finally, only sounds remained. One evening I stood in the middle of my living room and looked out at the blood-red sunset spreading out over the horizon of the Pacific. Suddenly I felt a strange sense of light at the back of my eyes and almost immediately saw a huge black centrifuge inside my head. I saw a tall figure in a floor-length evening gown approach the centrifuge with a vase-sized glass tube of blood in her hand. As the figure turned around I saw to my horror that it was me and that there was blood all over my dress, cape, and long white gloves. I watched as the figure carefully put the tube of blood into one of the holes in the rack of the centrifuge, closed the lid, and pushed a button on the front of the machine. The centrifuge began to whirl.

Then, horrifyingly, the image that previously had been inside my head now was completely outside of it. I was paralyzed by fright. The spinning of the centrifuge and the clanking of the glass tube against the metal became louder and louder, and then the machine splintered into a thousand pieces. Blood was everywhere. It spattered against the windowpanes, against the walls and paintings, and soaked down into the carpets. I looked out toward the ocean and saw that the blood on the window had merged into the sunset; I couldn't tell where one ended and the other began. I screamed at the top of my lungs. I couldn't get away from the sight of the blood and the echoes of the machine's clanking as it whirled faster and faster. Not only had my thoughts spun wild, they had turned into an awful phantasmagoria, an apt but terrifying vision of an entire life and mind out of control. I screamed again and again. Slowly the hallucination receded. I telephoned a colleague for help, poured myself a large scotch, and waited for his arrival.

* * *

At this point in my existence, I cannot imagine leading a normal life without both taking lithium and having had the benefits of psychotherapy. Lithium prevents my seductive but disastrous highs, diminishes my depressions, clears out the wool and webbing from my disordered thinking, slows me down, gentles me out, keeps me from ruining my career and relationships, keeps me out of a hospital, alive, and makes psychotherapy possible. But, ineffably, psychotherapy heals. It makes some sense of the confusion, reins in the terrifying thoughts and feelings, returns some control and hope and possibility of learning from it all. Pills cannot, do not, ease one back into reality; they only bring one back headlong, careening, and faster than can be endured at times. Psychotherapy is a sanctuary; it is a battleground; it is a place I have been psychotic, neurotic, elated, confused, and despairing beyond belief. But, always, it is where I have believed—or have learned to believe—that I might someday be able to contend with all of this.

No pill can help me deal with the problem of not wanting to take pills; likewise, no amount of psychotherapy alone can prevent my manias and depressions. I need both. It is an odd thing, owing life to pills, one's own quirks and tenacities, and this unique, strange, and ultimately profound relationship called psychotherapy.

Cyclothymia

Cyclothymia is generally considered to be a mild form of bipolar disorder. The symptoms of cyclothymia can often be almost as severe as those of bipolar disorder but may not be of sufficient intensity or duration to meet the criteria for that disorder. The age of onset for cyclothymia is most often in early adulthood; it begins gradually and persists chronically. Addictions, particularly alcoholism, are common among cyclothymic individuals.

Nikolai Leskov (1831–1895)

Nikolai Leskov was born in Gorokhovo, in the Orel province of Russia, into a well-educated, noble family. In his childhood he became familiar with the struggles and difficulties faced by the peasants who lived in his area. This knowledge of peasant life and their stories served him well in his later writings.

In 1861 Leskov moved to St. Petersburg and began his career as a journalist and writer. His first stories appeared in magazines. Leskov's work is marked by a growing criticism of the church, which led him into difficulties with the censors. He was an excellent observer of people, and his writing was filled with descriptions of cruelty, bravery, drunkenness, and adventure.

Leskov's collected works were published in 1902–1903. For a time his works were viewed with suspicion, but they have come to be seen as valuable for their insights into the common people. Anton Chekhov considered Leskov his teacher. With new printings and translations of his stories Leskhov has assumed a position of respect among Russian writers of the nineteenth century.

"The Amazon" offers an example of cyclothymic behavior. Domna is highly active and has mood swings that fluctuate from great happiness to sadness, including suicidal thoughts. In addition, she appears to have problems with alcohol that are severe enough to require her to "sew herself up."

"The Amazon"

. . . I feel I must describe Domna Platonovna to my readers at greater length.

Domna Platonovna is not a tall woman; in fact, she is rather short, but she looks big. This optical illusion is caused by the fact that Domna Platonovna is, as they say, broad in the beam, and what she lacks in height, she makes up for in breadth. Her health is not particularly good, although no one seems to remember her ever being ill, and to look at her you would never suspect that there was anything the matter with her. Her bosom alone is so immense that you cannot but be overcome at the sight of it. But she herself, Domna Platonovna, I mean, is always complaining about her poor health.

"To look at me," she'd say, "you would think I was robust, but there isn't any real strength in me as in other women of my size, and as for my sleep, it is just dreadful! Heavy is not the word for it. The minute my head touches the pillow, off I go and for all I care you can put me in the garden to scare away the birds. Until I've had my fill of sleep, I'm as good as dead. Yes, that's what I am, as good as dead!"

Domna Platonovna regarded her mighty sleep, too, as one of the ailments of her corpulent body and, as we shall see later, it had, in fact, given her a lot of trouble and caused her much unhappiness.

Domna Platonovna enjoyed nothing better than to pester people about the state of her health and ask them for medical advice. She would describe her ailments to them at great length, but she refused to take any medicines and believed only in "Haarlem" drops, which she called "Harem" drops, and a phial of which she always carried in the right-hand pocket of her capacious silk *capote*. According to her own account, she was always somewhere about forty-five years of age, but to judge by her fresh complexion and her cheerful mien, no one would give her more than forty. At the time of my first acquaintance with her, Domna Platonovna's hair was of a dark brown color, and there was not a single grey hair to be seen on her head. Her skin was quite unusually white and her red cheeks glowed with health, which, however, never satisfied her, for she used to buy some French *papier poudre* in the upper gallery of the Arcade, which greatly deepened the natural color of her cheeks, a color which steadfastly refused to be affected by any of her troubles or by the Finnish winds and fogs. Domna Platonovna's eyebrows looked as if they had been made of black satin: they were as black as jet and they shone with an unnatural glitter, for Domna Platonovna used to smear them thickly with a kind of black preparation and draw them into a thin line with her fingers. Her eyes were just like two black plums besprinkled with fresh morning dew. A mutual friend of ours, a Turkish prisoner of war by the name of Ispulat, who had been brought to St. Petersburg during the Crimean war, could never gaze calmly at Domna Platonovna's eyes. So potent was their influence on him that the poor fellow would completely lose his head and begin to give voice to his admiration in loud, ecstatic tones.

"Oh, what beautiful eyes! What lovely Greek eyes!"

Any other woman would, of course, be flattered by so sincere a compliment, but Domna Platonovna was never taken in by these Turkish blandishments and she always insisted on her pure Russian origin.

"Don't talk such rubbish, you damned infidel!" she'd reply with a merry twinkle in those "Greek" eyes of hers. "Don't you dare tell me such a thing again, you big-bellied toad! I come of a well-known and respectable family, I do, and there aren't any Greeks in the factory in our town and never have been!"

Domna Platonovna's nose was hardly what you might call a nose, so small, slender and straight was it. A nose like that you never come across on the Oka or the Zusha and, if you do, it is by mere accident. Her mouth, though, was rather big: you could tell at once that she'd been fed with a large spoon as a baby, but it was a pleasant mouth none the less and it looked so fresh, of a regular shape, with scarlet lips and teeth that might have been cut out of a young turnip. In a word, not only on an uninhabited island, but even in so big and populous a city as St. Petersburg any man who regarded the kissing of a pretty girl as a kind of duty would not by any means consider it a hardship to kiss Domna Platonovna. But there could be no doubt that the greatest attractions of Domna Platonovna's face were her chin, a chin that was a real peach, and the general expression of her features, which was so soft and child-like that if the thought ever crossed your mind how a woman whose face bespoke such bottomless good-nature could talk of nothing else but human treachery and malice, you could not help saying to yourself, "Oh, curse you a hundred times, Domna Platonovna, for, damn it! one look at your face is enough to conjure up such a multitude of the most dreadful problems in my head!"

Domna Platomnovna was of a very sociable disposition; she was a really cheerful soul, good-hearted, not given to taking offense easily, rather simple-minded, perhaps, and a bit superstitious, too, but, on the whole, honest and straightforward, although, to be sure, as in every Russian, there was a streak of cunning in her. Work and worry were Domna Platonovna's usual lot and she did not seem to be able to live without either. She was always busy, always rushing about, always worrying about something, devising some new scheme or other, or carrying it out.

"I live a lonely life," she used to say, "have no one except myself to look after in the whole world and yet to earn my bare living I have to lead a most aggravating sort of existence, running about the market like a scalded cat, and if it isn't one then it is another who's always trying to catch me by the tail."

"But," you'd sometimes say to her, "you can't possibly do everything at once, can you?"

"Well, perhaps not everything," she'd reply, "but all the same let me tell you that it's very trying. Well, so long at present, good-bye, dear: there are people waiting for me in a dozen different places!" and she'd actually rush off in a devil of a hurry.

Domna Platonovna quite often realized herself that she did not labor for her bread alone and that her hard and aggravating existence could be made considerably less hard and aggravating without any harm to her own personal interests; but she just could not restrain herself from bustling about.

"I can't bear the thought of losing any business," she used to say. "I'm jealous, you see, of anyone else getting it. To see something coming my way is enough to make my heart leap with joy."

But, as a matter of fact, what Domna Platonovna was jealous of was not that anybody should derive any profit from some business she might lose. No. That side often left her strangely cold. What did matter to her was that she might miss the worry and the bustle involved in bringing the business to successful issue.

"He's deceived me, the villain!" or "She's deceived me, the beast!" she'd go on complaining all day long, but next time you met her, she was again rushing about and worrying herself to death for the same villain or beast and telling herself beforehand that they would quite certainly deceive her again.

Domna Platonovna's business which gave her so much trouble was of a most diverse character. Officially, to be sure, she was just a seller of lace, that is to say, women of the artisan class and wives of poor merchants and priests used to send her from "their own parts" all kinds of lace collars, strips of lace material and cuffs which she hawked around Petersburg, or, in summer, around the different holiday resorts in the vicinity of the capital, sending back to "their own parts" the money she received after the deduction of her commission and expenses. But, besides her lace business, Domna Platonovna engaged in a most complicated business of a private character, in the carrying out of which the lace and the collars merely played the part of a pass to places where she would not otherwise have been admitted. Thus she found husbands and wives for all sorts of people, found purchasers for furniture and secondhand ladies' garments, raised loans for people with and without security, ran a kind of domestic agency of her own, finding jobs for governesses, caretakers and footmen, took confidential messages to the most famous *salons* and *boudoirs* in town of the sort that could not possibly be entrusted to the post and brought replies from the ladies in question, ladies surrounded by an atmosphere of frigid piety and devotion to good works.

But in spite of all her enthusiasm and connections, Domna Platonovna never got rich or even made a comfortable living. She had enough for her own needs, dressed, in her own words, "decently" and never begrudged herself anything; but she never had any spare money, either because she was too preoccupied with her different business worries or because her customers often deceived her, and, besides, all sorts of curious accidents always happened to her with her money.

Her chief trouble was that she was an artist: she got too much carried away by her own handiwork. Although she would invariably tell you that she had to work so hard for the sake of her daily bread, that claim of hers was scarcely just. Domna Platonovna loved her work as an artist loves his art: to contrive something, to collect something, to concoct something and then to admire her own handiwork—that was the main thing, that was what she really cared about, that was what she spent her money on and sacrificed any profit she might have obtained from the business in question which a more practical business woman would never have sacrificed.

Domna Platonovna found her vocation by sheer chance. At first she was quite satisfied with hawking her lace and it never entered her head to combine her trade with any other occupation; but the magic of our capital transformed this rather absurd Mtsensk woman into the accomplished factotum whom I knew as the inimitable Domna Platonovna, a woman who applied her native wit to any kind of business and who secured an entrée everywhere. Soon she had established herself so firmly that it was quite impossible for her not to get in wherever she wanted.

*   *   *

"I should like to ask you a question I've wanted to ask for a long time, Domna Platonovna," I said. "How old were you when your husband died? You were still quite a young woman, weren't you? Well, haven't you had any love affairs at all since then?"

"Love affairs?"

"Yes, I mean haven't you been in love with anyone?"

"Me in love? Good heavens, the nonsense you do sometimes talk, dear!"

"But why nonsense?"

"Because," she said, "it's only women who have nothing to do who have love-affairs. I'm much too busy rushing about day and night, leading so aggravating a life as I do, never a minute to myself . . . Why, such a thought never crosses my mind!"

"Doesn't it even cross your mind, Domna Platonovna?"

"No, dear, not as much as that even!" Domna Platonovna struck one finger-nail against another and added, "Besides, dear, let me tell you this love business is just a kind of craze: 'Oh, I can't live without him or her! Oh, I shall die!' That's all you hear from them. Now, if you ask me, dear, a man who's really in love with a woman should be always ready to help her, never let her down, that, I grant you, is real love. And as for the woman, she should never give way to temptation and should always behave decently."

"So I can take it, Domna Platonovna," I said, "that you've never been guilty of any such transgression and that in the eyes of God you're as pure as driven snow. Am I right?"

"Mind your own business, dear," she replied, "and don't you go meddling with my sins. For even if I did commit a sin, it's my sin, isn't it? Anyway, it's not yours and you're not a priest to whom I ought to confess my sins, are you?"

"I merely mentioned it, Domna Platonovna." I put it in propitiatingly, "because you were so young when you lost your husband and I can see that you must have been very beautiful."

"Whether I was beautiful or not, I can't say," she replied, "but I was never considered a plain woman."

"That's it!" I said, "Anybody can see it even now."

Domna Platonovna passed a finger over an eyebrow and fell into thought.

"I've often wondered," she began slowly, "whether or not I had been guilty of a particular sin. Tell me, O Lord, was I guilty of that sin or not? That was how

I'd ask for the Lord's guidance, but I never received a proper answer to that question from anyone. One nun once persuaded me to let her write down my story so that I could give it to the priest at confession. I let her write it down, but on my way to church I dropped the paper and couldn't find it."

"What story are you referring to, Domna Platonovna?"

"I don't rightly know to this day whether it was a sin or whether I imagined it all."

"Well, even if you did imagine it all, Domna Platonovna, I should very much like to hear it."

"It all happened a very long time ago when I was still living with my husband."

"What kind of life did you have with your husband, dear Domna Platonovna?"

"Not a bad kind of life. Our house was a little too small perhaps, but it occupied a very good position, for it stood on the market place, and we had many market days in our town, mostly for household goods and provisions of one sort or another, only there was precious little of either, that was the trouble. We were not particularly well off, but we were not exactly poor either. We sold fish, lard, liver and anything else we could. My husband, Fyodor Ilyich, was a young man, but a queer one, aye, a queer one, very haggard he was, but he had a pair of the most extraordinary lips. I never met a man with such lips in my life. He had, God forgive me, a terrible temper, very quarrelsome he was and quick to take offense, but I, too, was a real Amazon, dearly loved a fight as a girl, I did. Having married, I was at first as meek as a lamb, but that didn't please him at all, so that every morning before breakfast we used to have a grand old fight together. I was not very much in love with him, nor did we often agree, for we both were rare fighters, and, besides, you couldn't help fighting with him, for however nice you tried to be to him, he'd always look glum and glower at you. However, we carried on for eight whole years and did not separate. Now and again, of course, we'd have a row, but it was very rarely that we had a real fight. Once, it is true, he hit me over the head, but I was not altogether blameless myself, for I had been trimming his hair at the time and I cut off a bit of his ear with the scissors. We had no children, but we had friends at Nizhny to whose children I stood godmother. They weren't well off. He called himself a tailor and even had a diploma from a society, but he didn't earn his living by his needle, but by singing psalms for the dead and being a member of the Cathedral choir. As for earning a living, getting something for their home, it was his wife, Praskovya Ivanovna, who had to worry about it. She was a woman in a thousand, brought up all her children and made ends meet somehow.

"Well, once—it was in the same year that my husband died (everything was going topsy-turvy with us just then)—Praskovya Ivanovna invited us to her place to celebrate her birthday. We went and no sooner did we arrive than it began to pour and, as I had an awful headache at the time (I had had three glasses of punch and some Caucasian brandy and there's nothing worse than that Caucasian brandy for your head), I lay down for a bit on a couch in another room. 'Stay with your guests, dear,' I said to Praskovya Ivanovna, 'and I'll just go and lie down for a rest on the couch here.' But she wouldn't let me lie down on the couch, because, she said, it was too hard, so I went and lay down on their bed and dropped off to sleep immediately. Did I do anything wrong?" Domna Platonovna asked me.

"Why, no," I said, "you didn't do anything wrong."

"Very well, now listen to what happened. I felt in my sleep that somebody was embracing me and, you see, not just embracing me, either. I thought it was my husband, Fyodor Ilyich, and yet it didn't seem to be Fyodor Ilyich, for he was rather delicate, you know and shy, but I couldn't wake up, and when at last I did wake up, it was morning. I found myself in my friend's bed and beside me lay my friend's husband. I sort of scampered over him quickly, trembling all over, and there on the floor, on a feather bed, lay my friend and beside her was my husband, Fyodor Ilyich . . . I nudged her and then she, too, realized what had happened and began crossing herself. 'How did it all happen?' I asked her. 'Oh, dear,' she said, 'it's all my fault, for after everybody went away your husband and mine sat down to finish up the drinks and I didn't want to waken you in the darkness, so I lay down where I had made a bed for you and your husband, well, I just spat, so vexed was I.' 'What shall we do now?' I asked. But she said there was nothing we could do and that we'd better keep quiet about it. Yes, dear." Domna Platonovna said, "you're the first I ever told this story to after so many years, but it has been worrying me terribly all the time and whenever I think of it, I'm ready to curse that heavy sleep of mine."

"Don't distress yourself so much, Domna Platonovna," I said, "for whatever happened was against your will."

"Of course it happened against my will! I should think so! Still, it did worry me, I can tell you, and after that I was overtaken by one trouble after another. Fyodor Ilyich soon died, and not a natural death, either. Was crushed to death, he was, under a load of logs which collapsed on top him on the bank of a river. I had no notion of the Petersburg circumstances then and I didn't know what to do to distract myself, but sometimes of an evening when I'd remember what happened to me at that birthday party, I'd sit down at the window, all alone in the house, and sing, 'Take away my gold, take away my honors all,' and I'd burst out crying, tears gushing in a flood out of my eyes, so that it was a real wonder my heart didn't burst with sorrow. Oh, I felt so terrible when I'd remember the words of that song, 'My dear love in the dark ground lies sleeping,' that many a time I thought of putting a noose around my neck and ending it all. So I sold everything, gave up my business and left our town, for I decided that it was best to make a clean break with my past life."

"I can believe that, Domna Platonovna," I said, "for there's nothing worse than being depressed."

"Thank you, dear, for your kind words," said Domna Platonovna. "Indeed, there's nothing worse than that and may the Holy Virgin bless you and comfort you for your pity and understanding. But you can hardly be expected to know what I have been through, if I don't tell you how scurvily I was treated once and how shamelessly I was insulted. That my bag was stolen or that Lekanida Petrovana was so ungrateful to me, all that is nothing compared with what happened to me on another occasion. For there was such a day in my life, dear, when I prayed to God to send a serpent or a scorpion to suck my eyes out and devour my heart. And who do you think it was who did that wrong to me? I'll tell you: Ispulat, the Turk, that's who it was, that infidel Turk, in league with my own friends, Christians, baptized and anointed with myrrh!"

Poor Domna Platonovna burst into a flood of tears.

"A friend of mine, the wife of a government messenger," she went on, wiping her tears, "used to live in Lopatin's house on Nevsky Avenue and that Turkish war prisoner began to worry her about getting him a job. She asked me to see if I couldn't find some work for him. 'Find some situation for that devil, Domna Platonovna,' she said to me. But what sort of a job could I find for a Turk? A footman's job was all I could think of. Well, I found him such a place and I told him about it. 'Go there,' I said 'and you can start work at once.' So they decided to give a party to celebrate the occasion and they got a lot of drinks, for that damned Turk had renounced his religion and could now drink spirits. 'I don't want anything to drink,' I told them, but I did have a glass or two. That's the kind of silly character I have, dear, I always say 'no' at first, and drink afterwards. So it was there, too. I had a couple of drinks and got quite befuddled and lay down in the same bed with that woman friend of mine."

"And?"

"And . . . well . . . that's all there is to it and that's why now I always sew myself up before going to bed."

"Sew yourself up, Domna Platonovna?"

"Yes, dear. You see, dear, if I happen to be spending the night somewhere, I just get my feet into a kind of a sack and sew myself up, and, let me tell you, even when I am at home, I can no longer trust myself, seeing the kind of heavy sleeper I am, so I just sew myself up every night."

Domna Platonovna heaved a deep sigh and let fall her mournful head over he ample bosom.

"There you are, dear," she said after a long pause, "knowing the Petersburg circumstances as well as I do and yet I let such a thing happen to me!"

She got up, bid me good-bye and went back to her flat in Znamenskaya Street.

A few years later I had to take a poor fellow to an emergency hospital for typhus cases. Having seen him put to bed in one of the wards, I tried to find someone who could be relied on to look after him properly.

"You'd better see Sister," I was told.

"Won't you ask Sister if she will see me?" I asked.

A woman with a faded face and sagging cheeks entered the room.

"What can I do for you, sir?" she asked.

"Good heavens," I exclaimed, "Domna Platonovna!"

"Yes, sir," she said quietly, "it's me."

"How did you get here?"

"It was God's will, I suppose."

Discussion Questions

1.   Do you think that Richard Corey ever gave any indication that he was suicidal? Do some research on suicide and list several signs and symptoms that a person who is potentially suicidal might give.

2.   Two prominent features of dysthymia are low self-esteem and hopelessness. Can you identify these symptoms in Mr. Dumps? Mr. Dumps seems to take great pride in making other people miserable. Given the nature of his disorder do you feel that he is capable of genuine joy or happiness? Why or why not?

3.   Dr. Jamison and Leskhov describe the mood swings that occur in individuals with bipolar disorder and cyclothymia. Since mood swings are common to most people, discuss how you might be able to differentiate between the mood swings that reflect serious emotional problems and those related to the normal ups and downs most people face in their lives.

4.   It appears that mood disorders are diagnosed more often in women than in men. Why do you think this happens? Do you think that gender stereotypes play a role in the diagnosis of emotional disorders?

5.   Numerous individuals who have been diagnosed with emotional disturbances have gone on to become professionals in the mental health field. Some of these professionals end up treating the very disorders that they have been diagnosed as having. How do you feel about someone who has been diagnosed with an emotional disorder working with others as a treatment professional? Would you make a referral to such a professional? Why or why not?

Chapter 6

Anxiety Disorders

Individuals with anxiety disorders frequently experience anxiety, worry, and apprehension that is more intense and lasts for a longer period of time than the anxiety experienced by the average person. In response to this anxiety and worry these persons frequently develop avoidance behaviors, ritual acts, or repetitive thoughts as a means of protecting themselves from experiencing the anxiety.

In looking at the anxiety disorders it is often helpful to differentiate between anxiety and fear. Anxiety is a diffuse, highly unpleasant, often vague, feeling of apprehension, accompanied by one or more bodily sensations: for example, an empty feeling in the pit of the stomach, tightness in the chest, a pounding heart, perspiration, or headache. Often the individual feels restless and experiences the need to move around. Anxiety is an alerting signal; it warns of imminent danger and enables the person to take measures to deal with a threat. It is internal and is experienced in response to a threat that is unknown and vague. In contrast, fear is a response to a threat that is known, external, and definite.

In the anxiety disorders the individual is acutely aware of physiological sensations. These include such sensations as palpitations, sweating, butterflies, and shaking knees. Many of these individuals are aware of being nervous a great deal of the time. The anxiety tends to produce confusion and distortions of perception. Such distortions can interfere with learning. Anxiety is often responsible for lowering concentration, reducing recall, and impairing the ability to relate one item to another. Pathological anxiety is an inappropriate response to a given stimulus by virtue of either its intensity or its duration.

Panic Disorder

Panic disorder is characterized by the spontaneous, unexpected occurrence of panic attacks. A panic attack is marked by multiple physical sensations that often cause individuals to feel that they are having a heart attack. The first panic attack is often completely spontaneous. The major mental symptoms include extreme fear, a sense of impending doom, and an inability to name the source of the fear. Panic attacks generally last less than an hour. The symptoms may disappear quickly or gradually, and the person worries about having an attack between attacks. Major symptoms include palpitations, pounding heart, sweating, trembling or shaking, sensations of shortness of breath or smothering; a feeling of choking; chest pain or discomfort; nausea or abdominal distress; feeling dizzy, unsteady, lightheaded, or faint; fear of losing control or going crazy; fear of dying; and chills and hot flashes.

Vladimir Nabokov (1899–1977)

Vladimir Nabokov was born in St. Petersburg, Russia in 1899. He was born into a wealthy aristocratic family and was educated by British and French tutors.

His first novel, *Mashenka,* was published in 1926 in Russian. In 1940 Nabokov moved to the United States. He published works in both Russian and English. Nabokov wanted to be remembered as an American writer rather than a Russian writer. However, he enjoyed greater fame in the Soviet Union than in the West. His most famous work is *Lolita* (1955), which is one of the most controversial novels of the twentieth century. The story is about the desire of a middle-aged pedophile for a twelve-year-old girl.

In 1957 Nabokov published *Pnin,* the story of a Russian professor of literature teaching in an American college. In the following selection from *Pnin,* Nabokov describes the symptoms of panic disorder.

Pnin

. . . Pnin left the station, satisfied himself about the bus stop, and entered a coffee shop. He consumed a ham sandwich, ordered another, and consumed that too. At exactly five minutes to four, having paid for the food but not for an excellent toothpick which he carefully selected from a neat little cup in the shape of a pine cone near the cash register, Pnin walked back to the station for his bag.

A different man was now in charge. The first had been called home to drive his wife in all haste to the maternity hospital. He would be back in a few minutes.

"But I must obtain my valise!" cried Pnin.

The substitute was sorry but could not do a thing.

"It is there!" cried Pnin, leaning over and pointing.

This was unfortunate. He was still in the act of pointing when he realized that he was claiming the wrong bag. His index finger wavered. That hesitation was fatal.

"My bus to Cremona!" cried Pnin.

"There is another at eight," said the man.

What was our poor friend to do? Horrible situation! He glanced streetward. The bus had just come. The engagement meant an extra fifty dollars. His hand flew to his right side. *It* was there, *slava Bogu* (thank God)! Very well! He would not wear his black suit—*vot i vsyo* (that's all). He would retrieve it on his way back. He had lost, dumped, shed many more valuable things in his day. Energetically, almost lightheartedly, Pnin boarded the bus.

He had endured this new stage of his journey only for a few city blocks when an awful suspicion crossed his mind. Ever since he had been separated from his bag, the tip of his left forefinger had been alternating with the proximal edge of his right elbow in checking a precious presence in his inside coat pocket. All of a sudden he brutally yanked it out. It was Betty's paper.

Emitting what he thought were international exclamations of anxiety and entreaty, Pnin lurched out of his seat. Reeling, he reached the exit. With one hand the driver grimly milked out a handful of coins from his little machine, refunded him the price of the ticket, and stopped the bus. Poor Pnin landed in the middle of a strange town.

He was less strong than his powerfully puffed-out chest might imply, and the wave of hopeless fatigue that suddenly submerged his top heavy body, detaching him, as it were, from reality, was a sensation not utterly unknown to him. He found himself in a damp, green, purplish park, of the formal and funereal type, with the stress laid on somber rhododendrons, glossy laurels, sprayed shade trees and closely clipped lawns; and hardly had he turned into an alley of chestnut and oak, which the bus driver had curtly told him led back to the railway station, than that eerie feeling, that tingle of unreality overpowered him completely. Was it something he had eaten? That pickle with the ham? Was it a mysterious disease that none of his doctors had yet detected? My friend wondered, and I wonder, too.

I do not know if it has ever been noted before that one of the main characteristics of life is discreteness. Unless a film of flesh envelopes us, we die. Man exists only insofar as he is separated from his surroundings. The cranium is a space-traveler's helmet. Stay inside or you perish. Death is divestment, death is communion. It may be wonderful to mix with the landscape, but to do so is the end of the tender ego. The sensation poor Pnin experienced was something very like that divestment, that communion. He felt porous and pregnable. He was sweating. He was terrified. A stone bench among the laurels saved him from collapsing on the sidewalk. Was his seizure a heart attack? I doubt it. For the nonce I am his physician, and let me repeat, I doubt it. My patient was one of those singular and unfortunate people who regard their heart ("a hollow, muscular organ," according to the gruesome definition in *Webster's New Collegiate Dictionary*, which Pnin's orphaned bag contained) with a queasy dread, a nervous repulsion, a sick hate, as if it were some strong slimy untouchable monster that one had to be parasitized with, alas. Occasionally, when puzzled by his tumbling and tottering pulse, doctors examined him more thoroughly, the cardiograph outlined fabulous mountain ranges and indicated a dozen fatal diseases that excluded one another. He was afraid of touching his own wrist. He never attempted to sleep on his left side, even in those dismal hours of the night when the insomniac longs for a third side after trying the two he has.

And now, in the park of Whitchurch, Pnin felt what he had felt already on August 10, 1942, and February 15 (his birthday), 1937, and May 18, 1929, and July 4, 1920—that the repulsive automaton he lodged had developed a consciousness of its own and not only was grossly alive but was causing him pain and panic. He pressed his poor bald head against the stone back of the bench and recalled all the past occasions of similar discomfort and despair. Could it be pneumonia this time? He had been chilled to the bone a couple days before in one of those hearty American drafts that a host treats his guests to after a second round of drinks on a windy night. And suddenly Pnin (was he dying?) found himself sliding back into his own childhood. This sensation had the sharpness of retrospective detail that is said to be the dramatic privilege of drowning individuals, especially in the former Russian Navy—a phenomenon of suffocation that a veteran psychoanalyst, whose name escapes me, has explained as being the subconsciously evoked shock of one's baptism which causes an explosion of intervening recollections between the first immersion and the last. It all happened in a flash but there is no way of rendering it in less than so many conservative words . . .

* * *

A gray squirrel sitting on comfortable haunches on the ground before him was sampling a peach stone. The wind paused, and presently stirred the foliage again.

The seizure had left him a little frightened and shaky, but he argued that had it been a real heart attack, he would have surely felt a good deal more unsettled and concerned, and this roundabout piece of reasoning completely dispelled his fear. It was now four-twenty. He blew his nose and trudged to the station . . .

Phobia

Phobia is an irrational fear resulting in a conscious avoidance of the feared object, activity, or situation. Either the presence of the phobic activity or the anticipation of that activity produces severe distress in the affected person. Phobic individuals generally recognize that their reaction is excessive. The development of a specific phobia may result from the pairing of a specific object or situation with the emotion of fear and panic. Depression may be present in as many as one-third of the people with a phobia.

Graham Greene (1904–1991)

Graham Greene was born in Berkhamsted, Hertfordshire, England. He was educated at Balliol College, where he displayed a talent for writing. While in college he published more than sixty poems, stories, articles, and reviews, most of which appeared in the student magazine and newspaper.

In 1926 Greene moved to London where he worked for the *Times* of London (1926–30) and the *Spectator*, where he was a film critic and literary editor until 1940. Greene was a prolific writer, producing dramas, short stories, screen plays, reviews, and novels. The selection utilized here comes from his collected stories, published in 1972.

A phobia is an irrational fear. Graham Greene provides a chilling view of a young man's fear of the dark in his short story "The End of the Party."

"The End of the Party"

Peter Morton woke with a start to face the first light. Rain tapped against the glass. It was January the fifth.

He looked across a table on which a night-light had guttered into a pool of water, at the other bed. Francis Morton was still asleep, and Peter lay down again with his eyes on his brother. It amused him to imagine it was himself whom he watched, the same hair, the same eyes, the same lips and line of cheek. But the thought palled, and the mind went back to the fact which lent the day importance. It was the fifth of January. He could hardly believe a year had passed since Mrs. Henne-Falcon had given her last children's party.

Francis turned suddenly upon his back and threw an arm across his face, blocking his mouth. Peter's heart began to beat fast, not with pleasure now but with uneasiness. He sat up and called across the table, "Wake up." Francis's shoulders shook and he waved a clenched fist in the air, but his eyes remained closed. To Peter Morton the whole room seemed to darken, and he had the impression of a great bird swooping. He cried again, "Wake up," and once more there was silver light and the touch of rain on the windows. Francis rubbed his eyes. "Did you call out?" he asked.

"You are having a bad dream," Peter said. Already experience had taught him how far their minds reflected each other. But he was the elder, by a matter of minutes, and that brief extra interval of light, while his brother still struggled in pain and darkness, had given him self-reliance and an instinct of protection towards the other who was afraid of so many things.

"I dreamed that I was dead," Francis said.

"What was it like?" Peter asked.

"I can't remember," Francis said.

"You dreamed of a big bird."

"Did I?"

The two lay silent in bed facing each other, the same green eyes, the same nose tilting at the tip, the same firm lips, and the same premature modelling of the chin. The fifth of January, Peter thought again, his mind drifting idly from the image of cakes to the prizes which might be won. Egg-and-spoon races, spearing apples in basins of water, blind man's buff.

"I don't want to go," Francis said suddenly. "I suppose Joyce will be there . . . Mabel Warren." Hateful to him, the thought of a party shared with those two. They were older than he. Joyce was eleven and Mabel Warren thirteen. The long pigtails swung superciliously to a masculine stride. Their sex humiliated him, as they watched him fumble with his egg, from under lowered scornful lids. And last year . . . he turned his face away from Peter, his cheeks scarlet.

"What's the matter?" Peter asked.

"Oh, nothing. I don't think I'm well. I've got a cold. I oughtn't to go to the party." Peter was puzzled. "But Francis, is it a bad cold?"

"It will be a bad cold if I go to the party. Perhaps I shall die."

"Then you mustn't go," Peter said, prepared to solve all difficulties with one plain sentence, and Francis let his nerves relax, ready to leave everything to Peter. But though he was grateful he did not turn his face towards his brother. His cheeks still bore the badge of a shameful memory, of the game of hide and seek last year in the darkened house, and how he had screamed when Mabel Warren put her hand suddenly upon his arm. He had not heard her coming. Girls were like that. Their shoes never squeaked. No boards whined under the tread. They slunk like cats on padded claws.

When the nurse came in with hot water Francis lay tranquil leaving everything to Peter. Peter said, "Nurse, Francis has got a cold."

The tall starched woman laid the towels across the cans and said, without turning, "The washing won't be back till tomorrow. You must lend him some handkerchiefs."

"But, Nurse," Peter asked, "hadn't he better stay in bed?"

"We'll take him for a good walk this morning," the nurse said. "Wind'll blow away the germs. Get up now, both of you," and she closed the door behind her.

"I'm sorry," Peter said. "Why don't you just stay in bed? I'll tell mother you felt too ill to get up." But rebellion against destiny was not in Francis's power. If he stayed in bed they would come up and tap his chest and put a thermometer in his mouth and look at his tongue, and they would discover he was malingering. It was true he felt ill, a sick empty sensation in his stomach and a rapidly beating heart, but he knew the cause was only fear, fear of the party, fear of being made to hide by himself in the dark, uncompanioned by Peter and with no night-light to make a blessed breach.

"No, I'll get up," he said, and then with sudden desperation, "But I won't go to Mrs. Henne-Falcon's party. I swear on the Bible I won't."

Now surely all would be well, he thought. God would not allow him to break so solemn an oath. He would show him a way. There was all morning before him and all afternoon until four o'clock. No need to worry when the grass was still crisp with the early frost. Anything might happen. He might cut himself or break his leg or really catch a bad cold. God would manage somehow.

He had such confidence in God that when at breakfast his mother said, "I hear you have a cold, Francis," he made light of it. "We should have heard more about it," his mother said with irony, "if there was not a party this evening," and Francis smiled, amazed and daunted by her ignorance of him. His happiness would have lasted longer if, out for a walk that morning, he had not met Joyce. He was alone with his nurse, for Peter had leave to finish a rabbit-hutch in the woodshed. If Peter had been there he would have cared less; the nurse was Peter's nurse also, but now it was as though she were employed only for his sake, because he could not be trusted to go for a walk alone. Joyce was only two years older and she was by herself.

She came striding towards them, pigtails flapping. She glanced scornfully at Francis and spoke with ostentation to the nurse. "Hello, Nurse. Are you bringing Francis to the party this evening? Mabel and I are coming." And she was off again down the street in the direction of Mabel Warren's home, consciously alone and self-sufficient in the long empty road. "Such a nice girl," the nurse said. But Francis was silent, feeling again the jump-jump of his heart, realizing how soon the hour of the party would arrive. God had done nothing for him, and the minutes flew.

They flew too quickly to plan any evasion, or even to prepare his heart for the coming ordeal. Panic nearly overcame him when, all unready, he found himself standing on the doorstep, with coat-collar turned up against a cold wind, and the nurse's electric torch making a short trail through the darkness. Behind him were the lights of the hall and the sound of a servant laying the table for dinner, which his mother and father would eat alone. He was nearly overcome by the desire to run back into the house and call out to his mother that he would not go to the party, that he dared not go. They could not make him go. He could almost hear himself saying those final words, breaking down for ever the barrier of ignorance which saved his mind from his parents' knowledge. "I'm afraid of going. I won't go. I daren't go. They'll make me hide in the dark, and I'm afraid of the dark. I'll scream and scream and scream." He could see the expression of amazement on his mother's face, and then the cold confidence of a grown-up's retort.

"Don't be silly. You must go. We've accepted Mrs. Henne-Falcon's invitation." But they couldn't make him go; hesitating on the doorstep while the nurse's feet crunched across the frost-covered grass to the gate, he knew that. He would answer: "You can say I'm ill. I won't go. I'm afraid of the dark." And his mother: "Don't be silly. You know there's nothing to be afraid of in the dark." But he knew the falsity of that reasoning; he knew how they taught also that there was nothing to fear in death, and how fearfully they avoided the idea of it. But they couldn't make him go to the party. "I'll scream. I'll scream."

"Francis, come along." He heard the nurse's voice across the dimly phosphorescent lawn and saw the yellow circle of her torch wheel from tree to shrub. "I'm coming," he called with despair; he couldn't bring himself to lay bare his last secrets and end reserve between his mother and himself, for there was still in the last resort a further appeal possible to Mrs. Henne-Falcon. He comforted himself with that, as he advanced steadily across the hall, very small, towards her enormous bulk. His heart beat unevenly, but he had control now over his voice, as he said with meticulous accent, "Good evening, Mrs. Henne-Falcon. It was very good of you to ask me to your party." With his strained face lifted towards the curve of her breasts, and his polite set speech, he was like an old withered man. As a twin he was in many ways an only child. To address Peter was to speak to his own image in a mirror, an image a little altered by a flaw in the glass, so as to throw back less a likeness of what he was than of what he wished to be, what he would be without his unreasoning fear of darkness, footsteps of strangers, the flight of bats in dusk-filled gardens.

"Sweet child," said Mrs. Henne-Falcon absent-mindedly, before, with a wave of her arms, as though the children were a flock of chickens, she whirled them into her set programme of entertainments: egg-and-spoon races, three-legged races, the spearing of apples, games which held for Francis nothing worse than humiliation. And in the frequent intervals when nothing was required of him and he could stand alone in corners as far removed as possible from Mabel Warren's scornful gaze, he was able to plan how he might avoid the approaching terror of the dark. He knew there was nothing to fear until after tea, and not until he was sitting down in a pool of yellow radiance cast by ten candles on Colin Henne-Falcon's birthday cake did he become fully conscious of the imminence of what he feared. He heard Joyce's high voice down the table, "After tea we are going to play hide and seek in the dark."

"Oh, no," Peter said, watching Francis's troubled face, "don't let's. We play that every year."

"But it's in the programme," cried Mabel Warren. I saw it myself. I looked over Mrs. Henne-Falcon's shoulder. Five o'clock tea. A quarter to six to half past, hide and seek in the dark. It's all written down in the programme."

Peter did not argue, for if hide and seek had been inserted in Mrs. Henne-Falcon's programme, nothing which he could say would avert it. He asked for another piece of birthday cake and sipped his tea slowly. Perhaps it might be possible to delay the game for a quarter of an hour, allow Francis at least a few extra minutes to form a plan, but even in that Peter failed, for children were already leaving the table in twos and threes. It was his third failure, and again he saw a great bird darken his brother's face with its wings. But he upbraided himself silently for his folly, and finished his cake encouraged by the memory of that adult refrain, "There's nothing to fear in the dark." The last to leave the table, the brothers came together to the hall to meet the mustering and impatient eyes of Mrs. Henne-Falcon.

"And now," she said, "we will play hide and seek in the dark."

Peter watched his brother and saw the lips tighten. Francis, he knew, had feared this moment from the beginning of the party, had tried to meet it with courage and had abandoned the attempt. He must have prayed for cunning to evade the game, which was now welcomed with cries of excitement by all the other children. 'Oh, do let's.' "We must pick sides." "Is any of the house out of bounds?" "Where shall home be?"

"I think," said Francis Morton, approaching Mrs. Henne-Falcon, his eyes focused unwaveringly on her exuberant breasts, "it will be no use my playing. My nurse will be calling for me very soon."

"Oh, but your nurse can wait, Francis," said Mrs. Henne-Falcon, while she clapped her hands together to summon to her side a few children who were already straying up the wide staircase to upper floors. "Your mother will never mind."

That had been the limit of Francis's cunning. He had refused to believe that so well-prepared an excuse could fail. All that he could say now, still in the precise tone which other children hated, thinking it a symbol of conceit, was, "I think I had better not play." He stood motionless, retaining, though afraid, unmoved features. But the knowledge of his terror, or the reflection of the terror itself, reached his brother's brain. For the moment, Peter Morton could have cried aloud with the fear of bright lights going out, leaving him alone in an island of dark surrounded by the gentle lappings of strange footsteps. Then he remembered that the fear was not his own, but his brother's. He said impulsively to Mrs. Henne-Falcon, "Please, I don't think Francis should play. The dark makes him jump so. " They were wrong words. Six children began to sing, "Cowardy cowardy custard," turning torturing faces with the vacancy of wide sunflowers towards Francis Morton.

Without looking at his brother, Francis said, "Of course I'll play. I'm not afraid, I only thought . . ." But he was already forgotten by his human tormentors. The children scrambled round Mrs. Henne-Falcon, their shrill voices pecking at her with questions and suggestions. "Yes, anywhere in the house. We will turn out all the lights. Yes, you can hide in the cupboards. You must stay hidden as long as you can. There will be no home."

Peter stood apart, ashamed of the clumsy manner in which he had tried to help his brother. Now he could feel, creeping in at the corners of his brain, all Francis's resentment of his championing. Several children ran upstairs, and the lights on the top floor went out. Darkness came down like the wings of a bat and settled on the landing. Others began to put out the lights at the edge of the hall, till the children were all gathered in the central radiance of the chandelier, while the bats squatted round on hooded wings and waited for that, too, to be extinguished.

"You and Francis are on the hiding side," a tall girl said, and then the light was gone, and the carpet wavered under his feet with the sibilance of foothills, like small cold draughts, creeping away into corners.

"Where's Francis?" he wondered. "If I join him he'll be less frightened of all these sounds." "These sounds" were the casing of silence: the squeak of a loose board, the cautious closing of a cupboard door, the whine of a finger drawn along polished wood.

Peter stood in the center of the dark deserted floor, not listening but waiting for the idea of his brother's whereabouts to enter his brain. But Francis
crouched with fingers on his ears, eyes uselessly closed, mind numbed against
impressions, and only a sense of strain could cross the gap of dark. Then a voice
called "Coming", and as through his brother's self-possession had been shattered by the sudden cry, Peter Morton jumped with his fear. But it was not his
own fear. What in his brother was a burning panic was in him an altruistic
emotion that left the reason unimpaired. "Where, if I were Francis, should I
hide?" And because he was, if not Francis himself, at least a mirror to him, the
answer was immediate. "Between the oak bookcase on the left of the study
door, and the leather settee." Between the twins there could be no jargon of
telepathy. They had been together in the womb, and they could not be parted.

Peter Morton tiptoed towards Francis's hiding-place. Occasionally a board
rattled, and because he feared to be caught by one of the soft questers through
the dark, he bent and untied his laces. A tag struck the floor and the metallic
sound set a host of cautious feet moving in his direction. But by that time he
was in his stockings and would have laughed inwardly at the pursuit had not
the noise of someone stumbling on his abandoned shoes made his heart trip.
No more boards revealed Peter Morton's progress. On stockinged feet he moved
silently and unerringly towards his object. Instinct told him he was near the
wall, and extending a hand, he laid the fingers across his brother's face.

Francis did not cry out, but the leap of his own heart revealed to Peter a
proportion of Francis's terror. "It's all right," he whispered, feeling down the
squatting figure until he captured a clenched hand. "It's only me. I'll stay with
you." And grasping the other tightly, he listened to the cascade of whispers his
utterance had caused to fall. A hand touched the book-case close to Peter's
head and he was aware of how Francis's fear continued in spite of his presence.
It was less intense, more bearable, he hoped, but it remained. He knew that it
was his brother's fear and not his own that he experienced. The dark to him was
only an absence of light; the groping hand that of a familiar child. Patiently he
waited to be found.

He did not speak again, for between Francis and himself was the most intimate communion. By way of joined hands thought could flow more swiftly
than lips could shape themselves round words. He could experience the whole
progress of his brother's emotion, from the leap of panic at the unexpected contact to the steady pulse of fear, which now went on and on with the regularity
of a heart-beat. Peter Morton thought with intensity, "I am here. You needn't
be afraid. The lights will go on again soon. That rustle, that movement is nothing to fear. Only Joyce, only Mabel Warren." He bombarded the drooping form
with thoughts of safety, but he was conscious that the fear continued. "They
are beginning to whisper together. They are tired of looking for us. The lights
will go on soon. We shall have won. Don't be afraid. That was someone on the
stairs. I believe its Mrs. Henne-Falcon. Listen. They are feeling for the lights."
Feet moving on a carpet, hands brushing a wall, a curtain pulled apart, a click-

ing handle, the opening of a cupboard door. In the case above their heads a loose book shifted under a touch. "Only Joyce, only Mabel Warren, only Mrs. Henne-Falcon," a crescendo of reassuring thought before the chandelier burst, like a fruit-tree, into bloom.

The voices of the children rose shrilly into the radiance. "Where's Peter?" "Have you looked upstairs?" "Where's Francis?" but they were silenced again by Mrs. Henne-Falcon's scream. But she was not the first to notice Francis Morton's stillness, where he had collapsed against the wall at the touch of his brother's hand. Peter continued to hold the clenched fingers in an arid and puzzled grief. It was not merely that his brother was dead. His brain, too young to realize the full paradox, wondered with an obscure self-pity why it was that the pulse of his brother's fear went on and on, when Francis was now where he had always been told there was no more terror and no more darkness.

Obsessive-Compulsive Disorder

Obsessive-compulsive disorder is marked by the symptom of recurring obsessions or compulsions. These symptoms are described as severe enough to be time consuming or to cause marked distress. People with this disorder may have an obsession or a compulsion or both. An obsession is a recurrent and intrusive thought, feeling, idea, or sensation. A compulsion is a conscious, standardized, recurrent thought or behavior such as counting, checking, or avoiding. Obsessions increase a person's anxiety, whereas carrying out compulsions reduces the anxiety.

William Shakespeare (1564–1616)

One of the finest of Shakespeare's tragedies is *Macbeth*. Lady Macbeth is consumed by anxiety and guilt over her evil deeds. She presents an excellent example of obsessive-compulsive disorder through her behavior of compulsive hand-washing.

(Refer to chapter 4 for biographical material on Shakespeare.)

Macbeth, act V scene 1

Dunsinane. Macbeth's castle.

Enter a Doctor of Physic *and a* Waiting-Gentlewoman.

Doctor. I have two nights watch'd with you, but can perceive no truth in your report. When was it she last walk'd?

Gentlewoman. Since his Majesty went into the field, I have seen her rise from her bed, throw her nightgown upon her, unlock her closet, take forth paper, fold it, write upon't, read it, afterwards seal it, and again return to bed; yet all this while in a most fast sleep.

Doctor. A great perturbation in nature, to receive at once the benefit of sleep and do the effects of watching! In this slumb'ry agitation, besides her walking and other actual performances, what, at any time, have you heard her say?

Gentlewoman. That sir, which I will not report after her.

Doctor. You may to me; and 'tis most meet you should.

Gentlewoman. Neither to you nor any one, having no witness to confirm my speech.

Enter Lady Macbeth, with a taper

Lo you, here she comes! This is her very guise; and, upon my life, fast asleep. Observe her; stand close.

Doctor. How came she by that light?

Gentlewoman. Why, it stood by her. She has light by her continually; 'tis her command.

Doctor. You see her eyes are open.

Gentlewoman. Ay, but their sense is shut.

Doctor. What is it she does now? Look how she rubs her hands.

Gentlewoman. It is an accustomed action with her, to seem thus washing her hands; I have known her to continue in this a quarter of an hour.

Lady Macbeth. Yet here's a spot.

Doctor. Hark, she speaks. I will set down what comes from her, to satisfy my remembrance the more strongly.

Lady Macbeth. Out, damned spot! out, I say! One, two; why then 'tis time to do't. Hell is murky. Fie, my lord, fie! a soldier, and afeard? What need we fear who knows it, when none can call our pow'r to account? Yet who would have thought the old man to have had so much blood in him?

Doctor. Do you mark that?

Lady Macbeth. The Thane of Fife had a wife; where is she now? What, will these hands ne'er be clean? No more o' that, my lord, no more o' that; you mar all with this starting.

Doctor. Go to, go to; you have known what you should not.

Gentlewoman. She has spoke what should not, I am sure of that. Heaven knows what she has known.

Lady Macbeth. Here's the smell of blood still. All the perfumes of Arabia will not sweeten this little hand. Oh, oh, oh!

Doctor. What a sigh is there! The heart is sorely charg'd.

Gentlewoman. I would not have such a heart in my bosom for the dignity of the whole body.

Doctor. Well, well, well.

Gentlewoman. Pray God it be, sir.

Doctor. This disease is beyond my practice. Yet I have known those which have walk'd in their sleep who have died holily in their beds.

Lady Macbeth. Wash your hands, put on your nightgown, look not so pale. I tell you yet again, Banquo's buried; he cannot come out on's grave.

Doctor. Even so?

Lady Macbeth. To bed, to bed; there's knocking at the gate. Come, come, come, come, give me your hand. What's done cannot be undone. To bed, to bed, to bed.

Exit.

Doctor. Will she go now to bed?

Gentlewoman. Directly.

Doctor. Foul whisp'rings are abroad. Unnatural deeds
Do breed unnatural troubles; infected minds
To their deaf pillows will discharge their secrets.
More needs she the divine than the physician.
God, God forgive us all. Look after her;
Remove from her the means of all annoyance,
And still keep eyes upon her. So, good night.
My mind she has mated, and amaz'd my sight.
I think, but dare not speak.

Gentlewoman. Good night, good doctor. *Exeunt.*

Posttraumatic Stress Disorder

Individuals with posttraumatic stress disorder have experienced an emotional stress that was of a magnitude that would be traumatic for almost anyone. Such traumas include combat, natural disasters, assault, rape, serious auto accidents, and fires. The disorder consists of three phases: (1) reexperiencing the trauma through dreams and waking thoughts; (2) persistent avoidance of reminders of the trauma and numbing of responsiveness to such reminders; and (3) persistent hyperarousal. Associated symptoms include aggression, violence, poor impulse control, depression, and substance abuse.

Jonathan Shay (b. 1941)

Jonathan Shay, M.D., Ph.D., is a psychiatrist for the United States Department of Veterans Affairs in Boston. He is also a member of the faculty at Tufts Medical School.

Shay works in the treatment of Vietnam combat veterans for severe, chronic posttraumatic stress disorder. His groundbreaking work, *Achilles in Vietnam*, is a study of combat posttraumatic stress disorder. The selections utilized here are the accounts of the experience of posttraumatic stress disorder in the words of those veterans suffering from the disorder.

Achilles in Vietnam

I haven't really slept for twenty years. I lie down but I don't sleep. I'm always watching the door, the window, then back to the door. I get up at least five times to walk my perimeter, sometimes it's ten or fifteen times. There's always something within reach, maybe a baseball bat or a knife, at every door. I used to sleep with a gun under my pillow, another under my mattress, and another in the drawer next to the bed. . . .

* * *

I worked a lot of overtime and also went to school and had a second job. I didn't sleep any more then than now. Maybe two hours a night. But I sure made a lot of money. Workaholic. That's me—no, that *was* me. I was real lucky they kept me so long. They understood that sometimes I just had to leave work. And they never laughed at me when I hit the floor if there was a loud bang or something. . . .

* * *

I don't deserve my wife. What kind of life is it for her married to me? She says, "Let's take the kids out for dinner." And I say, "Sure, let's go." So we get to the restaurant and we walk in the door and I say, "Whoa!" when I look around and see all those people. So the hostess shows us to a table right in the middle, and I say, "How about there in the corner?" and she says, "There's people there," and I say, "We'll wait." Meantime my wife is looking at me and there's sweat running down my face. I can't sit with my back uncovered. If I know you're back there covering me, it's okay, but a bunch of strangers, and some of them Gooks—no way. I sit in the corner where I can see everyone who comes in and everyone who leaves. So after we wait thirty minutes for the table in the corner we start walking through the restaurant to it and my heart's pounding, pounding and the sweat's rolling off me and I say, "I gotta go." So they sit down and eat and I stand up in the parking garage, the second floor overlooking the entrance to the restaurant where I have a real good line on everything going on. . . .

* * *

I don't have very long to live. No, Doc, no, no, I'm not suicidal, it's just that sometimes I don't give a fuck. I don't care if I live or die. I've been waiting to die

ever since I got back from Vietnam. When I get that way, my wife, my kids—
and I really love them—it's "Get the fuck away from me!" Once when my
daughter was younger and I was that way, she came up behind me and before I
knew it I had her by the throat up against the wall. I can still see her eyes. I put
her down and just walked out of the house without saying anything to anybody
and didn't come back for a week. I felt lower than dogshit. I hate it that my kids
behave so *careful* around me. I made them that way, and I hate it. Every time I
see them being so careful I think of that look in her eyes and I get this feeling
here [puts his palm on his belly] like a big stone sitting there . . .

* * *

I never tried to kill myself, but a lot of the time I just don't care. For years
I used to go down to the Combat Zone [the Boston red-light district] after midnight and just walk the alleys. If I saw someone down an alley in the dark, I
wouldn't go the other way, I'd go down there thinking, "Maybe I'll get lucky."
I'm amazed I wasn't killed. I guess I wanted to be killed. . . .

* * *

I haven't spent a complete night in bed with my wife for at least ten years.
I always end up on the sofa. It's safer for her, and I don't have to worry about
waking her when I get up to walk the perimeter. When I was working sixteen
hours a day I'd come home; she'd already be in bed. I'd do a couple hours of
things around the house and meanwhile put away a case of beer and a fifth so
I'd be able to sleep. Then I'd get in bed with her for two, three hours until it was
time for work again. But after I couldn't work anymore, it got really worse and
it was really bad after I stopped drinking, I'd do this crazy shit at night. I once
threw her out of bed so hard it broke her shoulder. I thought there was an NVA
potato-masher [a grenade] come in on us. Another time I thought *she* was a
Gook, and I had my hands around her throat before I woke up. So since I
stopped drinking I never let myself fall asleep in bed with her. I lie there quiet
until she's asleep and then get up, check the perimeter, and lie down on the sofa
where I can see the door. . . .

* * *

My son asks me if I'll come to his Little League game and I can't ever promise. He wants me to promise, but I can't. It's not that I don't want to go. I was in
Little League myself, and I go sometimes just at the last minute and watch
from the tree line in the outfield. He has a great arm, and once he hit a home
run into the trees where I was standing. I had to pull back real quick. You can't
have somebody knowing where you'll be. . . .

* * *

I know it all kicks up around the time of year we went into _____. I can't
tell you what we were doing there, it's still secret and I've never been too

comfortable with these dropped ceilings here in the clinic. It's just too easy to hide a microphone here. Maybe someday I'll be able to talk about it, but for now you never know who might be listening, and I'm not allowed to say anything about it. I shouldn't even have said we were in _____. I guess they need to keep tabs, because you know we still have our people over there who'd be dead in a minute if the wrong thing was said. There've been times I took every stick of furniture out of my house, took all the plates off the plugs in the walls and replaced every light fixture, and I had a guy sweep my house for bugs—cost me $600, but I still had the feeling I was being watched. . . .

★   ★   ★

The people who read this book ain't going to believe any of this shit. And *you* better look out. Nobody's going to believe you when you tell them, and you'll end up an outcast like us.

Generalized Anxiety Disorder

Individuals with generalized anxiety disorder are anxious about almost everything. Symptoms include excessive and pervasive worry, a variety of somatic complaints, anxiety, muscle tension, restlessness, difficulty sleeping, and cognitive vigilance. They report that the anxiety is difficult for them to control and results in significant impairment in their lives. Generalized anxiety disorder is often diagnosed with a coexisting mental disorder, usually another anxiety disorder or mood disorder.

Guy de Maupassant (1850–1893)

Once again we call upon Guy de Maupassant to utilize his powerful storytelling ability. He provides us a clear picture of generalized anxiety disorder in his excellent story "He."

(Refer to chapter 4 for biographical information on de Maupassant.)

"He"

My dear friend, you cannot understand it by any possible means, you say, and I perfectly believe you. You think I am going mad? It may be so, but not for the reasons which you suppose.

Yes, I am going to get married, and I will tell you what has led me to take that step.

My ideas and my convictions have not changed at all. I look upon all legalized cohabitation as utterly stupid, for I am certain that nine husbands out of ten are cuckolds; and they get no more than their deserts for having been idiotic enough to fetter their lives and renounce their freedom in love, the only happy and good thing in the world, and for having clipped the wings of fancy which continually drives us on toward all women. You know what I mean. More than ever I feel that I am incapable of loving one woman alone, because

I shall always adore all the others too much. I should like to have a thousand arms, a thousand mouths, and a thousand—*temperaments*, to be able to strain an army of these charming creatures in my embrace at the same moment.

And yet I am going to get married!

I may add that I know very little of the girl who is going to become my wife to-morrow; I have only seen her four or five times. I know that there is nothing unpleasing about her, and that is enough for my purpose. She is small, fair, and stout; so of course the day after to-morrow I shall ardently wish for a tall, dark, thin woman.

She is not rich, and belongs to the middle classes. She is a girl such as you may find by the gross, well adapted for matrimony, without any apparent faults, and with no particularly striking qualities. People say of her: "Mlle. Lajolle is a very nice girl," and to-morrow they will say: "What a very nice woman Madame Raymon is." She belongs, in a word, to that immense number of girls who make very good wives for us till the moment comes when we discover that we happen to prefer all other women to that particular woman we have married.

"Well," you will say to me, "what on earth do you get married for?"

I hardly like to tell you the strange and seemingly improbable reason that urged me on to this senseless act; the fact, however, is that I am frightened of being alone!

I don't know how to tell you or to make you understand me, but my state of mind is so wretched that you will pity me and despise me.

I do not want to be alone any longer at night; I want to feel that there is someone close to me touching me, a being who can speak and say something, no matter what it be.

I wish to be able to awaken somebody by my side, so that I may be able to ask some sudden question, a stupid question even, if I feel inclined, so that I may hear a human voice, and feel that there is some waking soul close to me, some one whose reason is at work—so that when I hastily light the candle I may see some human face by my side—because—because I am ashamed to confess it—because I am afraid of being alone.

Oh! You don't understand me yet.

I am not afraid of any danger; if a man were to come into the room I should kill him without trembling. I am not afraid of ghosts, nor do I believe in the supernatural. I am not afraid of dead people, for I believe in the total annihilation of every being that disappears from the face of the earth.

Well,—yes, well, it must be told; I am afraid of myself, afraid of that horrible sensation of incomprehensible fear.

You may laugh, if you like. It is terrible and I cannot get over it. I am afraid of the walls, of the furniture, of the familiar objects, which are animated, as far as I am concerned, by a kind of animal life. Above all, I am afraid of my own dreadful thoughts of my reason, which seems as if it were about to leave me, driven away by a mysterious and invisible agony.

At first I feel a vague uneasiness in my mind which causes a cold shiver to run all over me. I look round, and of course nothing is to be seen, and I wish there were something there, no matter what, as long as it were something tangible: I am frightened, merely because I cannot understand my own terror.

If I speak, I am afraid of my own voice. If I walk, I am afraid of I know not what, behind the door, behind the curtains, in the cupboard, or under my bed, and yet all the time I know there is nothing anywhere, and I turn round suddenly because I am afraid of what is behind me, although there is nothing there, and I know it.

I get agitated; I feel that my fear increases, and so I shut myself up in my own room, get into bed, and hide under the clothes, and there cowering down rolled into a ball, I close my eyes in despair and remain thus for an indefinite time, remembering that my candle is alight on the table by my bedside, and that I ought to put it out, and yet—I dare not do it!

It is very terrible, is it not, to be like that?

Formerly I felt nothing of all that; I came home quite comfortably, and went up and down in my rooms without anything disturbing my calmness of mind. Had anyone told me that I should be attacked by a malady—for I can call it nothing else—of most improbable fear, such a stupid and terrible malady as it is, I should have laughed outright. I was certainly never afraid of opening the door in the dark; I used to go to bed slowly without locking it, and never got up in the middle of the night to make sure everything was firmly closed.

It began last year in a very strange manner, on a damp autumn evening. When my servant had left the room, after I had dined, I asked myself what I was going to do. I walked up and down my room for some time, feeling tired without a reason for it, unable to work, and without enough energy to read. A fine rain was falling, and I felt unhappy, a prey to one of those fits of casual despondency which make us feel inclined to cry, or to talk, no matter to whom, so as to shake off our depressing thoughts.

I felt that I was alone and that my rooms seemed to me to be more empty than they had ever been before. I was surrounded by a sensation of infinite and overwhelming solitude. What was I to do? I sat down, but then a kind of nervous impatience agitated my legs, so that I got up and began to walk about again. I was feverish, for my hands, which I had clasped behind me, as one often does when walking slowly, almost seemed to burn one another. Then suddenly a cold shiver ran down my back, and I thought the damp air might have penetrated into my room, so I lit the fire for the first time that year, and sat down again and looked at the flames. But soon I felt that I could not possibly remain quiet. So I got up again and determined to go out, to pull myself together, and to seek a friend to bear me company.

I could not find anyone, so I went on to the boulevards to try and meet some acquaintance or other there.

It was wretched everywhere, and the wet pavement glistened in the gaslight, while the oppressive mist of the almost impalpable rain lay heavily over the streets and seemed to obscure the light from the lamps.

I went on slowly, saying to myself, "I shall not find a soul to talk to."

I glanced into several *cafés,* from the Madeleine as far as the Faubourg Poissoniere, and saw many unhappy-looking individuals sitting at the tables, who did not seem even to have enough energy left to finish the refreshments they had ordered.

For a long time I wandered aimlessly up and down, and about midnight I started off for home; I was very calm and very tired. My *concierge* opened the door at once, which was quite unusual for him, and I thought that another lodger had no doubt just come in.

When I go out I always double-lock the door of my room. Now I found it merely closed, which surprised me; but I supposed that some letters had been brought up for me in the course of the evening.

I went in, and found my fire still burning so that it lighted up the room a little. In the act of taking up a candle, I noticed somebody sitting in my armchair by the fire, warming his feet, with his back toward me.

I was not in the slightest degree frightened. I thought very naturally that some friend or other had come to see me. No doubt the porter, whom I had told when I went out, had lent him his own key. In a moment I remembered all the circumstances of my return, how the street door had been opened immediately, and that my own door was only latched, and not locked.

I could see nothing of my friend but his head. He had evidently gone to sleep while waiting for me, so I went up to him to rouse him. I saw him quite clearly; his right arm was hanging down and his legs were crossed, while his head, which was somewhat inclined to the left of the armchair, seemed to indicate that he was asleep. "Who can it be?" I asked myself. I could not see clearly, as the room was rather dark, so I put out my hand to touch him on the shoulder, and it came in contact with the back of the chair. There was nobody there; the seat was empty.

I fairly jumped with fright. For a moment I drew back as if some terrible danger had suddenly appeared in my way; then I turned round again, impelled by some imperious desire to look at the armchair again. I remained standing upright, panting with fear, so upset that I could not collect my thoughts, and ready to drop.

But I am naturally a cool man, and soon recovered myself. I thought: "It is a mere hallucination, that is all," and I immediately began to reflect about this phenomenon. Thoughts fly very quickly at such moments.

I had been suffering from a hallucination, that was an incontestable fact. My mind had been perfectly lucid and had acted regularly and logically, so there was nothing the matter with the brain. It was only my eyes that had been deceived; they had had a vision, one of those visions which lead simple folk to believe in miracles. It was a nervous accident to the optical apparatus, nothing more; the eyes were rather overwrought, perhaps.

I lit my candle, and when I stooped down to the fire in so doing, I noticed that I was trembling, and I raised myself up with a jump, as if somebody had touched me from behind.

I was certainly not by any means reassured.

I walked up and down a little, and hummed a tune or two. Then I double-locked my door, and felt rather reassured; now, at any rate, nobody could come in.

I sat down again, and thought over my adventure for a long time; then I went to bed, and put out my light.

For some minutes all went well; I lay quietly on my back. Then an irresistible desire seized me to look round the room, and I turned on to my side.

My fire was nearly out and the few glowing embers threw a faint light on to the floor by the chair, where I fancied I saw the man sitting again.

I quickly struck a match, but I had been mistaken, for there was nothing there; I got up, however, and hid the chair behind my bed, and tried to get to sleep as the room was now dark. But I had not forgotten myself for more than five minutes when in my dream I saw all the scene which I had witnessed as clearly as if it were reality. I woke up with a start, and, having lit the candle, sat up in bed, without venturing even to try and go to sleep again.

Twice, however, sleep overcame me for a few moments in spite of myself, and twice I saw the same thing again, till I fancied I was going mad. When day broke, however, I thought that I was cured, and slept peacefully till noon.

It was all past and over, I had been feverish, had had the nightmare; I don't know what. I had been ill, in a word, but yet I thought that I was a great fool.

I enjoyed myself thoroughly that evening; I went and dined at a restaurant; afterward I went to the theater, and then started home. But as I got near the house I was seized by a strange feeling of uneasiness once more; I was afraid of *seeing* him again. I was not afraid of him, not afraid of his presence, in which I did not believe; but I was afraid of being deceived again; I was afraid of some fresh hallucination, afraid lest fear should take possession of me.

For more than an hour I wandered up and down the pavement; then I thought that I was really too foolish, and returned home. I panted so that I could scarcely get upstairs, and remained standing outside my door for more than ten minutes; then suddenly I took courage and pulled myself together. I inserted my key into the lock, and went in with a candle in my hand. I kicked open my half-open bedroom door, and gave a frightened look toward the fireplace; there was nothing there. A—h!

What relief and what a delight! What a deliverance! I walked up and down briskly and boldly, but I was not altogether reassured, and kept turning round with a jump; the very shadows in the corners disquieted me.

I slept badly, and was constantly disturbed by imaginary noises, but I did not see *him;* no, that was all over.

Since that time I have been afraid of being alone at night. I feel that the specter is there, close to me, around me; but it has not appeared to me again.

And supposing it did, what would it matter, since I do not believe in it and know that it is nothing?

It still worries me, however, because I am constantly thinking of it; *his right arm hanging down and his head inclined to the left like a man who was asleep*—Enough of that, in Heaven's name! I don't want to think about it!

Why, however, am I so persistently possessed with this idea? His feet were close to the fire!

He haunts me; it is very stupid, but so it is. Who and what is HE? I know that he does not exist except in my cowardly imagination, in my fears, and in my agony! There—enough of that!

Yes it is all very well for me to reason with myself, *to stiffen myself*, so to say; but I cannot remain at home, because I know he is there. I know I shall not see him again; he will not show himself again; that is all over. But he is there all the same in my thoughts. He remains invisible, but that does not prevent his being there. He is behind the doors, in the closed cupboards, in the wardrobe, under the bed, in every dark corner. If I open the door or the cupboard, if I take the candle to look under the bed and throw a light on to the dark places, he is there no longer, but I feel that he is behind me. I turn round, certain that I shall not see him, that I shall never see him again; but he is, none the less, behind me.

It is very stupid, it is dreadful; but what can I do? I cannot help it.

But if there were two of us in the place, I feel certain that he would not be there any longer, for he is there just because I am, alone, simply and solely because I am alone!

Discussion Questions

1. Is it possible for a person to die from a phobia, as Greene implies in "The End of the Party"? If you believe that it is possible, what might be the "official" cause of death in such a case?

2. Lady Macbeth engages in the obsessive-compulsive behavior of hand washing. List several other ways to express obsessive-compulsive behaviors.

3. Dr. Shay's work describes the most common cause of posttraumatic stress disorder in men, which is combat-related experiences. Do some research on posttraumatic stress disorder to see if you can find the most common cause of the disorder in women. Considering the differences between men and women in the development of this disorder, is a different treatment approach called for based on gender? Why or why not?

4. Anxiety disorder symptoms are sometimes divided into the categories of cognitive, affective, behavioral, and physiological. List the symptoms exhibited in *Pnin* utilizing these four categories.

5. Which of the anxiety disorders do you think would be the most difficult to work with? Why?

Chapter 7

Personality Disorders

These disorders represent persistent subjective patterns of ways in which individuals relate to and think about the environment and themselves. Disorders of personality result in patterns that are stable, rigid, pervasive, and maladaptive over time.

An individual's personality traits become personality disorders when they become inflexible and maladaptive and lead to unhappiness and impairment. Personality disorders should only be diagnosed when the characteristic features are typical of long-term functioning and not limited to discrete episodes of illness. Individuals with personality disorders rarely seek treatment on their own, and their disorders are often far more troubling to others than they are to themselves.

Schizoid Personality Disorder

Individuals with schizoid personality disorder display a lifelong pattern of social withdrawal and often a striking lack of warmth and tenderness. They are indifferent to social relationships and exhibit discomfort with human relationships. They often appear to be "in a fog," absentminded, detached from others, self-involved, and not connected. They tend to be loners, to gravitate to solitary jobs that involve little or no contact with others, and they may become very attached to animals.

Nathaniel Hawthorne (1804–1864)

Nathaniel Hawthorne was born in Salem, Massachusetts. He was descended from Puritan ancestors, who included John Hathorne, a presiding judge in the Salem witch trials. He was educated at Bowdin College, and among his classmates were Longfellow and future president Franklin Pierce.

Hawthorne's first novel, *Fanshawe*, published in 1828, did not receive much attention. His greatest works include *The Scarlet Letter* (1850) and *The House of the Seven Gables* (1851). *The Scarlet Letter* is considered the first American psychological novel. Hawthorne's novels and tales explore moral and spiritual conflicts. In addition to his importance as a novelist, Hawthorne helped to establish the American short story as a significant art form. His short stories are filled with loneliness, frustration, hypocrisy, eccentricity, and human frailty.

Hawthorne utilizes his finest skills to paint a picture of the schizoid personality disorder in his short story, "Wakefield." Mr. Wakefield's lack of need for human contact is obvious in his behavior. Wakefield is clearly a loner, and is detached, self-involved, and not interested in other people.

"Wakefield"

In some old magazine or newspaper I recollect a story, told as truth, of a man—let us call him Wakefield—who absented himself for a long time from his wife. The fact, thus abstractedly stated, is not very uncommon, nor—without a proper distinction of circumstances—to be condemned either as naughty or nonsensical. Howbeit, this, though far from the most aggravated, is perhaps the strangest, instance on record, of marital delinquency; and, moreover, as remarkable a freak as may found in the whole list of human oddities. The wedded couple lived in London. The man, under pretense of going on a journey, took lodgings in the next street to his own house, and there, unheard of by his wife or friends, and without the shadow of a reason for such self-banishment, dwelt upwards of twenty years. During that period, he beheld his home every day, and frequently the forlorn Mrs. Wakefield. And after so great a gap in his matrimonial felicity—when his death was reckoned certain, his estate settled, his name dismissed from memory, and his wife, long, long ago, resigned to her autumnal widowhood—he entered the door one evening, quietly, as from a day's absence, and became a loving spouse till death.

This outline is all that I remember. But the incident, though of the purest originality, unexampled, and probably never to be repeated, is one, I think, which appeals to the generous sympathies of mankind. We know, each for himself, that none of us would perpetrate such a folly, yet feel as if some other might. To my own contemplations, at least, it has often recurred, always exciting wonder, but with a sense that the story must be true, and a conception of its hero's character. Whenever any subject so forcibly affects the mind, time is well spent in thinking of it. If the reader choose, let him do his own meditation; or if he prefer to ramble with me through the twenty years of Wakefield's vagary, I bid him welcome; trusting that there will be a pervading spirit and a moral, even should we fail to find them, done up neatly, and condensed into the final sentence. Thought has always its efficacy, and every striking incident its moral.

What sort of a man was Wakefield? We are free to shape our own idea, and call it by his name. He was now in the meridian of life; his matrimonial affections, never violent, were sobered into a calm, habitual sentiment; of all husbands, he was likely to be the most constant, because a certain sluggishness would keep his heart at rest, wherever it might be placed. He was intellectual, but not actively so; his mind occupied itself in long and lazy musings, that ended to no purpose, or had not vigor to attain it; his thoughts were seldom so energetic as to seize hold of words. Imagination, in the proper meaning of the term, made no part of Wakefield's gifts. With a cold but not depraved nor wandering heart, and a mind never feverish with riotous thoughts, nor perplexed with originality, who could have anticipated that our friend would entitle himself to a foremost place among the doers of eccentric deeds? Had his acquaintances been asked, who was the man in London the surest to perform nothing to-day which should be remembered on the morrow, they would have thought of Wakefield. Only the wife of his bosom might have hesitated. She, without having analyzed his character, was partly aware of a quiet selfishness, that had rusted into his inactive mind; of a peculiar sort of vanity, the most uneasy attribute about him; of a disposition to craft, which had seldom produced more positive effects than the keeping of petty secrets, hardly worth revealing; and, lastly, of what she called a little strangeness, sometimes, in the good man. This latter quality is indefinable, and perhaps non-existent.

Let us now imagine Wakefield bidding adieu to his wife. It is the dusk of an October evening. His equipment is a drab greatcoat, a hat covered with an oilcloth, top-boots, an umbrella in one hand and a small portmanteau in the other. He has informed Mrs. Wakefield that he is to take the night coach into the country. She would fain inquire the length of his journey, its object, and the probable time of his return; but, indulgent to his harmless love of mystery, interrogates him only by a look. He tells her not to expect him positively by the return coach, nor to be alarmed should he tarry three or four days; but, at all events, to look for him at supper on Friday evening. Wakefield himself, be it considered, has no suspicion of what is before him. He holds out his hand, she gives her own, and meets his parting kiss in the matter-of-course way of a ten years' matrimony; and forth goes the middle-aged Mr. Wakefield, almost resolved to perplex his good lady by a whole week's absence. After the door has closed behind him, she perceives it thrust partly open, and a vision of her husband's face, through the aperture, smiling on her, and gone in a moment. For the time, this little incident is dismissed without a thought. But, long afterwards, when she has been more years a widow than a wife, that smile recurs, and flickers across all her reminiscences of Wakefield's visage. In her many musings, she surrounds the original smile with a multitude of fantasies, which make it strange and awful: as, for instance, if she imagines him in a coffin, that parting look is frozen on his pale features; or, if she dreams of him in heaven, still his blessed spirit wears a quiet and crafty smile. Yet, for its sake, when all others have given him up for dead, she sometimes doubts whether she is a widow.

But our business is with the husband. We must hurry after him along the street, ere he lose his individuality, and melt into the great mass of London life. It would be vain searching for him there. Let us follow close at his heels, therefore, until, after several superfluous turns and doublings, we find him comfortably established by the fireside of a small apartment, previously bespoken. He is in the next street to his own, and at his journey's end. He can scarcely trust his good fortune, in having got thither unperceived—recollecting that, at one time, he was delayed by the throng, in the very focus of a lighted lantern; and, again, there were footsteps that seemed to tread behind his own, distinct from the multitudinous tramp around him; and, anon, he heard a voice shouting afar, and fancied that it called his name. Doubtless, a dozen busybodies had been watching him, and told his wife the whole affair. Poor Wakefield! Little knowest thou thine own insignificance in this great world! No mortal eye but mine traced thee. Go quietly to thy bed, foolish man; and, on the morrow, if thou wilt be wise, get thee home to good Mrs. Wakefield, and tell her the truth. Remove not thyself, even for a little week, from thy place in her chaste bosom. Were she, for a single moment, to deem thee dead, or lost, or lastingly divided from her, thou wouldst be woefully conscious of a change in thy true wife forever after. It is perilous to make a chasm in human affections; not that they gape so long and wide—but so quickly close again!

Almost repenting of his frolic, or whatever it may be termed, Wakefield lies down betimes, and starting from his first nap, spreads forth his arms into the wide and solitary waste of the unaccustomed bed. "No,"—thinks he, gathering the bedclothes about him,—"I will not sleep alone another night."

In the morning he rises earlier than usual, and sets himself to consider what he really means to do. Such are his loose and rambling modes of thought that he has taken this very singular step with the consciousness of a purpose, indeed, but without being able to define it sufficiently for his own contemplation. The vagueness of the project, and the convulsive effort with which he plunges into the execution of it, are equally characteristic of a feeble-minded man. Wakefield sifts his ideas, however, as minutely as he may, and finds himself curious to know the process of matters at home—how his exemplary wife will endure her widowhood of a week; and, briefly, how the little sphere of creatures and circumstances, in which he was a central object, will be affected by his removal. A morbid vanity, therefore, lies nearest the bottom of the affair. But, how is he to attain his ends? Not, certainly, by keeping close in this comfortable lodging, where, though he slept and awoke in the next street to his home, he is as effectually abroad as if the stage-coach had been whirling him away all night. Yet, should he reappear, the whole project is knocked in the head. His poor brains being hopelessly puzzled with this dilemma, he at length ventures out partly resolving to cross the head of the street, and send one hasty glance towards his forsaken domicile. Habit—for he is a man of habits—takes him by the hand, and guides him, wholly unaware, to his own door, where, just at the critical moment, he is aroused by the scraping of his foot upon the step. Wakefield! whither are you going?

At that instant his fate was turning on the pivot. Little dreaming of the doom to which his first backward step devotes him, he hurries away, breathless with agitation hitherto unfelt, and hardly dares turn his head at the distant corner. Can it be that nobody caught sight of him? Will not the whole household—the decent Mrs. Wakefield, the smart maid servant, and the dirty little footboy—raise a hue and cry, through London streets, in pursuit of their fugitive lord and master? Wonderful escape! He gathers courage to pause and look homeward, but is perplexed with a sense of change about the familiar edifice, such as affects us all, when, after a separation of months or years, we again see some hill or lake, or work of art, with which we were friends of old. In ordinary cases, this indescribable impression is caused by the comparison and contrast between our imperfect reminiscences and the reality. In Wakefield, the magic of a single night has wrought a similar transformation, because, in that brief period, a great moral change has been effected. But this is a secret from himself. Before leaving the spot, he catches a far and momentary glimpse of his wife, passing athwart the front window, with her face turned towards the head of the street. The crafty nincompoop takes to his heels, scared with the idea that, among a thousand such atoms of mortality, her eye must have detected him. Right glad is his heart, though his brain be somewhat dizzy, when he finds himself by the coal fire of his lodgings.

So much for the commencement of this long whim-wham. After the initial conception, and the stirring up of the man's sluggish temperament to put it in practice, the whole matter evolves itself in a natural train. We may suppose him, as the result of deep deliberation, buying a new wig, of reddish hair, and selecting sundry garments, in a fashion unlike his customary suite of brown, from a Jew's old-clothes bag. It is accomplished. Wakefield is another man. The new system being now established, a retrograde movement to the old would be almost as difficult as the step that placed him in his unparalleled position. Furthermore, he is rendered obstinate by a sulkiness occasionally incident to his temper, and brought on at present by the inadequate sensation which he conceives to have been produced in the bosom of Mrs. Wakefield. He will not go back until she be frightened half to death. Well; twice or thrice has she passed before his sight, each time with a heavier step, a paler cheek, and more anxious brow; and in the third week of his non-appearance he detects a portent of evil entering the house, in the guise of an apothecary. Next day the knocker is muffled. Towards nightfall comes the chariot of a physician, and deposits its bigwigged and solemn burden at Wakefield's door, whence, after a quarter of an hour's visit, he emerges, perchance the herald of a funeral. Dear woman! Will she die? By this time, Wakefield is excited to something like energy of feeling, but still lingers away from his wife's bedside, pleading with his conscience that she must not be disturbed at such a juncture. If aught else restrains him, he does not know it. In the course of a few weeks she gradually recovers; the crisis is over; her heart is sad, perhaps, but quiet; and, let him return soon or late, it will never be feverish for him again. Such ideas glimmer through the mist of Wakefield's mind, and render him indistinctly conscious that an almost impassable gulf divides his hired apartment from his former home. "It is but in the next street!" he sometimes says. Fool! it is in another world. Hitherto, he has put off his return from one particular day to another; henceforward, he leaves the precise time undetermined. Not to-morrow—probably next week—pretty soon. Poor man! The dead have nearly as much chance of revisiting their earthly homes as the self-banished Wakefield.

Would that I had a folio to write, instead of an article of a dozen pages! Then I might exemplify how an influence beyond our control lays its strong hand on every deed which we do, and weaves its consequences into an iron tissue of necessity. Wakefield is spell-bound. We must leave him, for ten years or so, to haunt around his house, without once crossing the threshold, and to be faithful to his wife, with all the affection of which his heart is capable, while he is slowly fading out of hers. Long since, it must be remarked, he had lost the perception of singularity in his conduct.

Now for a scene! Amid the throng of a London street we distinguish a man, now waxing elderly, with few characteristics to attract careless observers, yet bearing, in his whole aspect, the handwriting of no common fate, for such as have the skill to read it. He is meagre; his low and narrow forehead is deeply wrinkled; his eyes, small and lusterless, sometimes wander apprehensively about him, but oftener seem to look inward. He bends his head, and moves with an indescribable obliquity of gait, as if unwilling to display his full front to the world. Watch him long enough to see what we have described, and you will allow that circumstances—which often produce remarkable men from nature's ordinary handiwork—have produced one such here. Next, leaving him to sidle along the footwalk, cast your eyes in the opposite direction, where a portly female, considerably in the wane of life, with prayer-book in her hand, is proceeding to yonder church. She has the placid mien of settled widowhood. Her regrets have either died away, or have become so essential to her heart, that they would be poorly exchanged for joy. Just as the lean man and well-conditioned woman are passing, a slight obstruction occurs, and brings these two figures directly in contact. Their hands touch; the pressure of the crowd forces her bosom against his shoulder; they stand, face to face, staring into each other's eyes. After a ten years' separation, thus Wakefield meets his wife!

The throng eddies away, and carries them asunder. The sober widow, resuming her former pace, proceeds to church, but pauses in the portal, and throws a perplexed glance along the street. She passes in, however, opening her prayer-book as she goes. And the man! with so wild a face that busy and selfish London stands to gaze after him, he hurries to his lodgings, bolts the door, and throws himself upon the bed. The latent feelings of years break out; his feeble mind acquires a brief energy from their strength; all the miserable strangeness of his life is revealed to him at a glance: and he cries out, passionately, "Wakefield! Wakefield! You are mad!"

Perhaps he was so. The singularity of his situation must have so moulded him to himself, that, considered in regard to his fellow-creatures and the business of life, he could not be said to possess his right mind. He had contrived, or rather he had happened, to dissever himself from the world—to vanish—to give up his place and privileges with living men, without being admitted among the dead. The life of a hermit is nowise parallel to his. He was in the bustle of the city, as of old; but the crowd swept by and saw him not; he was, we may figuratively say, always beside his wife and at his hearth, yet must never feel the warmth of the one nor the affection of the other. It was Wakefield's unprecedented fate to retain his original share of human sympathies, and to be still involved in human interests, while he had lost his reciprocal influence on them. It would be a most curious speculation to trace out the effect of such circumstances on his heart and intellect, separately, and in unison. Yet, changed as he was, he would seldom be conscious of it, but deem himself the same man as ever; glimpses of the truth, indeed, would come, but only for the moment; and still he would keep saying, "I shall soon go back!"—nor reflect that he had been saying so for twenty years.

I conceive, also, that these twenty years would appear, in the retrospect, scarcely longer than the week to which Wakefield had at first limited his absence. He would look on the affair as no more than an interlude in the main business of his life. When, after a little while more, he should deem it time to reenter his parlor, his wife would clap her hands for joy, on beholding the middle-aged Mr. Wakefield. Alas, what a mistake! Would Time but await the close of our favorite follies, we should be young men, all of us, and till Doomsday.

One evening, in the twentieth year since he vanished, Wakefield is taking his customary walk towards the dwelling which he still calls his own. It is a gusty night of autumn, with frequent showers that patter down upon the pavement, and are gone before a man can put up his umbrella. Pausing near the house, Wakefield discerns, through the parlor windows of the second floor, the red glow and the glimmer and fitful flash of a comfortable fire. On the ceiling appears a grotesque shadow of good Mrs. Wakefield. The cap, the nose and chin, and the broad waist, form an admirable caricature, which dances, moreover, with the up-flickering and down-sinking blaze, almost too merrily for the shade of an elderly widow. At this instant a shower chances to fall, and is driven, by the unmannerly gust, full into Wakefield's face and bosom. He is quite penetrated with its autumnal chill. Shall he stand, wet and shivering here, when his own hearth has a good fire to warm him, and his own wife will run to fetch the gray coat and small-clothes, which, doubtless, she has kept carefully in the closet of their bed chamber? No! Wakefield is no such fool. He ascends the steps—heavily!—for twenty years have stiffened his legs since he came down—but he knows it not. Stay, Wakefield! Would you go to the sole home that is left you? Then step into your grave! The door opens. As he passes in, we have a parting glimpse of his visage, and recognize the crafty smile, which was the precursor of the little joke that he has ever since been playing off at his wife's expense. How unmercifully has he quizzed the poor woman! Well, a good night's rest to Wakefield!

This happy event—supposing it to be such—could only have occurred at an unpremeditated moment. We will not follow our friend across the threshold. He has left us much food for thought, a portion of which shall lend its wisdom to a moral, and be shaped into a figure. Amid the seeming confusion of our mysterious world, individuals are so nicely adjusted to a system, and systems to one another and to a whole, that, by stepping aside for a moment, a man exposes himself to a fearful risk of losing his place forever. Like Wakefield, he may become, as it were, the Outcast of the Universe.

Schizotypal Personality Disorder

Individuals with this disorder appear to be strikingly odd or strange, with very limited capacity for interpersonal relationships. They exhibit cognitive or perceptual distortions and eccentric or odd behavior. They often participate in magical thinking, have peculiar ideas, and experience ideas of reference. Their thinking and communication are disturbed. They live in a world filled with weird thoughts, paranoid ideation, and telepathy. Current clinical thinking is that schizotypal personality disorder is the premorbid personality of the schizophrenic.

H. P. Lovecraft (1890–1937)

Howard Phillips Lovecraft was born in Providence, Rhode Island. When he was three his father had a nervous breakdown; the senior Lovecraft never recovered from his emotional problems, dying of syphilis five years later. Lovecraft's mother also experienced mental illness and suffered a complete mental breakdown in 1919. Lovecraft was a bright child, reciting poetry at age two, reading at age three, and writing at age six.

Lovecraft developed a strong interest in "weird" tales early in his life, fostered by his grandfather, who entertained him with such tales. The death of his grandfather in 1904 and the subsequent loss of the family home left him depressed and suicidal. In 1908, just prior to his high school graduation, he suffered a nervous breakdown and did not graduate. He was troubled for the rest of his life by the fact that he did not graduate and fulfill his dream of going on to Brown University.

After a period of isolation and living in New York, Lovecraft returned to Providence in 1926. It was during the last ten years of his life there that he produced his best works. He was content to have found his calling as a writer of weird tales.

H. P. Lovecraft was a master at creating clear pictures of horrifying visions. Much of his work deals with horror and monsters beyond the realm of real life. However, he does a remarkable job of capturing the important qualities of two schizotypal personalities, Edward Derby and Asena Wait, in "The Thing on the Doorstep."

"The Thing on the Doorstep"

. . . I have known Edward Pickman Derby all his life. Eight years my junior, he was so precocious that we had much in common from the time he was eight and I was sixteen. He was the most phenomenal child scholar I have ever known, and at seven was writing verse of a somber, fantastic, almost morbid cast which astonished the tutors surrounding him. Perhaps his private education and coddled seclusion had something to do with his premature flowering. An only child, he had organic weaknesses which startled his doting parents and caused them to keep him closely chained to their side. He was never allowed out without his nurse, and seldom had a chance to play unconstrainedly with other children. All this doubtless fostered a strange secretive life in the boy, with imagination as his one avenue of freedom.

At any rate, his juvenile learning was prodigious and bizarre; and his facile writings such as to captivate me despite my greater age. About that time I had leanings toward art of a somewhat grotesque cast, and I found in this younger child a rare kindred spirit. What lay behind our joint love of shadows and marvels was, no doubt, the ancient, moldering, and subtly fearsome town in which we lived—witch-cursed, legend-haunted Arkham, whose huddled, sagging gambrel roofs and crumbling Georgian balustrades brood out the centuries beside the darkly muttering Miskatonic.

As time went by I turned to architecture and gave up my design of illustrating a book of Edward's demonic poems, yet our comradeship suffered no lessening. Young Derby's odd genius developed remarkably, and in his eighteenth year his collected nightmare-lyrics made a real sensation when issued under the title *Azathoth and Other Horrors*. He was a close correspondent of the notorious Baudelairean poet Justin Geoffrey, who wrote *The People of the Monolith* and died screaming in a madhouse in 1926 after a visit to a sinister, ill-regarded village in Hungary.

In self-reliance and practical affairs, however, Derby was greatly retarded because of his coddled existence. His health had improved, but his habits of childish dependence were fostered by over-careful parents, so that he never traveled alone, made independent decisions, or assumed responsibilities. It was early seen that he would not be equal to a struggle in the business or professional arena, but the family fortune was so ample that this formed no tragedy. As he grew to years of manhood he retained a deceptive aspect of boyishness. Blond and blue-eyed, he had the fresh complexion of a child; and his attempts to raise a moustache were discernible only with difficulty. His voice was soft and light, and his unexercised life gave him a juvenile chubbiness rather than the paunchiness of premature middle age. He was of good height, and his handsome face would have made him a notable gallant had not his shyness held him to seclusion and bookishness.

Derby's parents took him abroad every summer, and he was quick to seize on the surface aspects of European thought and expression. His Poe-like talents turned more and more toward the decadent, and other artistic sensitivities and yearnings were half-aroused in him. We had great discussions in those days. I had been through Harvard, had studied in a Boston architect's office, had married, and had finally returned to Arkham to practice my profession—settling in the family homestead in Saltonstall Street since my father had moved to Florida for his health. Edward used to call almost every evening, till I came to regard him as one of the household. He had a characteristic way of ringing the doorbell or sounding the knocker that grew to be a veritable code signal, so that after dinner I always listened for the familiar three brisk strokes followed by two more after a pause. Less frequently I would visit at his house and note with envy the obscure volumes in his constantly growing library.

Derby went through Miskatonic University in Arkahm since his parents would not let him board away from them. He entered at sixteen and completed his course in three years, majoring in English and French literature and receiving high marks in everything but mathematics and the sciences. He mingled very little with the other students, though looking enviously at the "darling" or "Bohemian" set—whose superficially "smart" language and meaningless ironic pose he aped, and whose dubious conduct he wished he dared adopt.

What he did do was to become an almost fanatical devotee of subterranean magical lore, for which Miskatonic's library was and is famous. Always a dweller on the surface of fantasy and strangeness, he now delved deep into the actual runes and riddles left by a fabulous past for the guidance or puzzlement of posterity. He read things like the frightful *Book of Eibon*, the *Unaussprechlichen Kulten* of von Junzt, and the forbidden *Necronomicon* of the mad Arab Abdul Alhazred, though he did not tell his parents he had seen them. Edward was twenty when my son and only child was born, and seemed pleased when I named the newcomer Edward Derby Upton, after him.

By the time he was twenty-five Edward Derby was a prodigiously learned man and a fairly well-known poet and fantaisiste, though his lack of contacts and responsibilities had slowed down his literary growth by making his products derivative and over-bookish. I was perhaps his closest friend—finding him an inexhaustible mine of vital theoretical topics, while he relied on me for advice in whatever matters he did not wish to refer to his parents. He remained single—more through shyness, inertia, and parental protectiveness than through inclination—and moved in society only to the slightest and most perfunctory extent. When the war came both health and ingrained timidity kept him at home. I went to Plattsburg for a commission, but never got overseas.

So the years wore on. Edward's mother died when he was thirty-four, and for months he was incapacitated by some odd psychological malady. His father took him to Europe, however, and he managed to pull out of his trouble without visible effects. Afterward he seemed to feel a sort of grotesque exhilaration, as if of partial escape from some unseen bondage. He began to mingle in the more "advanced" college set despite his middle age, and was present at some extremely wild doings—on one occasion paying heavy blackmail (which he borrowed of me) to keep his presence at a certain affair from his father's notice. Some of the whispered rumors about the wild Miskatonic set were extremely singular. There was even talk of black magic and of happenings utterly beyond credibility.

II

Edward was thirty-eight when he met Asenath Waite. She was, I judge, about twenty-eight at the time; and was taking a special course in mediaeval metaphysics at Miskatonic. The daughter of a friend of mine had met her before—in the Hall School at Kingsport—and had been inclined to shun her because of her odd reputation. She was dark, smallish, and very good-looking except for overprotuberant eyes; but something in her expression alienated extremely sensitive people. It was, however, largely her origin and conversation which caused average folk to avoid her. She was one of the Innsmouth Waites, and dark legends have clustered for generations about crumbling, half-deserted Innsmouth and its people. There are tales of horrible bargains about the year 1850, and of a strange element "not quite human" in the ancient families of the run-down fishing port—tales such as only old-time Yankees can devise and repeat with proper awesomeness.

Asenath's case was aggravated by the fact that she was Ephraim Waite's daughter—the child of his old age by an unknown wife who always went veiled. Ephraim lived in a half-decayed mansion in Washington Street, Innsmouth, and those who had seen the place (Arkham folk avoid going to Insmouth whenever they can) declared that the attic windows were always boarded, and that strange sounds sometimes floated from within as evening drew on. The old man was known to have been a prodigious magical student in his day, and legend averred that he could raise or quell storms at sea according to his whim. I had seen him once or twice in my youth as he came to Arkham to consult forbidden tomes at the college library, and had hated his wolfish, saturnine face with its tangle of iron–grey beard. He had died insane—under rather queer circumstances—just before his daughter (by his will made a nominal ward of the principal) entered the Hall School, but she had been his morbidly avid pupil and looked fiendishly like him at times.

The friend whose daughter had gone to school with Asenath Waite repeated many curious things when the news of Edward's acquaintance with her began to spread about. Asenath, it seemed, had posed as a kind of magician at school; and had really seemed able to accomplish some highly baffling marvels. She professed to be able to raise thunderstorms, though her seeming success was generally laid to some uncanny knack at prediction. All animals markedly disliked her, and she could make any dog howl by certain motions of her right hand. There were times when she displayed snatches of knowledge and language very singular—and very shocking—for a young girl; when she would frighten her schoolmates with leers and winks of an inexplicable kind, and would seem to extract an obscene zestful irony from her present situation.

Most unusual, though, were the well-attested cases of her influence over other persons. She was, beyond question, a genuine hypnotist. By gazing peculiarly at a fellow-student she would often give the latter a distinct feeling of *exchanged personality*— as if the subject were placed momentarily in the magician's body and able to stare half across the room at her real body, whose eyes blazed and protruded with an alien expression. Asenath often made wild claims about the nature of consciousness and about its independence of the physical frame—or at least from the life-process of the physical frame. Her crowning rage, however, was that she was not a man; since she believed a male brain had certain unique and far-reaching cosmic powers. Given a man's brain, she declared, she could not only equal but surpass her father in mastery of unknown forces.

Edward met Asenath at a gathering of "intelligentsia" held in one of the student's rooms, and could talk of nothing else when he came to see me the next day. He had found her full of the interests and erudition which engrossed him most, and was in addition wildly taken with her appearance. I had never seen the young woman, and recalled casual references only faintly, but I knew who she was. It seemed rather regrettable that Derby should become so upheaved about her; but I said nothing to discourage him, since infatuation thrives on opposition. He was not, he said, mentioning her to his father.

In the next few weeks I heard of very little but Asenath from young Derby. Others now remarked Edward's autumnal gallantry, though they agreed that he did not look even nearly his actual age, or seemed at all inappropriate as an escort for his bizarre divinity. He was only a trifle paunchy despite his indolence and self-indulgence, and his face was absolutely without lines. Asenath, on the other hand, had the premature crow's feet which come from the exercises of an intense will.

About this time Edward brought the girl to call on me, and I at once saw that his interest was by no means one-sided. She eyed him continually with an almost predatory air, and I perceived that their intimacy was beyond untangling. Soon afterward I had a visit from old Mr. Derby, whom I had always admired and respected. He had heard the tales of his son's new friendship, and had wormed the whole truth out of "the boy." Edward meant to marry Asenath, and had even been looking at houses in the suburbs. Knowing my usually great influence with his son, the father wondered if I could help to break the ill-advised affair off; but I regretfully expressed my doubts. This time it was not a question of Edward's weak will but of the woman's strong will. The perennial child had transferred his dependence from the parental image to a new and stronger image, and nothing could be done about it.

Antisocial Personality Disorder

These individuals often present a normal, even charming and ingratiating exterior. Their history often includes lying, truancy, running away form home, thefts, fights, drug abuse, and illegal activity. They demonstrate a lack of anxiety or depression that is often grossly incongruous with their situation. Family history reveals a pattern of parental desertion, separation, divorce, early deaths, frequent moves, brutal discipline, neglect, indifference or substance abuse. They can readily manipulate, exploit, control, deceive, and intimidate others. They seem incapable of shame, guilt, loyalty, love, or any persistently sincere emotion. They crave excitement and live solely in the "now." They are unconcerned with the consequences of their actions and are unable to learn from experience. The threat of punishment affords little restraint.

Oliver Goldsmith (1728–1774)

Oliver Goldsmith was born in Roscommon, Ireland. He was graduated from Trinity College, Dublin in 1749. His ungainliness and crude manners prevented him from making many friends in college.

He moved to London in 1756 and became a writer. Intemperance and gambling brought Goldsmith significant debt and he wrote on a wide variety of subjects mostly to keep out of debtors' prison. The publication of *The Bee* (a weekly essay paper) and *the Life of Beau Nash* brought Goldsmith popularity, and his fortunes began to improve. "The Traveler" was published in 1764, and his reputation as a poet was established. Goldsmith's drinking and his fondness for gambling returned him to debt once again, and broken in health and mind he died in 1774 at the age of forty-six.

One of the finest of Goldsmith's works was *The Vicar of Wakefield*, written in 1766. "An Elegy on the Death of a Mad Dog" comes from that excellent novel. A striking feature of the antisocial individual is their superficial charm and their ability to deceive others. Oliver Goldsmith captures this quality in his little poem "An Elegy on the Death of a Mad Dog."

"An Elegy on the Death of a Mad Dog"

Good people all, of every sort,
Give ear unto my song,
And if you find it wondrous short,
It cannot hold you long.

In Islington there was a man,
Of whom the world might say,
That still a godly race he ran,
Whene'er he went to pray.

A kind and gentle heart he had,
To comfort friends and foes;
The naked every day he clad,
When he put on his clothes.

And in that town a dog was found,
As many dogs there be,
Both mongrel, puppy, whelp, and hound,
And curs of low degree.

This dog and man at first were friends;
But when a pique began,
The dog, to gain some private ends,
Went mad, and bit the man.

Around from all the neighboring streets
The wond'ring neighbors ran
And swore the dog had lost his wits,
To bite so good a man.

The wound it seemed both sore and sad
To every Christian eye;
And while they swore the dog was mad,
They swore the man would die.

But soon a wonder came to light,
That showed the rogues they lied:
The man recovered of the bite—
The dog it was that died.

O. Henry (William Sydney Porter) (1862–1910)

William Sydney Porter was born in 1862 in Greensboro, North Carolina. At the age of twenty he moved to Texas, primarily for his health. In 1898 Porter was found guilty of embezzlement and sentenced to prison. Three years and about a dozen short stories later, he emerged from prison as O. Henry.

After his release from prison, O. Henry moved to New York City, and over the next ten years he published over 300 short stories and gained worldwide fame. O. Henry wrote with realistic detail based on firsthand experiences. He died a penniless alcoholic in New York City in 1910 at the age of forty-seven.

O. Henry had ample time to study the ways of the antisocial personality while serving his term in the penitentiary. In his outstanding short story "The Marionettes," he provides an excellent portrait of two variants of the disorder in the persons of Dr. James and Mr. Chandler, who just happen to encounter each other in the middle of the night.

"The Marionettes"

The policeman was standing at the corner of Twenty-Fourth Street and a prodigiously dark alley near where the elevated railroad crosses the street. The time was two o'clock in the morning; the outlook a stretch of cold, drizzling, unsociable blackness until the dawn.

A man, wearing a long overcoat, with his hat tilted down in front, and carrying something in one hand, walked softly but rapidly out of the black alley. The policeman accosted him civilly, but with the assured air that is linked with conscious authority. The hour, the alley's musty reputation, the pedestrian's haste, the burden he carried—these easily combined into the "suspicious circumstances" that required illumination at the officer's hands.

The "suspect" halted readily and tilted back his hat, exposing, in the flicker of the electric lights, an emotionless, smooth countenance with a rather long nose and steady dark eyes. Thrusting his gloved hand into a side pocket of his overcoat, he drew out a card and handed it to the policeman. Holding it to catch the uncertain light, the officer read the name "Charles Spencer James, M.D." The street and number of the address were of a neighborhood so solid and respectable as to subdue even curiosity. The policeman's downward glance at the article carried in the doctor's hand—a handsome medicine case of black leather, with small silver mountings—further endorsed the guaranty of the card.

"All right, doctor," said the officer, stepping aside, with an air of bulky affability. "Orders are to be extra careful. Good many burglars and hold-ups lately. Bad night to be out. Not so cold, but—clammy."

With a formal inclination of his head, and a word or two corroborative of the officer's estimate of the weather, Doctor James continued his somewhat rapid progress. Three times that night had a patrolman accepted his professional card and the sight of his paragon of a medicine case as vouchers for his honesty of person and purpose. Had any one of those officers seen fit, on the morrow, to test the evidence of that card he would have found it borne out by the doctor's name and a handsome doorplate, his presence, calm and well dressed, in his well-equipped office—provided it were not too early, Doctor James being a late riser—and the testimony of the neighborhood to his good citizenship, his devotion to his family, and his success as a practitioner the two years he had lived among them.

Therefore, it would have much surprised any one of those zealous guardians of the peace could they have taken a peep into that immaculate medicine case. Upon opening it, the first article to be seen would have been an elegant set of the latest conceived tools used by the "box man," as the ingenious safe burglar now denominates himself. Specifically designed and constructed were the implements—the short but powerful "jimmy," the collection of curiously fashioned keys, the blued drills and punches of the finest temper—capable of eating their way into chilled steel as a mouse eats into a cheese, and the clamps that fasten like a leech to the polished door of a safe and pull out the combination knob as a dentist extracts a tooth. In a little pouch in the inner side of the "medicine" case was a four-ounce vial of nitroglycerine, now half empty. Underneath the tools was a mass of crumpled banknotes and a few handfuls of gold coin, the money, altogether, amounting to eight hundred and thirty dollars.

To a very limited circle of friends Doctor James was known as "The Swell 'Greek.'" Half of the mysterious term was a tribute to his cool and gentlemanlike manners; the other half denoted, in the argot of the brotherhood, the leader, the planner, the one who, by the power and prestige of his address and position, secured the information upon which they based their plans and desperate enterprises.

Of this elect circle the other members were Skitsie Morgan and Gum Decker, expert "box men," and Leopold Pretzfelder, a jeweller downtown, who manipulated the "sparklers" and other ornaments collected by the working trio. All good and loyal men, as loose-tongued as Memnon and as fickle as the North Star.

That night's work had not been considered by the firm to have yielded more than a moderate repayal for their plans. An old-style two-story side-bolt safe in the dingy office of a very wealthy old-style dry-goods firm on a Saturday night should have excreted more than twenty-five hundred dollars. But that was all they found, and they had divided it, the three of them, into equal shares upon the spot, as was their custom. Ten or twelve thousand was what they expected. But one of the proprietors had proved to be just a trifle too old style. Just after dark he had carried home in a shirt box most of the funds on hand.

Doctor James proceeded up Twenty-fourth Street, which was, to all appearance, depopulated. Even the theatrical folk, who affect this district as a place of residence, were long since abed. The drizzle had accumulated upon the street, puddles of it among the stones received the fire of the arc lights, and returned it, shattered into a myriad liquid spangles. A captious wind, shower-soaked and chilling, coughed from the laryngeal flues between the houses.

As the practitioner's foot struck even with the corner of a tall brick residence of more pretension than its fellows the front door popped open, and a bawling negress clattered down the steps to the pavement. Some medley of words came forth from her mouth, addressed, like as not, to herself—the recourse of her race when alone and beset by evil. She looked to be one of that old vassal class of the South—voluble, familiar, loyal, irrepressible; her person pictured it—fat, neat, aproned, kerchiefed.

This sudden apparition, spewed from the silent house, reached the bottom of the steps as Doctor James came opposite. Her brain transferring its energies from sound to sight, she ceased her clamor and affixed her pop-eyes upon the case the doctor carried.

"Bress de Lawd!" was the benison the sight drew from her. "Is you a doctor, suh?"

"Yes, I am a physician," said Doctor James, pausing.

"Den fo God's sake come and see Mister Chandler, suh. He done had a fit or sump'n. He layin' jist like he wuz dead. Miss Amy sont me to git a doctor. Lawd knows whar old Cindy'd a skeared one up from, if you, suh, hadn't come along. Ef old Mars' knowed one tenhundredth part of dese doin's dey'd be shootin' gwine on, suh—pistol shootin'—leb'm feet marked off on de ground, and ev'ybody a-duellin'. And dat po' lamb, Miss Amy—"

"Lead the way," said Doctor James, setting his foot upon the step, "if you want me as a doctor. As an auditor I'm not open to engagements."

The negress preceded him into the house and up a flight of thickly carpeted stairs. Twice they came to dimly lighted branching hallways. At the second one the now panting conductress turned down a hall, stopping at a door and opening it.

"I done brought de doctor, Miss Amy."

Doctor James entered the room, and bowed slightly to a young lady standing by the side of a bed. He set his medicine case upon a chair, removed his overcoat, throwing it over the case and the back of the chair, and advanced with quiet self-possession to the bedside.

There lay a man, sprawling as he had fallen—a man dressed richly in the prevailing mode, with only his shoes removed; lying relaxed, and as still as the dead.

There emanated from Doctor James an aura of calm force and reserve strength that was as manna in the desert to the weak and desolate among his patrons. Always had women, especially, been attracted by something in his sick-room manner. It was not the indulgent suavity of the fashionable healer, but a manner of poise, of sureness, of ability to overcome fate, of deference and protection and devotion. There was an exploring magnetism in his steadfast, luminous brown eyes; a latent authority in the impassive, even priestly, tranquillity of his smooth countenance that outwardly fitted him for the part of confidant and consoler. Sometimes, at his first professional visit, women would tell him where they hid their diamonds at night from burglars.

With the ease of much practice, Doctor James's unroving eyes estimated the order and quality of the room's furnishings. The appointments were rich and costly. The same glance had secured cognizance of the lady's appearance. She was small and scarcely past twenty. Her face possessed the title to a winsome prettiness, now obscured by (you would say) rather a fixed melancholy than the more violent imprint of a sudden sorrow. Upon her forehead, above one eyebrow, was a livid bruise, suffered, the physician's eye told him, within the past six hours.

Doctor James's fingers went to the man's wrist. His almost vocal eyes questioned the lady.

"I am Mrs. Chandler," she responded, speaking with the plaintive Southern slur and intonation. "My husband was taken suddenly ill about ten minutes before you came. He has had attacks of heart trouble before—some of them were very bad." His clothed state and late hour seemed to prompt her to further explanation. "He had been out late; to—a supper, I believe."

Doctor James now turned his attention to his patient. In which ever of his "professions" he happened to be engaged he was wont to honor the "case" or the "job" with his whole interest.

The sick man appeared to be about thirty. His countenance bore a look of boldness and dissipation, but was not without a symmetry of feature and the fine lines drawn by a taste and indulgence in humor that gave the redeeming touch. There was an odor of spilled wine about his clothes.

The physician laid back his outer garments, and then, with a penknife, slit the shirt-front from collar to waist. The obstacles cleared, he laid his ear to the heart and listened intently.

"Mitral regurgitation?" he said, softly, when he rose. The words ended with rising inflection of uncertainty. Again he listened long; and this time he said, "Mitral insufficiency," with the accent of an assured diagnosis.

"Madam," he began, in the reassuring tones that had so often allayed anxiety, "there is a probability—" As he slowly turned his head to face the lady, he saw her fall, white and swooning into the arms of the old negress.

"Po' lamb! po' lamb! Has dey done killed Aunt Cindy's own blessed child? May de Lawd 'stroy wid His wrath dem what stole her away; what break dat angel heart; what left—"

"Lift her feet," said Doctor James, assisting to support the drooping form. "Where is her room? She must be put to bed."

"In here, suh." The woman nodded her kerchiefed head toward a door. "Dat's Miss Amy's room."

They carried her in there, and laid her on the bed. Her pulse was faint, but regular. She passed from the swoon, without recovering consciousness, into a profound slumber.

"She is quite exhausted," said the physician. "Sleep is a good remedy. When she wakes, give her a toddy—with an egg in it, if she can take it. How did she get that bruise upon her forehead?"

"She done got a lick there, suh. De po' lamb fell—No, suh"—the old woman's racial mutability swept her in a sudden flare of indignation—"old Cindy ain't gwineter lie for dat debble. He done it, suh. May de Lawd wither de hand what—dar now! Cindy promise her sweet lamb she ain't gwine tell. Miss Amy got hurt, suh, on de head."

Doctor James stepped to a stand where a handsome lamp burned, and turned the flame low.

"Stay here with your mistress," he ordered, "and keep quiet so she will sleep. If she wakes, give her the toddy. If she grows any weaker, let me know. There is something strange about it."

"Dar's mo' strange t'ings dan dat' round here," began the negress, but the physician hushed her in a seldom-employed, peremptory, concentrated voice with which he had often allayed hysteria itself. He returned to the other room, closing the door softly behind him. The man on the bed had not moved, but his eyes were open. His lips seemed to form words. Doctor James bent his head to listen. "The money! the money!" was what they were whispering.

"Can you understand what I say?" asked the doctor, speaking low, but distinctly.

The head nodded slightly

"I am a physician, sent for by your wife. You are Mr. Chandler, I am told. You are quite ill. You must not excite or distress yourself at all."

The patient's eyes seemed to beckon to him. The doctor stopped to catch the same faint words.

"The money—the twenty thousand dollars."

"Where is this money?—in the bank?"

The eyes expressed a negative. "Tell her"—the whisper was growing fainter—the twenty thousand dollars—her money"—his eyes wandered about the room.

"You have placed this money somewhere?" Doctor James's voice was toiling like a siren's to conjure the secret from the man's failing intelligence—"Is it in this room?"

He thought he saw a fluttering assent in the dimming eyes. The pulse under his fingers was as fine and small as a silk thread.

There arose in Doctor James's brain and heart the instincts of his other profession. Promptly, as he acted in everything, he decided to learn the whereabouts of this money, and at the calculated and certain cost of a human life.

Drawing from his pocket a little pad of prescription blanks, he scribbled upon one of them a formula suited, according to the best practice, to the needs of the sufferer. Going to the door of the inner room, he softly called the old woman, gave her the prescription, and bade her take it to some drug store and fetch the medicine.

When she had gone, muttering to herself, the doctor stepped to the bedside of the lady. She still slept soundly; her pulse was a little stronger; her forehead was cool, save where the inflammation of the bruse extended, and a slight moisture covered it. Unless disturbed, she would yet sleep for hours. He found the key in the door, and locked it after him when he returned.

Doctor James looked at his watch. He could call half an hour his own, since before that time the old woman could scarcely return from her mission. Then he sought and found water in a pitcher and a glass tumbler. Opening his medicine case he took out the vial containing the nitroglycerine—"the oil," as his brethren of the brace-and-bit term it.

One drop of the faint yellow, thickish liquid he let fall in the tumbler. He took out his silver hypodermic syringe case, and screwed the needle into its place. Carefully measuring each modicum of water in the graduated glass barrel of the syringe, he diluted the one drop with nearly half a tumbler of water.

Two hours earlier that night Doctor James had, with that syringe, injected the undiluted liquid into a hole drilled in the lock of a safe, and had destroyed, with one dull explosion, the machinery that controlled the movement of the bolts. He now purposed, with the same means, to shiver the prime machinery of a human being—to rend its heart—and each shock was for the sake of the money to follow.

The same means, but in a different guise. Whereas, that was the giant in its rude, primary dynamic strength, this was the courtier, whose no less deadly arms were concealed by velvet and lace. For the liquid in the tumbler and in the syringe that the physician carefully filled was now a solution of glonoin, the most powerful heart stimulant known to medical science. Two ounces had riven the solid door of the iron safe; with one fiftieth part of a minim he was now about to still forever the intricate mechanism of a human life.

But not immediately. It was not so intended. First there would be a quick increase of vitality; a powerful impetus given to every organ and faculty. The heart would respond bravely to the fatal spur; the blood in the veins return more rapidly to its source.

But, as Doctor James well knew, over-stimulation in this form of heart disease means death, as sure as by a rifle shot. When the clogged arteries should suffer congestion from the increased flow of blood pumped into them by the power of the burglar's "oil," they would rapidly become "no thoroughfare," and the fountain of life would cease to flow.

The physician bared the chest of the unconscious Chandler. Easily and skillfully he injected, subcutaneously, the contents of the syringe into the muscles of the region over the heart. True to his neat habits in both professions, he next carefully dried his needle and re-inserted the fine wire that threaded it when not in use.

In three minutes Chandler opened his eyes, and spoke, in a voice faint but audible, inquiring who attended upon him. Doctor James again explained his presence there.

"Where is my wife?" asked the patient.

"She is asleep—from exhaustion and worry," said the doctor. "I would not awaken her unless—"

"It isn't—necessary." Chandler spoke with spaces between his words caused by his short breath that some demon was driving too fast. "She wouldn't—thank you to disturb her—on my—account."

Doctor James drew a chair to the bedside. Conversation must not be squandered.

"A few minutes ago," he began, in the grave, candid tones of his other profession, "you were trying to tell me something regarding some money. I do not seek your confidence, but it is my duty to advise you that anxiety and worry will work against your recovery. If you have any communication to make about this—to relieve your mind about this—twenty thousand dollars, I think was the amount you mentioned—you would better do so."

Chandler could not turn his head, but he rolled his eyes in the direction of the speaker.

"Did I—say where this—money is?"

"No," answered the physician. "I only inferred, from your scarcely intelligible words, that you felt a solicitude concerning its safety. If it is in this room—"

Doctor James paused. Did he only seem to perceive a flicker of understanding, a gleam of suspicion upon the ironical features of his patient? Had he seemed too eager? Had he said too much? Chandler's next words restored his confidence.

"Where—should it be," he gasped, "but in—the safe—there?"

With his eyes he indicated a corner of the room, where now, for the first time, the doctor perceived a small iron safe, half-concealed by the trailing end of a window curtain.

Rising, he took the sick man's wrist. His pulse was beating in great throbs, with ominous intervals between.

"Lift your arm," said Doctor James.

"You know—I can't move, Doctor."

The physician stepped swiftly to the hall door, opened it, and listened. All was still. Without further circumvention he went to the safe and examined it. Of a primitive make and simple design, it afforded little more security than protection against light-fingered servants. To his skill it was a mere toy, a thing of straw and pasteboard. The money was as good as in his hands. With his clamps he could draw the knob, punch the tumblers, and open the door in two minutes. Perhaps, in another way, he might open it in one.

Kneeling upon the floor, he laid his ear to the combination plate, and slowly turned the knob. As he had surmised, it was locked at only a "day com."—upon one number. His keen ear caught the faint warning click as the tumbler was disturbed; he used the clue—the handle turned. He swung the door wide open.

The interior of the safe was bare—not even a scrap of paper rested within the hollow iron cube.

Doctor James rose to his feet and walked back to the bed.

A thick dew had formed upon the dying man's brow, but there was a mocking, grim smile on his lips and in his eyes. "I never—saw it before," he said, painfully, "medicine and—burglary wedded! Do you—make the—combination pay—dear Doctor?"

Than that situation afforded, there was never a more rigorous test of Doctor James's greatness. Trapped by the diabolic humor of his victim into a position both ridiculous and unsafe, he maintained his dignity as well as his presence of mind. Taking out his watch, he waited for the man to die.

"You were—just a shade—too—anxious—about that money. But it never was—in any danger—from you, dear Doctor. It's safe. Perfectly safe. It's all— In the hands of the bookmakers. Twenty—thousand—Amy's money. I played it at the races—lost every—cent of it. I've been a pretty bad boy, Burglar—excuse me—Doctor, but I've been a square sport. I don't think—I ever met—such an—eighteen-carat rascal as you are, Doctor—excuse me Burglar, in all my rounds. Is it contrary—to the ethics—of your—gang, Burglar, to give a victim—excuse me—patient, a drink of water?"

Doctor James brought him a drink. He could scarcely swallow it. The reaction from the powerful drug was coming in regular, intensifying waves. But his moribund fancy must have one more grating fling.

"Gambler—drunkard—spendthrift—I've been those, but—a doctor-burglar!"

The physician indulged himself to but one reply to the other's caustic taunts. Bending low to catch Chandler's fast crystallizing gaze, he pointed to the sleeping lady's door with a gesture so stern and significant that the prostrate man half lifted his head, with his remaining strength, to see. He saw nothing; but he caught the cold words of the doctor—the last sounds he was to hear:

"I never yet—struck a woman."

It were vain to attempt to con such men. There is no curriculum that can reckon with them in its ken. They are offshots from the types whereof men say, "He will do this," or "He will do that." We only know that they exist; and that we can observe them, and tell one another of their bare performances, as children watch and speak of the marionettes.

Yet it were a droll study in egoism to consider these two—one an assassin and a robber, standing above his victim; the other baser in his offenses, if a lesser law-breaker, lying, abhorred, in the house of the wife he had persecuted, spoiled, and smitten, one a tiger, the other a dog-wolf—to consider each of them sickening at the foulness of the other; and each flourishing out of the mire of his manifest guilt his own immaculate standard—of conduct, if not of honor.

The one retort of Doctor James must have struck home to the other's remaining shreds of shame and manhood, for it proved the *coup de grace*. A deep blush suffused his face—an ignominious *rose mortis*; the respiration ceased, and, with scarcely a tremor, Chandler expired.

Close following upon his last breath came the negress, bringing the medicine. With a hand gently pressing upon the closed eyelids, Doctor James told her of the end. Not grief, but a hereditary *rapprochement* with death in the abstract, moved her to a dismal, watery sniffing, accompanied by her usual jeremiad.

"Dar now! It's in de Lawd's hands. He am de jedge ob de transgressor, and de suppo't of dem in distress. He gwine hab suppo't us now. Cindy done paid out de last quarter fer dis bottle of physic, and it nebber come to no use."

"Do I understand," asked Doctor James, "that Mrs. Chandler has no money?"

"Money, suh? You know what make Miss Amy fall down and so weak? Stahvation, suh. Nothin' to eat in dis house but some crumbly crackers in three days. Dat angel sell her finger rings and watch mont's ago. Dis fine house, suh, wid de red cyarpets and shiny bureaus, it's all hired; and de man talkin' scan'los about de rent. Dat debble—'scuse me, Lawd—he done in Yo' hands for jedgment, now—he made way wid everything."

The physician's silence encouraged her to continue. The history that he gleaned from Cindy's disordered monologue was an old one, of illusion, wilfulness, disaster, cruelty, and pride. Standing out from the blurred panorama of her gabble were little clear pictures—an ideal home in the far South; a quickly repented marriage; an unhappy season, full of wrongs and abuse, and, of late, an inheritance of money that promised deliverance; its seizure and waste by the dog-wolf during a two months' absence, and his return in the midst of a scandalous carouse. Unobtruded, but visible between every line, ran a pure white thread through the smudged warp of the story—the simple, all-enduring, sublime love of the old negress, following her mistress unswervingly through everything to the end.

When at last she paused, the physician spoke, asking if the house contained whiskey or liquor of any sort. There was, the old woman informed him, half a bottle of brandy left in the sideboard by the dog-wolf.

"Prepare a toddy as I told you," said Doctor James. "Wake your mistress; have her drink it, and tell her what has happened."

Some ten minutes afterward, Mrs. Chandler entered, supported by old Cindy's arm. She appeared to be a little stronger since her sleep and the stimulant she had taken. Doctor James had covered, with a sheet, the form upon the bed.

The lady turned her mournful eyes once, with a half-frightened look, toward it, and pressed closer to her protector. Her eyes were dry and bright. Sorrow seemed to have done its utmost with her. The fount of tears was dried; feeling itself paralyzed.

Doctor James was standing near the table, his overcoat donned, his hat and medicine case in his hand. His face was calm and impassive—practice had inured him to the sight of human suffering. His lambent brown eyes alone expressed a discreet professional sympathy.

He spoke kindly and briefly, stating that, as the hour was late, and assistance, no doubt, difficult to procure, he would himself send the proper persons to attend to the necessary finalities.

"One matter, in conclusion," said the doctor, pointing to the safe with its still wide-open door. "Your husband, Mrs. Chandler, toward the end, felt that he could not live; and directed me to open that safe, giving me the number upon which the combination is set. In case you may need to use it, you will remember that the number is forty-one. Turn several times to the right; then to the left once; stop at forty-one. He would not permit me to waken you, though he knew the end was near.

"In that safe he said he had placed a sum of money not large—but enough to enable you to carry out his last request. That was that you should return to your old home, and, in after days, when time shall have made it easier, forgive his many sins against you."

He pointed to the table, where lay an orderly pile of banknotes, surmounted by two stacks of gold coins.

"The money is there—as he described it—eight hundred and thirty dollars. I beg to leave my card with you, in case I can be of any service later on."

So, he had thought of her—and kindly—at the last! So late! And yet the lie fanned into life one last spark of tenderness where she had thought all was turned to ashes and dust. She cried aloud "Rob! Rob!" She turned, and, upon the ready bosom of her true servitor, diluted her grief in relieving tears. It is well to think, also, that in the years to follow, the murderer's falsehood shone like a little star above the grave of love, comforting her, and gaining the forgiveness that is good in itself, whether asked for or no.

Hushed and soothed upon the dark bosom, like a child, by a crooning, babbling sympathy, at last she raised her head—but the doctor was gone.

Borderline Personality Disorder

These individuals are characterized by their extraordinarily unstable affect, mood, behavior, interpersonal relationships, and self-image. Mood swings are common, and behavior is highly unpredictable. They engage in repetitive self-destructive acts. They cannot tolerate being alone and often pursue a frantic search for companionship. They distort their present relationships by putting people into either an all-good or an all-bad category (splitting). As a result of this splitting, the good person is idealized and the bad person devalued, and shifts in loyalty from one person or group to another are frequent. Such individuals feel chronically bored and empty, and as a result they desperately seek stimulation. They often gamble, act out sexually, abuse drugs, overdose, instigate fights, or attempt suicide. Moods are reactive and intense, and they often allow trivial problems to mushroom into calamities.

Susanna Kaysen (b. 1948)

Susanna Kaysen is a writer whose works are related to her own personal life experiences. She began her literary career as a freelance editor and proofreader. Her first novel, *Asa, as I Knew Him*, published in 1987, received very positive reviews. Kaysen followed her initial success with a second novel, *Far Afield*, in 1990. Her third book, *Girl, Interrupted*, won her both critical and popular accolades. *Girl, Interrupted*, was turned into a successful movie, and Kaysen gained considerable media attention for her work.

In *Girl, Interrupted*, Kaysen provides a first-person account of her struggles with borderline personality disorder. Her emotional problems resulted in a suicide attempt and hospitalization. *Girl, Interrupted* is an account of her experiences and was written after attaining her actual hospital records. These excerpts reflect the real-life difficulties encountered by individuals suffering from borderline personality disorder.

Girl, Interrupted

Something also was happening to my perceptions of people. When I looked at someone's face, I often did not maintain an unbroken connection to the concept of a face. Once you start parsing a face, it's a peculiar item: squishy, pointy, with lots of air vents and wet spots. This was the reverse of my problem with patterns. Instead of seeing too much meaning, I didn't see any meaning. . . .

* * *

Now, I would say to myself, you are feeling alienated from people and unlike other people; therefore you are projecting your discomfort onto them. When you look at a face, you see a blob of rubber because you are worried that your face is a blob of rubber. . . .

* * *

I have to admit, though, that I knew I wasn't mad.

It was a different precondition that tipped the balance: the state of contrariety. My ambition was to negate. The world, whether dense or hollow, provoked only my negations. When I was supposed to be awake, I was asleep; when I was supposed to speak, I was silent; when a pleasure offered itself to me, I avoided it. My hunger, my thirst, my loneliness and boredom and fear were all weapons aimed at my enemy, the world. They didn't matter a whit to the world, of course, and they tormented me, but I got a gruesome satisfaction from my sufferings. They proved my existence. All my integrity seemed to lie in saying No. . . .

* * *

I sat in my yellow vinyl chair not thinking about Torrey. Instead, I looked at my hand. It occurred to me that my palm looked like a monkey's palm. The crinkle of the three lines running across it and the way my fingers curled in seemed simian to me. If I spread my fingers out, my hand looked more human, so I did that. But it was tiring holding my fingers apart. I let them relax, and then the monkey idea came back.

I turned my hand over quickly. The back of it wasn't much better. My veins bulged—maybe because it was such a hot day—and the skin around my knuckles was wrinkly and loose. If I moved my hand I could see the three long bones that stretched out from the wrist to the first joints of my fingers. Or perhaps those weren't bones but tendons? I poked one; it was resilient, so probably it was a tendon. Underneath, though, were bones. At least I hoped so.

I poked deeper, to feel the bones. They were hard to find. Knucklebones were easy, but I wanted to find the hand bones, the long ones going from my wrist to my fingers.

I started getting worried. Where were my bones? I put my hand in my mouth and bit it, to see if I crunched down on something hard. Everything slid away from me. There were nerves; there were blood vessels; there were tendons: All these things were slippery and elusive.

"Damn," I said.

Georgina and Polly weren't paying attention.

I began scratching the back of my hand. My plan was to get hold of a flap of skin and peel it away, just to have a look. I wanted to see that my hand was a normal human hand, with bones. My hand got red and white—sort of like Polly's hands—but I couldn't get my skin to open up and let me in.

I put my hand in my mouth and chomped. Success! A bubble of blood came out near my last knuckle, where my incisor had pierced the skin.

"What the fuck are you doing?" Georgina asked.

"I'm trying to get to the bottom of this," I said.

"Bottom of what?" Georgina looked angry.

"My hand," I said, waving it around. A dribble of blood went down my wrist.

"Well, stop it," she said.

"It's my hand," I said. I was angry too. And I was getting really nervous. Oh God, I thought, there aren't any bones in there, there's nothing in there.

"Do I have any bones?" I asked them. "Do I have any bones? Do you think I have any bones?" I couldn't stop asking.

"Everybody has bones," said Polly.

"But do *I* have any bones."

"You've got them," said Georgina. Then she ran out of the room. She came back in half a minute with Valerie.

"Look at her," Georgina said, pointing at me.

Valerie looked at me and went away.

"I just want to see them," I said. "I just have to be sure."

"They're in there—I promise you," said Georgina.

"I'm not safe," I said suddenly.

Valerie was back, with a full medication cup.

"Valerie, I'm not safe," I said.

"You take this." She gave me the cup.

I could tell it was Thorazine from the color. I'd never had it before. I tipped my head back and drank. . . .

* * *

So these were the charges against me. I didn't read them until twenty-five years later. "A character disorder" is what they'd told me then.

I had to find a lawyer to help me get my records from the hospital; I had to read line 32a of form A1 of the Case Record, and entry G on the Discharge on Visit Summary, and entry B of part IV of the Case Report; then I had to locate a copy of the *Diagnostic and Statistical Manual of Mental Disorders* and look up Borderline Personality to see what they really thought about me.

It's a fairly accurate picture of me at eighteen, minus a few quirks like reckless driving and eating binges. It's accurate but it isn't profound. Of course, it doesn't aim to be profound. It's not even a case study. It's a set of guidelines, a generalization.

I'm tempted to try refuting it, but then I would be open to the further charges of "defensiveness" and "resistance."

All I can do is give the particulars: an annotated diagnosis.

"[U]ncertainty about several life issues, such as self-image, sexual orientation, long-term goals or career choice, types of friends or lovers to have . . ." I relish that last phrase. Its awkwardness (the "to have" seems superfluous) gives it substance and heft. I still have that uncertainty. Is this the type of friend or lover I want to have? I ask myself every time I meet someone new. Charming but shallow; good-hearted but a bit conventional; too handsome for his own good; fascinating but probably unreliable; and so forth. I guess I've had my share of unreliables. More than my share? How many would constitute more than my share?

Fewer than for somebody else—somebody who'd never been called a borderline personality?

That's the nub of my problem here.

If my diagnosis had been bipolar illness, for instance, the reaction to me and to this story would be slightly different. That's a chemical problem, you'd say to yourself, manic-depression, Lithium, all that. I would be blameless, somehow. And what about schizophrenia—that would send a chill up your spine. After all, that's real insanity. People don't "recover" from schizophrenia. You'd have to wonder how much of what I'm telling you is true and how much imagined. . . .

* * *

"[I]nstability of self-image, interpersonal relationships, and mood . . . uncertainty about . . . long-term goals or career choice . . ." Isn't this a good description of adolescence? Moody, fickle, faddish, insecure: in short, impossible.

"[S]elf-mutilating behavior (e.g., wrist-scratching) . . ." I've skipped forward a bit. This is one that caught me by surprise as I sat on the floor of the book-store reading my diagnosis. Wrist-scratching! I thought I'd invented it. Wrist-banging, to be precise.

This is where people stop being able to follow me. This is the sort of stuff you get locked up for. Nobody knew I was doing it, though. I never told anyone, until now.

I had a butterfly chair. In the sixties, everyone in Cambridge had a butterfly chair. The metal edge of its upturned seat was perfectly placed for wrist-banging. I had tried breaking ashtrays and walking on the shards, but I didn't have the nerve to tread firmly. Wrist-banging—slow, steady, mindless—was a better solution. It was cumulative injury, so each bang was tolerable.

A solution to what? I quote from the *Manual:* "This behavior may . . . counteract feelings of 'numbness' and depersonalization that arise during periods of extreme stress."

I spent hours in my butterfly chair banging my wrist. I did it in the evenings, like homework. I'd do some homework, then I'd spend half an hour wrist-banging, then finish my homework, then back in the chair for some more banging before brushing my teeth and going to bed. I banged the inside, where the veins converge. It swelled and turned a bit blue, but considering how hard and how much I banged it, the visible damage was slight. That was yet one more recommendation of it to me.

I'd had an earlier period of face-scratching. If my finger-nails hadn't been quite short, I couldn't have gotten away with it. As it was, I definitely looked puffy and peculiar the next day. I used to scratch my cheeks and then rub soap on them. Maybe the soap prevented me from looking worse. But I looked bad enough that people asked, "Is something wrong with your face?" So I switched to wrist-banging. . . .

* * *

"Quite often social contrariness and a generally pessimistic outlook are observed." What do you suppose they mean by "social contrariness"? Putting my elbows on the table? Refusing to get a job as a dental technician? Disappointing my parents' hope that I would go to a first-rate university?

They don't define "social contrariness," and I can't define it, so I think it ought to be excluded from the list. I'll admit to the generally pessimistic outlook. Freud had one too. . . .

* * *

"The person often experiences this instability of self-image as chronic feelings of emptiness or boredom." My chronic feelings of emptiness and boredom came from the fact that I was living a life based on my incapacities, which were numerous. A partial list follows. I could not and did not want to: ski, play tennis, or go to gym class; attend to any subject in school other than English and biology; write papers on any assigned topics (I wrote poems instead of papers for English topics; I got F's), plan to go or apply to college; give any reasonable explanation for these refusals.

My self-image was not unstable. I saw myself, quite correctly, as unfit for the educational and social systems. . . .

* * *

Back then I didn't know that I—or anyone—could make a life out of boyfriends and literature. As far as I could see, life demanded skills I didn't have. The result was chronic emptiness and boredom. There were more pernicious results as well: self-loathing, alternating with "inappropriately intense anger with frequent displays of temper. . . ."

* * *

What would have been an appropriate level of intensity for my anger at feeling shut out of life? My classmates were spinning their fantasies for the future: lawyer, ethnobotanist, Buddhist monk (it was a very progressive high school). Even the dumb, uninteresting ones who were there to provide "balance" looked forward to their marriages and their children. I knew I wasn't going to have any of this because I knew I didn't want it. But did that mean I would have nothing?

* * *

I often ask myself if I'm crazy. I ask other people too.

"Is this a crazy thing to say?" I'll ask before saying something that probably isn't crazy.

I start a lot of sentences with, "Maybe I'm totally nuts," or "Maybe I've gone 'round the bend."

If I do something out of the ordinary—take two baths in one day, for example—I say to myself: Are you crazy?

It's a common phrase, I know. But it means something particular to me: the tunnels, the security screens, the plastic forks, the shimmering, ever-shifting borderline that like all boundaries beckons and asks to be crossed. I do not want to cross it again. . . .

Histrionic Personality Disorder

This disorder is marked by a pattern of excessive emotionality and attention-seeking behavior. These individuals are colorful, dramatic, extroverted, excitable, and emotional people. They show a high degree of attention-seeking behavior, exaggerating their thoughts and feelings, making everything seem more important than it really is. Their need for reassurance seems endless; they are sensation seekers and may get into difficulty with the law, abuse substances, or act promiscuously.

Anton Chekhov (1860–1904)

Once again we turn to the marvelous storytelling ability of Anton Chekhov. His keen perceptions regarding human behavior are portrayed in "An Enigmatic Nature." Chekhov has captured the excessive emotionality, exaggeration of thoughts and feelings, and attention-seeking qualities of the histrionic personality in this delightful tale.

(Refer to chapter 4 for biographical information on Chekhov.)

"An Enigmatic Nature"

On the red velvet seat of a first-class railway carriage a pretty lady sits half reclining. An expensive fluffy fan trembles in her tightly closed fingers, a pince-nez keeps dropping off her pretty little nose, the brooch heaves and falls on her bosom, like a boat on the ocean. She is greatly agitated.

On the seat opposite sits the Provincial Secretary of Special Commissions, a budding young author, who from time to time publishes long stories of high life, or "Novelli" as he calls them, in the leading paper of the province. He is gazing into her face, gazing intently, with the eyes of a connoisseur. He is watching, studying, catching every shade of this exceptional, enigmatic nature. He understands it, he fathoms it. Her soul, her whole psychology lies open before him.

"Oh, I understand, I understand you to your inmost depths!" says the Secretary of Special Commissions, kissing her hand near the bracelet. "Your sensitive, responsive soul is seeking to escape from the maze of—

Yes, the struggle is terrific, titanic. But do not lose heart, you will be triumphant! Yes!"

"Write about me, Voldemar!" says the pretty lady, with a mournful smile. "My life has been so full, so varied, so chequered. Above all, I am unhappy. I am a suffering soul in some page of Dostoevsky. Reveal my soul to the world, Voldemar. Reveal that hapless soul. You are a psychologist. We have not been in the train an hour together, and you have already fathomed my heart."

"Tell me! I beseech you, tell me!"

"Listen. My father was a poor clerk in the Service. He had a good heart and was not without intelligence; but the spirit of the age—of his environment— *vous comprenez?*—I do not blame my poor father. He drank, gambled, took bribes. My mother—but why say more? Poverty, the struggle for daily bread, the consciousness of insignificance—ah, do not force me to recall it! I had to make my own way. You know the monstrous education at a boarding-school, foolish novel-reading, the errors of early youth, the first timid flutter of love. It was awful! The vacillation! And the agonies of losing faith in life, in oneself! Ah, you are an author. You know us women. You will understand. Unhappily I have an intense nature. I looked for happiness—and what happiness! I longed to set my soul free. Yes. In fact I saw my happiness!"

"Exquisite creature!" murmured the author, kissing her hand close to the bracelet. "It's not you I am kissing, but the suffering of humanity. Do you remember Raskolnikov and his kiss?"

"Oh, Voldemar, I longed for glory, renown, success, like every—why affect modesty?—every nature above the commonplace. I yearned for something extraordinary, above the common lot of woman! And then—and then—there crossed my path—an old general—very well off. Understand me, Voldemar! It was self-sacrifice, renunciation! You must see that! I could do nothing else. I restored the family fortunes, was able to travel, to do good. Yet how I suffered, how revolting, how loathsome to me were his embraces—though I will be fair to him—he had fought nobly in his day. There were moments—terrible moments—but I was kept up by the thought that from day to day the old man might die, that then I would begin to live as I liked, to give myself to the man I adore—be happy. There is such a man, Voldemar, indeed there is!"

The pretty lady flutters her fan more violently. Her face takes a lachrymose expression. She goes on:

"But at last the old man died. He left me something. I was free as a bird of the air. Now is the moment for me to be happy, isn't it. Voldemar? Happiness comes tapping at my window, I had only to let it in—but—Voldemar, listen, I implore you! Now is the time for me to give myself to the man I love, to become the partner of his life, to help, to uphold his ideals, to be happy—to find rest—but—how ignoble, repulsive, and senseless all our life is! How mean it all is, Voldemar. I am wretched, wretched, wretched! Again there is an obstacle in my path! Again I feel that my happiness is far, far away! Ah, what anguish!— if only you knew what anguish!"

"But what—what stands in your way? I implore you to tell me! What is it?"

"Another old general, very well off—"

The broken fan conceals the pretty little face. The author props on his fist his thought-heavy brow and ponders with the air of a master in psychology. The engine is whistling and hissing while the window curtains flush red with the glow of the setting sun.

Narcissistic Personality Disorder

These individuals demonstrate a pervasive pattern of grandiosity. They see themselves as special and demonstrate a striking sense of entitlement. They have a heightened sense of self-importance; they feel that they are unique and are frequently ambitious. Interpersonal difficulties, rejection, loss, and occupational difficulties are common. To the narcissist, appearance is more important than substance. They do not sustain genuine positive regard for anyone. Narcissistic personalities are driven in the pursuit of recognition and they are seldom satisfied with their accomplishments.

Charles Dickens (1812–1870)

Charles Dickens captures the sense of entitlement and grandiosity of the narcissistic personality in the character of Chevy Slime from his novel *Martin Chuzzlewit*. Even though Chevy is obviously not very special or successful, he continues to see himself as special and unique. His heightened sense of self-importance seems out of character for the circumstances in which he finds himself.

(Refer to chapter 2 for biographical information on Dickens.)

Martin Chuzzlewit

The rosy hostess scarcely needed Mr. Pinch's word as a preliminary to the release of her two visitors, of whom she was glad to be rid on any terms: indeed, their brief detention had originated mainly with Mr. Tapley, who entertained a constitutional dislike to gentlemen out-at-elbows who flourished on false pretenses; and had conceived a particular aversion to Mr. Tigg and his friend, as choice specimens of the species. The business in hand thus easily settled, Mr. Pinch and Martin would have withdrawn immediately, but for the urgent entreaties of Mr. Tigg that they would allow him the honor of presenting them to his friend Slyme, which were so very difficult of resistance that, yielding partly to these persuasions and partly to their own curiosity, they suffered themselves to be ushered into the presence of that distinguished gentleman.

He was brooding over the remains of yesterday's decanter of brandy, and was engaged in the thoughtful occupation of making a chain of rings on the top of the table with the wet foot of his drinking-glass. Wretched and forlorn as he looked, Mr. Slyme had once been, in his way, the choicest of swaggers: putting forth his pretensions, boldly, as a man of infinite taste and most undoubted promise. The stock-in trade requisite to set up an amateur in this department of business is very slight and easily got together; a trick of the nose and a curl of the lip sufficient to compound a tolerable sneer, being ample provision for any exigency. But, in an evil hour, this off-shoot of the Chuzzlewit trunk, being lazy, and ill qualified for any regular pursuit, and having dissipated such means as he ever possessed, had formally established himself as a professor of

Taste for a livelihood; and finding, too late, that something more than his old amount of qualifications were necessary to sustain him in this calling, had quickly fallen to his present level, where he retained nothing of his old self but his boastfulness and his bile, and seemed to have no existence separate or apart from his friend Tigg. And now so abject and so pitiful was he—at once so maudlin, insolent, beggarly, and proud—that even his friend and parasite, standing erect beside him, swelled into a Man by contrast.

"Chiv," said Mr. Tigg, clapping him on the back, "my friend Pecksniff not being at home, I have arranged our trifling piece of business with Mr. Pinch and friend. Mr. Pinch and friend, Mr. Chevy Slyme! Chiv, Mr. Pinch and friend!"

"These are agreeable circumstances in which to be introduced to strangers," said Chevy Slyme, turning his bloodshot eyes towards Tom Pinch. "I am the most miserable man in the world, I believe!"

Tom begged he wouldn't mention it; and finding him in this condition, retired, after an awkward pause, followed by Martin. But Mr. Tigg so urgently conjured them, by coughs and signs, to remain in the shadow of the door, that they stopped there.

"I swear," cried Mr. Slyme, giving the table an imbecile blow with his fist, and then feebly leaning his head upon his hand, while some drunken drops oozed from his eyes, "that I am the wretchedest creature on record. Society is in a conspiracy against me. I'm the most literary man alive. I'm full of scholarship; I'm full of genius; I'm full of information; I'm full of novel views on every subject; yet look at my condition! I'm at this moment obliged to two strangers for a tavern bill!"

Mr. Tigg replenished his friend's glass, pressed it into his hand, and nodded an intimation to the visitors that they would see him in a better aspect immediately.

"Obliged to two strangers for a tavern bill, eh!" repeated Mr. Slyme, after a sulky application to his glass. "Very pretty! And crowds of impostors, the while becoming famous: men who are no more on a level with me than—Tigg, I take you to witness that I am the most persecuted hound on the face of the earth."

With a whine, not unlike the cry of the animal he named, in its lowest state of humiliation, he raised his glass to his mouth again. He found some encouragement in it; for when he set it down, he laughed scornfully. Upon that Mr. Tigg gesticulated to the visitors once more, and with great expression: implying that now the time was come when they would see Chiv in his greatness.

"Ha, ha, ha," laughed Mr. Slyme. "Obliged to two strangers for a tavern bill! Yet I think I've a rich uncle, Tigg, who could buy up the uncles of fifty strangers! Have I, or have I not? I come of a good family, I believe! Do I, or do I not? I'm not a man of common capacity or accomplishments, I think! Am I, or am I not?"

"You are the American aloe of the human race, my dear Chiv," said Mr. Tigg, "which only blooms once in a hundred years!"

"Ha, ha, ha!" laughed Mr. Slyme, again. "Obliged to two strangers for a tavern bill! I! Obliged to two architect's apprentices. Fellows who measure earth with iron chains, and build houses like bricklayers. Give me the names of those two apprentices. How dare they oblige me!"

Mr. Tigg was quite lost in admiration of this noble trait in his friend's character; as he made known to Mr. Pinch in a neat little ballet of action, spontaneously invented for the purpose.

"I'll let 'em know, and I'll let all men know," cried Chevy Slyme, "that I'm none of the mean, groveling, tame characters they meet with commonly. I have an independent spirit. I have a heart that swells in my bosom. I have a soul that rises superior to base considerations."

"Oh Chiv, Chiv," murmured Mr. Tigg, "you have a nobly independent nature, Chiv!"

"You go and do your duty, sir," said Mr. Slyme, angrily, "and borrow money for traveling expenses; and whoever you borrow it of, let 'em know that I possess a haughty spirit, and a proud spirit, and have infernally finely-touched chords in my nature, which won't brook patronage. Do you hear? Tell 'em I hate 'em, and that that's the way I preserve my self-respect; and tell 'em that no man ever respected himself more than I do!"

Obsessive-Compulsive Personality Disorder

This disorder is characterized by emotional constriction, orderliness, perseverance, stubbornness, and indecisiveness. The essential feature is a pervasive pattern of perfectionism and inflexibility. They are preoccupied with rules, regulations, orderliness, neatness, details, and achievement of perfection. Their interpersonal skills are limited, and they are unable to compromise. They fear making mistakes and thus are indecisive. Obsessive-compulsive individuals see the parts but not the whole. They tend to be boring, annoying, and self-righteous. They are known for having problems with control and authority figures.

Nicolai Vasilyevitch Gogol (1809–1852)

Nicolai Gogol was born in Sorochintsi, Ukraine, and grew up on his parents' country estate. His father was an educated and talented man who was also a writer of plays and poetry. Gogol's literary career began in 1835 after he proved to be a failure as a world history lecturer at the University of St. Petersburg.

In 1835 Gogol published *Mirgorod* and *St. Petersburg Stories*, a collection of stories that examined mental disorders and social problems. Gogol is best known for his novel *Dead Souls*, published in 1842. His reputation as a major literary figure of the nineteenth century was established with the first edition of his collected tales in 1842. Gogol's literary works include plays, novels, and short stories and are considered among the masterpieces of realist literature. His work is ranked with such Russian literary giants as Tolstoy, Turgenev, and Dostoyevsky.

In his later years Gogol came under the influence of a fanatical priest who influenced him to fast and pray day and night. Before he died of starvation, Gogol slipped to the verge of madness.

Our selection comes from one of his finest works, "The Overcoat," published in 1835. In this segment from this wonderful story, Gogol provides us with a detailed description of the thoughts and feelings of an obsessive-compulsive personality disorder in the person of Akaky Akayevitich.

"The Overcoat"

In the department of . . . but I had better not mention in what department. There is nothing in the world more readily moved to wrath than a department, a regiment, a government office, and in fact any sort of official body. Nowadays every private individual considers all society insulted in his person. I have been told that very lately a petition was handed in from a police-captain of what town I don't recollect, and that in this petition he set forth clearly that the institutions of the State were in danger and that its sacred name was being taken in vain; and, in proof thereof, he appended to his petition an enormously long volume of some work of romance in which a police-captain appeared on every tenth page, occasionally, indeed, in an intoxicated condition. And so, to avoid any unpleasantness, we had better call the department of which we are speaking a certain department.

And so, in a certain department there was a government clerk; a clerk of whom it cannot be said that he was very remarkable; he was short, somewhat pock-marked, with rather reddish hair and rather dim, bleary eyes, with a small bald patch on the top of his head, with wrinkles on both sides of his cheeks and the sort of complexion which is usually associated with hemorrhoids . . . no help for that, it is the Petersburg climate. As for his grade in service (for among us the grade is what must be put first), he was what is called a perpetual titular councillor, a class at which, we all know, various writers who indulge in the praiseworthy habit of attacking those who cannot defend themselves jeer and jibe to their hearts' content. This clerk's surname was Bashmatchkin. From the very name it is clear that it must have been derived from a shoe (*bashmak*); but when and under what circumstances it was derived from a shoe, it is impossible to say. Both his father and his grandfather and even his brother-in-law, and all the Bashmatchkins without exception wore boots, which they simply re-soled two or three times a year. His name was Akaky Akakyevitch. Perhaps it may strike the reader as a rather strange and far-fetched name, but I can assure him that it was not far-fetched at all, that the circumstances were such that it was quite out of the question to give him any other name. Akaky Akakyevitch was born towards nightfall, if my memory does not deceive me, on the twenty-third of March. His mother, the wife of a government clerk, a very good woman, made arrangements in due course to christen the child. She was still lying in bed, facing the door, while on her right hand stood the godfather, an excellent man called Ivan Ivanovitch Yeroshkin, one of the head clerks in the Senate, and the godmother, the wife of a police official, and a woman of rare qualities, Arina Semyonovna Byelobryushkov. Three names were offered to the happy mother for selection—Moky, Sossy, or the name of the martyr Hozdazat. "No," thought the poor lady, "they are all such names!" To satisfy her, they opened the calendar at another place, and the names which turned up were: Trifily, Dula, Varahasy. "What an infliction!" said the mother. "What names they all are! I really never heard such names. Varadat or Varuh would be bad enough, but Trifily and Varahasy!" They turned over another page and the names were: Pavsikahy and Vahtisy. "Well, I see," said the mother, "it is clear that it is his fate. Since that is how it is, he had better be called after his father, his father is Akaky, let the son be Akaky, too." This was how he came to be Akaky Akakyevitch. The baby was christened and cried and made faces during the ceremony, as though he foresaw that he would be a titular councillor. So that was how it all came to pass. We have recalled it here so that the reader may see for himself that it happened quite inevitably and that to give him any other name was out of the question. No one has been able to remember when and how long ago he entered the department, nor who gave him the job. However many directors and higher officials of all sorts came and went, he was always seen in the same place, in the same position, at the very same duty, precisely the same copying clerk, so that they used to declare that he must have been born a copying clerk in uniform all complete and with a bald patch on his head. No respect at all was shown him in the department. The porters, far from getting up from their seats when he came in, took no more notice of him than if a simple fly had flown across the vestibule. His superiors treated him with a sort of domineering chilliness. The head clerk's assistant used to throw papers under his nose without even saying: "Copy this" or "Here is an interesting, nice little case" or some agreeable remark of the sort, as is usually done in well-behaved offices. And he would take it, gazing only at the paper without looking to see who had put it there and whether he had the right to do so: he would take it and at once set to work to copy it. The young clerks jeered and made jokes at him to the best of their clerkly wit, and told before his face all sorts of stories of their own invention about him; they would say of his landlady, an old woman of seventy, that she beat him, would enquire when the wedding was to take place, and would scatter bits of paper on his head, calling them snow. Akaky Akakyevitch never answered a word, however, but behaved as though there were no one there. It had no influence on his work even; in the midst of all this teasing, he never made a single mistake in his copying. Only when the jokes were too unbearable, when they jolted his arm and prevented him from going on with his work, he would bring out:

"Leave me alone! Why do you insult me?" and there was something strange in the words and in the voice in which they were uttered. There was a note in it of something that aroused compassion, so that one young man, new to the office, who, following the example of the rest, had allowed himself to mock at him, suddenly stopped as though cut to the heart, and from that time forth, everything was, as it were, changed and appeared in a different light to him. Some unnatural force seemed to thrust him away from the companions with whom he had become acquainted, accepting them as well-bred, polished people. And long afterwards, at moments of the greatest gaiety, the figure of the humble little clerk with a bald patch on his head rose before him with his heart-rending words: "Leave me alone! Why do you insult me?" and in those heart-rending words he heard others: "I am your brother." And the poor young man hid his face in his hands, and many times afterwards in his life he shuddered, seeing how much inhumanity there is in man, how much savage brutality lies hidden under refined, cultured politeness, and, my God! Even in a man whom the world accepts as a gentleman and a man of honor. . . .

It would be hard to find a man who lived in his work as did Akaky Akakyevitch. To say that he was zealous in his work is not enough; no, he loved his work. In it, in that copying, he found a varied and agreeable world of his own. There was a look of enjoyment on his face; certain letters were favorites with him, and when he came to them he was delighted; he chuckled to himself and winked and moved his lips, so that it seemed as though every letter his pen was forming could be read in his face. If rewards had been given according to the measure of zeal in the service, he might to his amazement have even found himself a civil councillor; but all he gained in the service, as the wits, his fellow-clerks expressed it, was a buckle in his button-hole and a pain in his back. It cannot be said, however, that no notice had ever been taken of him. One director, being a good-natured man and anxious to reward him for his long service, sent him something a little more important than his ordinary copying; he was instructed from a finished document to make some sort of report for another office; the work consisted only of altering the headings and in places changing the first person into the third. This cost him such an effort that it threw him into a regular perspiration: he mopped his brow and said at last, "No, better let me copy something."

From that time forth they left him to go on copying for ever. It seemed as though nothing in the world existed for him outside his copying. He gave no thought at all to his clothes; his uniform was—well, not green but some sort of rusty, muddy color. His collar was very short and narrow, so that, although his neck was not particularly long, yet, standing out of the collar, it looked as immensely long as those of the plaster kittens that wag their heads and are carried about on trays on the heads of dozens of foreigners living in Russia. And there were always things sticking to his uniform, either bits of hay or threads; moreover, he had a special art of passing under a window at the very moment when various rubbish was being flung out into the street, and so was continually carrying off bits of melon rind and similar litter on his hat. He had never once in his life noticed what was being done and going on in the street, all those things at which, as we all know, his colleagues, the young clerks, always stare, carrying their sharp sight so far even as to notice anyone on the other side of the pavement with a trouser strap hanging loose—a detail which always calls forth a sly grin. Whatever Akaky Akakyevitch looked at, he saw nothing anywhere but his clear, evenly written lines, and only perhaps when a horse's head suddenly appeared from nowhere just on his shoulder, and its nostrils blew a perfect gale upon his cheek, did he notice that he was not in the middle of his writing, but rather in the middle of the street.

On reaching home, he would sit down at once to the table, hurriedly sup his soup and eat a piece of beef with an onion; he did not notice the taste at all, but ate it all up together with the flies and anything else that Providence chanced to send him. When he felt that his stomach was beginning to be full, he would rise up from the table, get out a bottle of ink and set to copying the papers he had brought home with him. When he had none to do, he would make a copy expressly for his own pleasure, particularly if the document were remarkable not for the beauty of its style but for the fact of its being addressed to some new or important personage.

Even at those hours when the grey Petersburg sky is completely overcast and the whole population of clerks have dined and eaten their fill, each as best he can, according to the salary he receives and his personal tastes; when they are all resting after the scratching of pens and bustle of the office, their own necessary work and other people's, and all the tasks that an over-zealous man voluntarily sets himself even beyond what is necessary; when the clerks are hastening to devote what is left of their time to pleasure; some more enterprising are flying to the theatre, others to the street to spend their leisure, staring at women's hats, some to spend the evening paying compliments to some attractive girl, the star of a little official circle, while some—and this is the most frequent of all—go simply to a fellow-clerk's flat on the third or fourth storey, two little rooms with an entry or a kitchen, with some pretensions to style, with a lamp or some such article that cost many sacrifices of dinners and excursions—at the time when all the clerks are scattered about the little flats of their friends, playing a tempestuous game of whist, sipping tea out of glasses to the accompaniment of farthing rusks, sucking in smoke from long pipes, telling, as the cards are dealt, some scandal that has floated down from higher circles, a pleasure which the Russian can never by any possibility deny himself, or, when there is nothing better to talk about, repeating the everlasting anecdote of the commanding officer who was told that the tail had been cut off his horse on the Falconet monument—in short, even when every one was eagerly seeking entertainment, Akaky Akakyevitch did not give himself up to any amusement. No one could say that they had ever seen him at an evening party. After working to his heart's content, he would go to bed, smiling at the thought of the next day and wondering what God would send him to copy. So flowed on the peaceful life of a man who knew how to be content with his fate on a salary of four hundred rubles, and so perhaps it would have flowed on to extreme old age, had it not been for the various calamities that bestrew the path through life, not only of titular, but even of privy, actual court and all other councillors, even those who neither give counsel to others nor accept it themselves.

There is in Petersburg a mighty foe of all who receive a salary of four hundred rubles or about that sum. That foe is none other than our northern frost, although it is said to be very good for the health. Between eight and nine in the morning, precisely at the hour when the streets are full of clerks going to their departments, the frost begins giving such sharp and stinging flips at all their noses indiscriminately that the poor fellows don't know what to do with them. At that time, when even those in the higher grade have a pain in their brows and tears in their eyes from the frost, the poor titular councillors are sometimes almost defenceless. Their only protection lies in running as fast as they can through five or six streets in a wretched, thin little overcoat and then warming their feet thoroughly in the porter's room, till all their faculties and qualifications for their various duties thaw again after being frozen on the way. Akaky Akakyevitch had for some time been feeling that his back and shoulders were particularly nipped by the cold, although he did try to run the regular distance as fast as he could. He wondered at last whether there were any defects in his overcoat. After examining it thoroughly in the privacy of his home, he discovered that in two or three places, to wit on the back and the shoulders, it had become a regular sieve; the cloth was so worn that you could see through it and the lining was coming out. I must observe that Akaky Akakyevitch's overcoat had also served as a butt for the jibes of the clerks. It had even been deprived of the honorable name of overcoat and had been referred to as the "dressing jacket." It was indeed of rather a strange make. Its collar had been growing smaller year by year as it served to patch the other parts. The patches were not good specimens of the tailor's art, and they certainly looked clumsy and ugly. On seeing what was wrong, Akaky Akakyevitch decided that he would have to take the overcoat to Petrovitch, a tailor who lived on a fourth storey up a back staircase, and, in spite of having only one eye and being pockmarked all over his face, was rather successful in repairing the trousers and coats of clerks and others—that is, when he was sober, be it understood, and had no other enterprise in his mind. Of this tailor I ought not, of course, to say much, but since it is now the rule that the character of every person in a novel must be completely drawn, well, there is no help for it, here is Petrovitch too. At first he was called simply Grigory, and was a serf belonging to some gentleman or other. He began to be called Petrovitch from the time that he got his freedom and began to drink rather heavily on every holiday, at first only on the chief holidays, but afterwards on all church holidays indiscriminately, wherever there is a cross in the calendar. On that side he was true to the customs of his forefathers, and when he quarreled with his wife used to call her "a worldly woman and a German." Since we have now mentioned the wife, it will be necessary to say a few words about her too, but unfortunately not much is known about her, except indeed that Petrovitch had a wife and that she wore a cap and not a kerchief, but apparently she could not boast of beauty; anyway, none but soldiers of the Guards peeped under her cap when they met her, and they twitched their moustaches and gave vent to a rather peculiar sound.

As he climbed the stairs leading to Petrovitch's— which, to do them justice, were all soaked with water and slops and saturated through and through with that smell of spirits which makes the eyes smart, and is, as we all know, inseparable from the backstairs of Petersburg houses—Akaky Akakyevitch was already wondering how much Petrovitch would ask for the job, and inwardly resolving not to give more than two rubles. The door was open, for Petrovitch's wife was frying some fish and had so filled the kitchen with smoke that you could not even see the black-beetles. Akaky Akakyevitch crossed the kitchen unnoticed by the good woman, and walked at last into a room where he saw Petrovitch sitting on a big, wooden, unpainted table with his legs tucked under him like a Turkish Pasha. The feet, as is usual with tailors when they sit at work, were bare; and the first object that caught Akaky Akakyevitch's eye was the big toe, with which he was already familiar, with a misshapen nail as thick and strong as the shell of a tortoise. Round Petrovitch's neck hung a skein of silk and another of thread and on his knees was a rag of some sort. He had for the last three minutes been trying to thread his needle, but could not get the thread into the eye and so was very angry with the darkness and indeed with the thread itself, muttering in an undertone: "It won't go in, the savage! You wear me out, you rascal." Akaky Akakyevitch was vexed that he had come just at the minute when Petrovitch was in a bad humor; he liked to give him an order when he was a little "elevated," or, as his wife expressed it, "had fortified himself with fizz, the one-eyed devil." In such circumstances Petrovitch was as a rule very ready to give way and agree, and invariably bowed and thanked him, indeed. Afterwards, it is true, his wife would come wailing that her husband had been drunk and so had asked too little, but adding a single ten-kopeck piece would settle that. But on this occasion Petrovitch was apparently sober and consequently curt, unwilling to bargain, and the devil knows what price he would be ready to lay on. Akaky Akakyevitch perceived this, and was, as the saying is, beating a retreat, but things had gone too far, for Petrovitch was screwing up his solitary eye very attentively at him and Akaky Akakyevitch involuntarily brought out: "Good day, Petrovitch!" "I wish you a good day, sir," said Petrovitch, and squinted at Akaky Akakyevitch's hands, trying to discover what sort of goods he had brought.

"Here I have come to you, Petrovitch, do you see . . . !"

It must be noticed that Akaky Akakyevitch for the most part explained himself by apologies, vague phrases, and particles which have absolutely no significance whatever. If the subject were a very difficult one, it was his habit indeed to leave his sentences quite unfinished, so that very often after a sentence had begun with words, "It really is, don't you know . . ." nothing at all would follow and he himself would be quite oblivious, supposing he had said all that was necessary.

"What is it?" said Petrovitch, and at the same time with his solitary eye he scrutinized his whole uniform from the collar to the sleeves, the back, the skirts, the button-holes—with all of which he was very familiar, they were all his own work. Such scrutiny is habitual with tailors, it is the first thing they do on meeting one.

"It's like this, Petrovitch . . . the overcoat, the cloth . . . you see everywhere else it is quite strong; it's a little dusty and looks as though it were old, but it is new and it is only in one place just a little . . . on the back, and just a little worn on one shoulder and on this shoulder, too, a little . . . do you see? that's all, and it's not much work . . . "

Petrovitch took the "dressing jacket," first spread it out over the table, examined it for a long time, shook his head and put his hand out to the window for a round snuff-box with a portrait on the lid of some general—which precisely I can't say, for a finger had been thrust through the spot where a face should have been, and the hole had been pasted up with a square bit of paper. After taking a pinch of snuff, Petrovitch held the "dressing jacket" up in his hands and looked at it against the light, and again he shook his head; then turned it with the lining upwards and once more shook his head; again he took off the lid with the general pasted up with paper and stuffed a pinch into his nose, shut the box, put it away and at last said: "No, it can't be repaired; a wretched garment!" Akaky Akakyevitch's heart sank at those words.

"Why can't it, Petrovitch?" he said, almost in the imploring voice of a child. "Why, the only thing is it is a bit worn on the shoulders; why, you have got some little pieces . . . ."

"Yes, the pieces will be found alright," said Petrovitch, "but it can't be patched, the stuff is quite rotten; if you put a needle in it, it would give way."

"Let it give way, but you just put a patch on it."

"There is nothing to put a patch on. There is nothing for it to hold on to; there is a great stain on it, it is not worth calling cloth, it would fly away at a breath of wind."

"Well, then, strengthen it with something—upon my word, really, this is . . . !"

"No," said Petrovitch resolutely, "there is nothing to be done, the thing is no good at all. You had far better, when the cold winter weather comes, make yourself leg wrappings out of it, for there is no warmth in stockings, the Germans invented them just to make money." (Petrovitch was fond of a dig at the Germans occasionally.) "And as for the overcoat, it is clear that you will have to have a new one."

At the word "new" there was a mist before Akaky Akakyevitch's eyes, and everything in the room seemed blurred. He could see nothing clearly but the general with the piece of paper over his face on the lid of Petrvitch's snuff-box.

"A new one?" he said, still feeling as though he were in a dream; "why, I haven't the money for it."

"Yes, a new one," Petrovitch repeated with barbarous composure.

"Well, and if I did have a new one, how much would it . . . ?"

"You mean what will it cost?"

"Yes."

"Well, three fifty-ruble notes or more," said Petrovitch, and he compressed his lips significantly. He was very fond of making an effect, he was fond of suddenly disconcerting a man completely and then squinting sideways to see what sort of a face he made.

"A hundred and fifty rubles for an overcoat," screamed poor Akaky Akakyevitch—it was perhaps the first time he had screamed in his life, for he was always distinguished by the softness of his voice.

"Yes," said Petrovitch, "and even then it's according to the coat. If I were to put marten on the collar, add a hood with silk linings, it would come to two hundred."

"Petrovitch, please," said Akaky Akakyevitch in an imploring voice, not hearing and not trying to hear what Petrovitch said, and missing all his effects, "do repair it somehow, so that it will serve a little longer."

"No, that would be wasting work and spending money for nothing," said Petrovitch, and after that Akaky Akakyevitch went away completely crushed, and when he had gone Petrovitch remained standing for a long time with his lips pursed up significantly before he took up his work again, feeling pleased that he had not demeaned himself nor lowered the dignity of the tailor's art.

When he got into the street, Akaky Akakyevitch was as though in a dream. "So that is how it is," he said to himself. "I really did not think it would be so . . ." and then after a pause he added, "So there it is! so that's how it is at last! and I really could never have supposed it would have been so. And there . . ." There followed another long silence, after which he brought out: "So there it is! well, it really is so utterly unexpected . . . who would have thought . . . what a circumstance . . ." Saying this, instead of going home he walked off in quite the opposite direction without suspecting what he was doing. On the way a clumsy sweep brushed the whole of his sooty side against him and blackened all his shoulder; a regular hatful of plaster scattered upon him from the top of a house that was being built. He noticed nothing of this, and only after he had jostled against a sentry who had set his halberd down beside him and was shaking some snuff out of his horn into his rough fist, he came to himself a little and then only because the sentry said: "Why are you poking yourself right in one's face, haven't you the pavement to yourself?" This made him look round and turn homeward; only there he began to collect his thoughts, to see his position in a clear light and began talking no longer incoherently but reasonably and openly as with a sensible friend with whom one can discuss the most intimate and vital matters. "No, indeed," said Akaky Akakyevitch, "it is no use talking to Petrovitch now; just now he really is . . . his wife must have been giving it to him. I had better go to him on Sunday morning; after the Saturday evening he will be squinting and sleepy, so he'll want a little drink to carry it off and his wife won't give him a penny. I'll slip ten kopecks into his hand and then he will be more accommodating and maybe take the overcoat . . . ."

So reasoning with himself, Akaky Akakyevitch cheered up and waited until the next Sunday; then, seeing from a distance Petrovitch's wife leaving the house, he went straight in. Petrovitch certainly was very tipsy after the Saturday. He could hardly hold his head up and was very drowsy: but, for all that, as soon as he heard what he was speaking about, it seemed as though the devil had nudged him. "I can't," he said, "you must kindly order a new one." Akaky Akakyevitch at once slipped a ten-kopeck piece into his hand. "I thank you, sir, I will have just a drop to your health, but don't trouble yourself about the overcoat; it is not a bit of good for anything. I'll make you a fine new coat, you can trust me for that."

Akaky Akakyevitch would have said more about repairs, but Petrovitch, without listening, said: "A new one now I'll make you without fail; you can rely on that, I'll do my best. It could even be like the fashion that has come in with the collar to button with silver claws under appliqué."

Then Akaky Akakyevitch saw that there was no escape from a new overcoat and he was utterly depressed. How indeed, for what, with what money could he get it? Of course he could to some extent rely on the bonus for the coming holiday, but that money had long ago been appropriated and its use determined beforehand. It was needed for new trousers and to pay the cobbler an old debt for putting some new tops to some old boot-legs, and he had to order three shirts from a seamstress as well as two specimens of an under-garment which it is improper to mention in print; in short, all that money absolutely must be spent, and even if the director were to be so gracious as to assign him a gratuity of forty-five or even fifty, instead of forty rubles, there would be still left a mere trifle, which would be but as a drop in the ocean beside the fortune needed for an overcoat. Though, of course, he knew that Petrovitch had a strange craze for suddenly putting on the devil knows what enormous price, so that at times his own wife could not help crying out: "Why, you are out of your wits, you idiot! Another time he'll undertake a job for nothing, and here the devil has bewitched him to ask more than he is worth himself." Though, of course, he knew that Petrovitch would undertake to make it for eighty rubles, still where would he get those eighty rubles? He might manage half of that sum; half of it could be found, perhaps even a little more; but where could he get the other half? But, first of all, the reader ought to know where the first half was to be found. Akaky Akakyevitch had the habit every time he spent a ruble of putting aside two kopecks in a little locked-up box with a slit in the lid for slipping the money in. At the end of every half-year he would inspect the pile of coppers there and change them for small silver. He had done this for a long time, and in the course of many years the sum had mounted up to forty rubles and so he had half the money in his hands, but where was he to get the other half, where was he to get another forty rubles? Akaky Akakyevitch pondered and pondered and decided at last that he would have to diminish his ordinary expenses, at least for a year; give up burning candles in the evening, and if he had to do anything he must go into the landlady's room and work by her candle; that as he walked along the streets he must walk as lightly and carefully as possible, almost on tiptoe, on the cobbles and flagstones, so that his soles might last a little longer than usual; that he must send his linen to the wash less frequently, and that, to preserve it from being worn, he must take it off every day when he came home and sit in a thin cotton-shoddy dressing-gown, a very ancient garment which Time itself had spared. To tell the truth, he found it at first rather hard to get used to these privations, but after a while it became a habit and went smoothly enough—he even became quite accustomed to being hungry in the evening; on the other hand, he had spiritual nourishment, for he carried ever in his thoughts the idea of his future overcoat. His whole existence had in a sense become fuller, as though he had married, as though some other person were present with him, as though he were no longer alone, but an agreeable companion had consented to walk the path of life hand in hand with him, and that companion was no other than the new overcoat with its thick wadding and its strong, durable lining. He became, as it were, more alive, even more strong willed, like a man who has set before himself a definite aim. Uncertainty, indecision, in fact all the hesitating and vague characteristics vanished from his face and his manners. At times there was a gleam in his eyes, indeed, the most bold and audacious ideas flashed through his mind. Why not really have marten on the collar? Meditation on the subject always made him absentminded. On one occasion when he was copying a document, he very nearly made a mistake, so that he almost cried out "ough" aloud and crossed himself. At least once every month he went to Petrovitvh to talk about the overcoat, where it would be best to buy the cloth, and what color it should be, and what price, and, though he returned home a little anxious, he was always pleased at the thought that at last the time was at hand when everything would be bought and the overcoat would be made. Things moved even faster than he had anticipated. Contrary to all expectations the director bestowed on Akaky Akakyevitch a gratuity of no less than sixty rubles. Whether it was that he had an inkling that Akaky Akakyevitch needed a greatcoat, or whether it happened so by chance, owing to this he found he had twenty rubles extra. This circumstance hastened the course of affairs. Another two or three months of partial fasting and Akaky Akakyevitch had actually saved up nearly eighty rubles. His heart, as a rule very tranquil, began to throb. The very first day he set off in company with Petrovitch to the shops. They bought some very good cloth, and no wonder, since they had been thinking of it for more than six months before, and scarcely a month had passed without their going to the shop to compare prices; now Petrovitch himself declared that there was no better cloth to be had. For the lining they chose calico, but of a stout quality, which in Petrovitch's words was even better than silk, and actually as strong and handsome to look at. Marten they did not buy, because it certainly was dear, but instead they chose cat fur, the best to be found in the shop—cat which in the distance might almost be taken for marten. Petrovitch was busy over the coat for a whole fortnight, because there were a great many buttonholes, otherwise it would have been ready sooner. Pertovitch asked twelve rubles for the work; less than that it hardly could have been, everything was sewn with silk, with fine double seams, and Petrovitch went over every seam afterwards with his own teeth imprinting various figures with them. It was . . . it is hard to say precisely on what day, but probably on the most triumphant day of the life of Akaky Akakyevitch that Petrovitch at last brought home the overcoat . . . .

Discussion Questions

1. Histrionic personality disorder includes the symptoms of attention-seeking and the need to be the center of attention. Describe each of these behaviors in detail, as demonstrated by Anton Chekhov's "An Enigmatic Nature."

2. Common symptoms of schizotypal personality disorder include ideas of reference, odd beliefs, magical thinking, peculiar behavior and appearance, and odd thinking. Document as many of these behaviors as you can from Lovecraft's descriptions of Edward Derby and Asena Wait.

3. Discuss the differences between obsessive-compulsive disorder and obsessive-compulsive personality disorder? Which of these disorders do you think is the most difficult to treat? Why?

4. What aspects of Dr. James's and Mr. Chandler's behavior indicate antisocial personality disorder? Discuss what might cause antisocial personality disorder.

5. Borderline personality disorder involves mood changes, unstable relationships, and identity problems. Describe these characteristics the selections from Kaysen's *Girl, Interrupted*.

Chapter 8

Disorders of Infancy, Childhood, or Adolescence

Children's disorders are noted primarily by the time of onset rather than their phenomenology. These disorders are also primarily those of abnormal maturation and development. We will address mental retardation, attention-deficit/hyperactivity disorder and the disruptive behavior disorders of oppositional defiant disorder, and conduct disorder. The chapter concludes with eating disorders, which affect significant numbers of adolescents although they normally constitute a separate diagnostic category.

Mental Retardation

Mental retardation is characterized by low intellectual functioning, which is determined by an IQ of 70 or below. This disorder has an onset before age eighteen and results in problems related to adaptive functioning. Mental retardation is classified as mild, moderate, severe, or profound, depending on the severity of the deficits in intellectual functioning.

Jack London (1876–1916)

In this selection Jack London tells a fascinating tale of life in a state institution as seen through the eyes of a mildly retarded resident. London utilizes his amazing insight and storytelling ability to demonstrate the worldly wisdom of his so-called feebleminded narrator.

(Refer to chapter 3 for biographical information on Jack London.)

"Told in the Drooling Ward"

Me? I'm not a drooler. I'm the assistant. I don't know what Miss Jones or Miss Kelsey could do without me. There are fifty-five low-grade droolers in this ward, and how could they ever all be fed if I wasn't around? I like to feed droolers. They don't make trouble. They can't. Something's wrong with most of their legs and arms, and they can't talk. They're very low-grade. I can walk, and talk, and do things. You must be careful with the droolers and not feed them too fast. Then they choke. Miss Jones says I'm an expert. When a new nurse comes I show her how to do it. Its funny watching a new nurse try to feed them. She goes at it so slow and careful that supper time would be around before she finished shoving down their breakfast. Then I show her, because I'm an expert. Dr. Dalrymple says I am, and he ought to know. A drooler can eat twice as fast if you know how to make him.

My name's Tom. I'm twenty-eight years old. Everybody knows me in the institution. This is an institution, you know. It belongs to the State of California and is run by politics. I know. I've been here a long time. Everybody trusts me. I run errands all over the place, when I'm not busy with the droolers. I like droolers. It makes me think how lucky I am that I ain't a drooler.

I like it here in the Home. I don't like the outside. I know. I've been around a bit, and run away, and adopted. Me for the Home, and for the drooling ward best of all. I don't look like a drooler, do I? You can tell the difference soon as you look at me. I'm an assistant, expert assistant. That's going some for a feeb. Feeb? Oh, that's feeble-minded. I thought you knew. We're all feebs in here.

But I'm a high-grade feeb. Dr. Dalrymple says I'm too smart to be in the Home, but I never let on. It's a pretty good place. And I don't throw fits like lots of the feebs. You see that house up there through the trees. The high-grade epilecs all live in it by themselves. They're stuck up because they ain't just ordinary feebs. They call it the club house, and they say they're just as good as anybody outside, only they're sick. I don't like them much. They laugh at me, when they ain't busy throwing fits. But I don't care. I never have to be scared about falling down and busting my head. Sometimes they run around in circles trying to find a place to sit down quick, only they don't. Low-grade epilecs are disgusting, and high-grade epileptics put on airs. I'm glad I ain't an epilecs. There ain't anything to them. They just talk big, that's all.

Miss Kelsey says I talk too much. But I talk sense, and that's more than the other feebs do. Dr. Dalrymple says I have the gift of language. I know it. You ought to hear me talk when I'm by myself, or when I've got a drooler to listen. Sometimes I think I'd like to be a politician, only it's too much trouble. They're all great talkers; that's how they hold their jobs.

Nobody's crazy in this institution. They're just feeble in their minds. Let me tell you something funny. There's about a dozen high-grade girls that set the tables in the big dining-room. Sometimes when they're done ahead of time, they all sit down in chairs in a circle and talk. I sneak up to the door and listen, and I nearly die to keep from laughing. Do you want to know what they talk? It's like this. They don't say a word for a long time. And then one says, "Thank God I'm not feeble-minded." And all the rest nod their heads and look pleased. And then nobody says anything for a time. After which the next girl in the circle says, "Thank God I'm not feeble-minded," and they nod their heads all over again. And it goes on around the circle, and they never say anything else.

Now they're real feebs, ain't they? I leave it to you. I'm not that kind of a feeb, thank God.

Sometimes I don't think I'm a feeb at all. I play in the band and read music. We're all supposed to be feebs in the band except the leader. He's crazy. We know it, but we never talk about it except amongst ourselves. His job is politics, too, and we don't want him to lose it. I play the drum. They can't get along without me in this institution. I was sick once, so I know. It's a wonder the drooling ward didn't break down while I was in hospital.

I could get out of here if I wanted to. I'm not so feeble as some might think. But I don't let on. I have too good a time. Besides, everything would run down if I went away. I'm afraid some time they'll find out I'm not a feeb and send me out into the world to earn my own living. I know the world, and I don't like it. The Home is fine enough for me.

You see how I grin sometimes. I can't help that. But I can put it on a lot. I'm not bad, though. I look at myself in the glass. My mouth is funny, I know that, and it lops down, and my teeth are bad. You can tell a feeb anywhere by looking at his mouth and teeth. But that doesn't prove I'm a feeb. It's just because I'm lucky that I look like one.

I know a lot. If I told you all I know, you'd be surprised. But when I don't want to know, or when they want me to do something I don't want to do, I just let my mouth lop down and laugh and make foolish noises. I watch the foolish noises by the low-grades, and I can fool anybody. And I know a lot of foolish noises. Miss Kelsey called me a fool the other day. She was very angry, and that was where I fooled her.

Miss Kelsey asked me why I don't write a book about feebs. I was telling her what was the matter with little Albert. He's a drooler, you know, and I can always tell the way he twists his left eye what's the matter with him. So I was explaining it to Miss Kelsey, and, because she didn't know, it made her mad. But some day, mebbe, I'll write that book. Only it's so much trouble. Besides, I'd sooner talk.

Do you know what a micro is? It's the kind with the little heads no bigger than your fist. They're usually droolers, and they live a long time. The hydros don't drool. They have the big heads, and they're smarter. But they never grow up. They always die. I never look at one without thinking he's going to die. Sometimes, when I'm feeling lazy, or the nurse is mad at me, I wish I was a drooler with nothing to do and somebody to feed me. But I guess I'd sooner talk and be what I am.

Only yesterday Doctor Dalrymple said to me, "Tom," he said, "I just don't know what I'd do without you." And he ought to know, seeing as he's had the bossing of a thousand feebs for going on two years. Dr. Whatcomb was before him. They get appointed, you know. It's politics. I've seen a whole lot of doctors here in my time. I was here before any of them. I've been in this institution twenty-five years. No, I've got no complaints. The institution couldn't be run better.

It's a snap to be a high-grade feeb. Just look at Doctor Dalrymple. He has troubles. He holds his job by politics. You bet we high-graders talk politics. We know all about it, and it's bad. An institution like this oughtn't to be run on politics. Look at Doctor Dalrymple. He's been here two years and learned a lot. Then politics will come along and throw him out and send a new doctor who don't know anything about feebs.

I've been acquainted with just thousands of nurses in my time. Some of them are nice. But they come and go. Most of the women get married. Sometimes I think I'd like to get married. I spoke to Dr. Whatcomb about it once, but he told me he was very sorry, because feebs ain't allowed to get married. I've been in love. She was a nurse. I won't tell her name. She had blue eyes, and yellow hair, and a kind voice, and she liked me. She told me so. And she always told me to be a good boy. And I was, too, until afterward, and then I ran away. You see, she went off and got married, and she didn't tell me about it.

I guess being married ain't what it's cracked up to be. Dr. Anglin and his wife used to fight. I've seen them. And once I heard her call him a feeb. Now nobody has a right to call anybody a feeb that ain't. Dr. Anglin got awful mad when she called him that. But he didn't last long. Politics drove him out, and Doctor Mandeville came. He didn't have a wife. I heard him talking one time with the engineer. The engineer and his wife fought like cats and dogs, and that day Doctor Mandeville told him he was damn glad he wasn't tied to no petticoats. A petticoat is a skirt. I knew what he meant, if I was a feeb. But I never let on. You hear lots when you don't let on.

I've seen a lot in my time. Once I was adopted, and went away on the railroad over forty miles to live with a man named Peter Bopp and his wife. They had a ranch. Doctor Anglin said I was strong and bright, and I said I was, too. That was because I wanted to be adopted. And Peter Bopp said he'd give me a good home, and the lawyers fixed up the papers.

But I soon made up my mind that a ranch was no place for me. Mrs. Bopp was scared to death of me and wouldn't let me sleep in the house. They fixed up the woodshed and made me sleep there. I had to get up at four o'clock and feed the horses, and milk cows, and carry the milk to the neighbors. They called it chores, but it kept me going all day. I chopped wood, and cleaned chicken houses, and weeded vegetables, and did most everything on the place. I never had any fun. I hadn't no time.

Let me tell you one thing. I'd sooner feed mush and milk to feebs than milk cows with the frost on the ground. Mrs. Bopp was scared to let me play with her children. And I was scared, too. They used to make faces at me when nobody was looking, and call me "Looney." Everybody called me Looney Tom. And the other boys in the neighborhood threw rocks at me. You never see anything like that in the Home here. The feebs are better behaved.

Mrs. Bopp used to pinch me and pull my hair when she thought I was too slow, and I only made foolish noises and went slower. She said I'd be the death of her someday. I left the boards off the old well in the pasture, and the pretty new calf fell in and drowned. Then Peter Bopp said he was going to give me a licking. He did, too. He took a strap halter and went at me. It was awful. I'd never had a licking in my life. They don't do such things in the Home, which is why I say the Home is the place for me.

I know the law, and I knew he had no right to lick me with a strap halter. That was being cruel, and the guardianship papers said he mustn't be cruel. I didn't say anything. I just waited, which shows you what kind of a feeb I am. I waited a long time, and got slower, and made more foolish noises; but he wouldn't send me back to the Home, which was what I wanted. But one day, it was the first of the month, Mrs. Brown gave me three dollars, which was for her milk bill with Peter Bopp. That was in the morning. When I brought the milk in the evening I was to bring back the receipt. But I didn't. I just walked down to the station, bought a ticket like any one, and rode on the train back to the Home. That's the kind of feeb I am.

Doctor Anglin was gone then, and Doctor Mandeville had his place. I walked right into his office. He didn't know me. "Hello," he said, "this ain't visiting day." "I ain't a visitor," I said. "I'm Tom. I belong here." Then he whistled and showed he was surprised. I told him all about it, and showed him the marks of the strap halter, and he got madder and madder all the time and said he'd attend to Mr. Peter Bopp's case.

And mebbe you think some of them little droolers weren't glad to see me.

I walked right into the ward. There was a new nurse feeding little Albert. "Hold on," I said. "That ain't the way. Don't you see how he's twisting that left eye? Let me show you." Mebbe she thought I was a new doctor, for she just gave me the spoon, and I guess I filled little Albert up with the most comfortable meal he'd had since I went away. Droolers ain't bad when you understand them. I heard Miss Jones tell Miss Kelsey once that I had an amazing gift in handling droolers.

Some day, mebbe, I'm going to talk with Doctor Dalrymple and get him to give me a declaration that I ain't a feeb. Then I'll get him to make me a real assistant in the drooling ward, with forty dollars a month and my board. And then I'll marry Miss Jones and live right on here. And if she won't have me, I'll marry Miss Kelsey or some other nurse. There's lots of them that want to get married. And I won't care if my wife gets mad and calls me a feeb. What's the good? And I guess when one's learned to put up with droolers a wife won't be much worse.

I didn't tell you about when I ran away. I hadn't no idea of such a thing, and it was Charley and Joe who put me up to it. They're high-grade epilecs, you know. I'd been up to Doctor Wilson's office with a message, and was going back to the drooling ward, when I saw Charley and Joe hiding around the corner of the gymnasium and making motions to me. I went over to them.

"Hello," Joe said. "How's droolers?"

"Fine," I said. "Had any fits lately?"

That made them mad, and I was going on, when Joe said, "We're running away. Come on."

"What for?" I said.

"We're going over the top of the mountain," Joe said.

"And find a gold mine," said Charley. "We don't have fits any more. We're cured."

"All right," I said. And we sneaked around back of the gymnasium and in among the trees. Mebbe we walked along about ten minutes, when I stopped.

"What's the matter?" said Joe.

"Wait," I said. "I got to go back."

"What for?" said Joe.

And I said, "To get little Albert."

And they said I couldn't, and got mad. But I didn't care. I knew they'd wait. You see, I've been here twenty-five years, and I know the back trails that lead up the mountain, and Charley and Joe didn't know those trails. That's why they wanted me to come.

So I went back and got little Albert. He can't walk, or talk, or do anything except drool, and I had to carry him in my arms. We went on past the last hayfield, which was as far as I'd ever gone. Then the woods and brush got so thick, and me not finding any more trails, we followed the cow-path down to a big creek and crawled through the fence which showed where the Home land stopped.

We climbed up the big hill on the other side of the creek. It was all big trees, and no brush, but it was so steep and slippery with dead leaves we could hardly walk. By and by we came to a real bad place. It was forty feet across, and if you slipped you'd fall a thousand feet, or mebbe a hundred. Anyway, you wouldn't fall—just slide. I went across first, carrying little Albert. Joe came next. But Charley got scared right in the middle and sat down.

"I'm going to have a fit," he said.

"No, you're not," said Joe. "Because if you was you wouldn't 'a' sat down. You take all your fits standing."

"This is a different kind of a fit," said Charley, beginning to cry.

He shook and shook, but just because he wanted to he couldn't scare up the least kind of a fit.

Joe got mad and used awful language. But that didn't help none. So I talked soft and kind to Charley. That's the way to handle feebs. If you get mad, they get worse. I know. I'm that way myself. That's why I was almost the death of Mrs. Bopp. She got mad.

It was getting along in the afternoon, and I knew we had to be on our way, so I said to Joe: "Here, stop your cussing and hold Albert. I'll go back and get him."

And I did, too; but he was so scared and dizzy he crawled along on hands and knees while I helped him. When I got him across and took Albert back in my arms, I heard somebody laugh and looked down. And there was a man and woman on horseback looking up at us. He had a gun on his saddle, and it was her who was laughing.

"Who in hell's that?" said Joe, getting scared. "Somebody to catch us?"

"Shut up your cussing," I said to him. "That is the man who owns this ranch and writes books."

"How do you do, Mr. Endicott," I said down to him.

"Hello," he said. "What are you doing here?"

"We're running away," I said.

And then both he and his wife laughed.

"All right," he said. "Good luck just the same. But watch out the bears and mountain lions don't get you when it gets dark."

Then they rode away laughing, pleasant like; but I wished he hadn't said that about the bears and mountain lions.

After we got around the hill, I found a trail, and we went much faster. Charley didn't have any more signs of fits, and began laughing and talking about gold mines. The trouble was with little Albert. He was almost as big as me. You see, all the time I'd been calling him little Albert, he'd been growing up. He was so heavy I couldn't keep up with Joe and Charley. I was all out of breath. So I told them they'd have to take turns in carrying him, which they said they wouldn't. Then I said I'd leave them and they'd get lost, and the mountain lions and bears would eat them. Charley looked like he was going to have a fit right there, and Joe said, "Give him to me." And after that we carried him in turn.

We kept right on up that mountain. I don't think there was any gold mine, but we might 'a' got to the top and found it, if we hadn't lost the trail, and if it hadn't got dark, and if little Albert hadn't tired us all out carrying him. Lots of feebs are scared of the dark, and Joe said he was going to have a fit right there. Only he didn't. I never saw such an unlucky boy. He never could throw a fit when he wanted to. Some of the feebs can throw a fit as quick as a wink.

By and by it got real black, and we were hungry, and we didn't have no fire. You see, they don't let feebs carry matches, and all we could do was just shiver. And we'd never thought about being hungry. You see, feebs always have their food ready for them, and that's why it's better to be a feeb than earning your living in the world.

And worse than everything was the quiet. There was only one thing worse, and it was the noises. There was all kinds of noises every once in a while, with quiet spells in between. I recon they were rabbits, but they made noises in the brush like wild animals—you know, rustle rustle, thump, bump, crackle, just like that. First Charley got a fit, a real one, and Joe threw a terrible one. I don't mind fits in the Home with everybody around. But out in the woods on a dark night is different. You listen to me, and never go hunting gold mines with epilecs, even if they are high-grade.

I never had such an awful night. When Joe and Charley weren't throwing fits they were making believe, and in the darkness the shivers from the cold which I couldn't see seemed like fits, too. And I shivered so hard I thought I was getting fits myself. And little Albert, with nothing to eat, just drooled and drooled. I never seen him as bad as that before. Why, he twisted that left eye of his until it ought to have dropped out. I couldn't see it, but I could tell from the movements he made. And Joe just lay and cussed and cussed, and Charley cried and wished he was back in the Home.

We didn't die, and next morning we went right back the way we'd come. And little Albert got awful heavy. Doctor Wilson was mad as could be, and said I was the worst feeb in the institution, along with Joe and Charley. But Miss Striker, who was a nurse in the drooling ward then, just put her arms around me and cried, she was that happy I'd got back. I thought right there that mebbe I'd marry her. But only a month afterward she got married to the plumber that came up from the city to fix the gutter-pipes of the new hospital. And little Albert never twisted his eye for two days, it was that tired.

Next time I run away I'm going right over that mountain. But I ain't going to take epilecs along. They ain't never cured, and when they get scared or excited they throw fits to beat the band. But I'll take little Albert. Somehow I can't get along without him. And anyway, I ain't going to run away. The drooling ward's a better snap than gold mines, and I hear there's a new nurse coming. Besides, little Albert's bigger than I am now, and I could never carry him over a mountain. And he's growing bigger every day. It's astonishing.

Attention-Deficit/Hyperactivity Disorder

Attention-deficit/hyperactivity Disorder (ADHD) is marked by a persistent pattern of inattention and/or hyperactive and impulsive behavior that is inappropriate for children of the same age and level of development.

Associated inattention behaviors include failure to give attention to details, making careless mistakes in schoolwork or other activities, difficulty sustaining attention to tasks or play activities, inability to listen when spoken to directly, failure to follow through on instructions, and failure to finish schoolwork or chores, These persons often lose things, are easily distracted, and are often forgetful.

Associated hyperactivity behaviors include fidgeting with hands and feet or squirming in seat, having difficulty remaining seated in classrooms, running or climbing excessively, difficulty playing quietly, often being "on the go" or behaving as if "driven by a motor," and often talking excessively.

Associated impulsive behaviors include blurting out answers before questions have been completed, having difficulty awaiting turn, and interrupting or intruding on others (e.g., butting into conversations or games).

Caroline Janover (b. 1943)

Caroline Janover completed her undergraduate degree at Sara Lawrence College and earned master's degrees from Boston University and Farleigh Dickinson University in special education. She is a learning disabilities consultant in the New Jersey public school system and she lectures nationally regarding the talents and academic challenges of children with dyslexia and ADHD. Janover has dyslexia herself and is knowledgeable about ADHD from her academic and professional work. In her wonderful work on ADHD, *Zipper: The Kid with ADHD*, she describes the disorder with humor, insight, and compassion.

Zipper

Zach yanked the letter out of his book bag. His teacher had written "To The Parents Of Zachary Winson" on the envelope. Mrs. Ginsberg only wrote letters home if something very good or very bad had happened. As usual, Zach knew the letter talked about something very bad. He hid the envelope under his pillow and jumped down the stairs two at a time for supper.

Zach tapped the dinner plate with his fork.

"Stop tapping," said his little sister. "Can't you ever sit still?" Isabel had brushed her hair before dinner. She sat up straight and put her napkin in her lap. Zack began to tap a quick rhythm on the table with his fork. "If you don't stop tapping," Isabel said slowly, "I'm going to tell Mom you got sent to the principal's office."

"How did you know that?" asked Zach, looking up surprised.

"Because when my class went to the library, I saw you sitting in the 'big trouble chair' waiting for Dr. Jacobs to come out of her office."

Zach stopped tapping. He swung one leg back and forth under the chair and called into the kitchen, "So what's for supper?"

"Meatloaf and mashed potatoes," his mother replied as she carried the salad bowl into the dining room.

"Yuck!" Zack made a face. "I *hate* meatloaf."

"You liked it last week," his mother said, walking back into the kitchen.

"Now I'm sick of it. I want plain hamburgers."

"Too late now," his mother called in an irritated voice. "I spent the last hour making a delicious meal and you tell me you don't like it even before you take one bite?"

"I love meatloaf," said Isabel smiling sweetly.

Zach tapped out a rhythm on his chest with the fingers on both hands. Maybe his mother was in a bad mood because his dad was late for dinner.

"I said sit *still!*" Isabel snarled. "I'm telling Mom you got in trouble. You're the worst fifth grader in the history of the Valley School."

Zach gave his sister a desperate look. "I'll do your math homework," he pleaded.

"I don't have any math homework. Besides, I love math. I just have ten stupid spelling sentences to write. The list words for second graders are too easy. I only like bonus words like Tyrannosaurus Rex."

"When is Dad getting home?" Zach called into the kitchen.

His mother carried in two glasses of milk and sank wearily into her chair. "Your father has a school board meeting tonight. He won't be home for supper."

"Zipper got into more trouble today," Isabel said smugly, tasting a bite of meatloaf. She always called her brother by his nickname. Gramps had nicknamed him "Zach the Zipper" because when he was a baby he jumped up and down and up and down in his crib.

"Not again. What did you do this time?"

"It wasn't my fault, Mom."

"You always say that," replied Isabel. "It had to be your fault or Dr. Jacobs wouldn't make you go into her office."

"How was your day, Mom? Did you get any big orders at the flower shop?" Zach squirmed in his chair.

"Stop trying to change the subject, Zipper. What is this I hear about being sent to Dr. Jacobs' office?"

Zach punched holes in the meatloaf with his fork. He wished that he was outside playing baseball.

"Tuck in your shirt and stop playing with your food," his mother ordered.

"I can't eat this garbage. It looks like brown, baked sponge with gravy on top."

"Then you can go to your room," his mother snapped.

"I'm sorry, Mom."

"I said go to your room."

Zach grabbed the apple from his dessert plate. He ran up the stairs and slammed his bedroom door. He lay on his pillow and took a big bite of apple. He hadn't eaten anything since school got out. The teacher at homework club had shared her bag of pretzels but Zach had only gotten a few. His stomach rumbled as he opened his L.L. Bean backpack. Zach took out his assignment book and flipped through the pages, most of which were empty. He used to be able to remember all his assignments. Now that he was at the end of the fifth grade, it was getting harder to keep all his homework straight. He had finished his math homework in science class. All he had left to do was to begin the research project about the Native Americans of Northern New Jersey. He could put that off. The five-page report wasn't due for another three days.

Zach flopped onto his bed and listened for sounds. He could hear things that other people didn't pay attention to, like chirping birds and bees buzzing up against the classroom window. Once in school Mrs. Ginsberg had asked the class to write down three wishes. Zach's first wish was to have more friends, especially a best friend. His second wish was to be able to fly. He'd be an eagle and soar high above the earth in blue sky. The last wish was to have a million dollars. He would buy his own pitching machine for the back yard and all the Nintendo games ever made. The rest of the money he would invest to help take care of his parents when they got old.

Zach heard a knock on his bedroom door. "The scoutmaster is on the telephone. You can take the call in our room."

Zach twisted the phone chord and paced in circles around his parents' double bed. When he hung up, his mother was waiting in his bedroom. She handed Zach a peanut butter and jelly sandwich on a paper plate.

"I'm sorry," she said, "I shouldn't have yelled at you like that at the dinner table."

"That's okay, Mom. You're a good cook, only I just suddenly hate meatloaf."

"What did the scoutmaster want?" His mother lay down on Zach's black and white checkered bedspread.

"He just reminded me about tomorrow. The troop is meeting in front of the school at 3:05. We're planting flowers at some old age home."

"I'll write a note to excuse you from homework club."

"How come I have to go to that stupid homework club anyway? I'm the only smart kid in there. The rest are dorks and dummies and Mantimer's mentals."

"Don't talk that way about students in Mrs. Mantimer's special class." His mother sat up on the bed and looked Zach in the eye. "Everyone knows you are intelligent, Zipper, but you don't work up to your potential. You are *totally* disorganized. You either procrastinate or you finish your work and forget to pass it in. A quiet place to do your homework in school won't do you any harm."

"I'd rather be playing baseball," said Zack.

"When you show us that you are responsible enough to complete all your assignments, you can play baseball." His mother tucked her straight, shiny hair behind her ears. "Until then, it's homework club every day from 3:00 to 4:00."

Zach tapped his foot against the desk. "It's not fair," he muttered. "Mrs. Ginsberg sent you a note, Mom," he said slowly. "It's under the pillow."

Zach watched his mother's expression as she read the letter from his teacher. Her face looked pained, like she'd just been smacked in the shins with a baseball bat.

"We'll discuss this situation when your father gets home," his mother announced in an icy voice. Zach looked out his bedroom window. He wished he was the cardinal flying on strawberry red wings high above the houses toward the moon.

*   *   *

Zach woke up feeling hungry. He could hear his dad in the kitchen making breakfast. His mother always left for work before 7 o'clock to buy fresh flowers at the wholesale market. Zach liked eating breakfast with his father. He wasn't mad at him every single minute of the day. His dad was 6'4" tall. He'd played varsity basketball in college. Zach wished that his father had become an NBA All Star player instead of a house builder.

"I understand Mrs. Ginsberg sent another letter," his father said, reaching for the box of cornflakes. "Your mother is pretty upset."

"It wasn't my fault, Dad," said Zach. "Mrs. Dracula Breath blames me for everything. Even when I'm totally innocent, she yells at me. Just because I accidentally flipped an eraser into Kelly's milk and *whispered* the F word, Mrs. Gambini sends me to the principal."

"You've got to *think*, Zipper! Even if you are innocent, watch your language and never talk back, especially to an adult." His father stood up and lifted the whistling tea kettle off the burner.

"But Dad, Mrs. Gambini is such a big, fat jerk! I had to stand up for my rights." Zach wiggled his feet under the chair as he watched his father pour boiling water into his hot chocolate mix.

"Don't drink this yet," his father warned.

Zach picked up the mug. He took a little sip and winced in pain.

"What did I just tell you about letting that cool down?" his father asked.

Zach pushed away the mug of hot chocolate and quickly slurped a large spoonful of cornflakes in cold milk.

"I suggest you write the lunch aide a note of apology."

"Dad, you've got to be kidding! That lady owes ME an apology."

"Don't argue. Just do what I say."

Zach shook his head and grabbed a pencil. By the time his father had finished his coffee, Zach had finished the note.

Wednesday

Dear Mrs. Gambini.

I'm sorry I said a bad word. I'll never do it again. Please stop yelling at me every day at lunch time.

> Sincerely Yours,
> Zachary Winson

Zach tucked the note in the pocket of his blue jeans. After making a peanut butter, banana, and bacon bit sandwich, he carried his New York Yankee lunchbox into the living room. Isabel was watching a nature program about seals on the VCR. She had already made her lunch and finished her hot chocolate and bowl of cereal.

"Zipper, do me a favor. Run upstairs and get the laundry," his dad yelled from the cellar. "Hurry . . . the bus should be here any minute."

Zach rushed up the stairs and grabbed the dirty clothes out of the hamper and off his bedroom floor. Bending down, he noticed his Boy Scout uniform lying under the bed. Ripping off his New York Yankee T-shirt, he quickly buttoned his rumpled shirt with the merit badges sewed onto the sleeve. Zach wrapped the dirty clothes in a damp towel and raced down the cellar stairs to the washing machine.

"Thanks, Zip," his dad said, pouring liquid detergent on top of the clothes.

"You and Isabel had better go wait outside for the bus. Your mother said to give you this note. It's something about not going to homework club today."

Zach snatched the envelope out of his father's hand and raced upstairs to the bathroom. After he brushed his teeth, he glanced into the mirror. He liked his new layered haircut, long on top and shaved around the bottom. It made him look more like a teenager than an eleven-year-old. Zach wished that he'd grow as tall as his father. After baseball, basketball was his second favorite sport.

"Here comes the bus!" Isabel yelled, turning off the VCR. Zach grabbed his backpack and baseball jacket. "Bye, Dad," he called. Leaving the front door wide open, Zach hopped over the wet grass to the school bus waiting at the end of Orchard Lane.

Zach sat down alone in the back of the bus. Isabel always sat in the middle of the bus with her best friend, Liz. The ride to Valley Elementary School took about twenty minutes. Halfway to school, Zach jumped up out of his seat. He ran down the narrow aisle to talk to Henry. Henry was in his Boy Scout troop.

"Sit down, Zipper," yelled the bus driver. "How many times have I told you to stay in your seat?"

Zach sat down quickly next to Henry. "You coming to the old age home this afternoon?" he asked. Henry nodded. Zach noticed that Henry's uniform looked like it had been pressed at the dry cleaners. "Scoutmaster Holmes says we're going to plant some kind of flowers. I'd rather be playing baseball," said Zach.

"Me too," said Henry. "I'm allergic to pollen."

"See you after school," said Zach. Crouching down, he waited to make sure the bus driver wasn't looking in her rearview mirror. On the way back to his seat, Zach noticed that Charlie had a new haircut. Pointing his finger, he blurted out, "Hi dweeb head!"

Zach pulled his backpack onto the seat next to him and reached inside for a snack. With a sinking feeling, he realized that he had left his New York Yankee lunch box sitting on top of the television set.

"Stop the bus!" Zach yelled, running up the aisle toward the driver. "Stop . . . I forgot my lunch!"

"SIT DOWN!" shrieked the bus driver. Her voice was so sharp that all the children on the bus stopped talking. They stared at Zach.

"That kid's an idiot," a sixth grader joked.

Zach felt an angry panic rise like steam inside him. He grabbed the back of Isabel's seat as the bus swerved around the corner.

"I'll give you my sandwich," his sister said suddenly. "Liz and all my friends will share their food." She handed Zach her tomato and cream cheese sandwich and a carton of apple juice. "You better sit down," she whispered, "before the bus driver kills you."

Zach gave his sister a grateful look. Without a word, he slumped back down, alone, on the very last seat in the school bus.

＊ ＊ ＊

Zach stuffed the loose pages of his social studies report into his backpack. He'd planned to organize them in the plastic binder before he went to school, but now there wasn't time. He'd overslept.

"Hurry up!" Isabel shrieked.

Zach's dad leapt up the stairs. "What happened?" he called.

Zach stood in the middle of the room in his Power Rangers pajamas, holding his backpack. "Dad, help me find my shoes. I can't find them anywhere." He quickly dressed and grabbed a banana from the fruit basket.

"The bus is here," Isabel announced. "I made you a sandwich for lunch so you better be nice to me."

"Thanks," Zach said, jamming the sandwich into his backpack. "Dad, did you find my sneakers?" he hollered up the stairs.

"For some strange reason, your shoes were on the bathroom window sill holding down the shade."

Zach grabbed the sneakers out of his father's hand and shoved his foot into the right shoe. He hopped out the front door and jumped onto the school bus. Frank stopped him as he made his way to the back of the bus.

"Where were you yesterday, Zipper? We sure did miss you, man. We got killed by the Sluggers!"

Zach stood in the aisle, unsure what to say.

"SIT DOWN!" yelled the bus driver.

"I better get in my seat," Zach said quickly. As he tied his shoelaces, he tried to decide what to tell the team. He could say that he had developed a high fever and couldn't make the game. Except that if he'd had a high fever, his dad would be keeping him home from school. He could say he was overcome with grief because his goldfish died, but Moby and Dick were still swimming happily in their bowl. He could say that he had an unbelievable amount of homework, but no one on the team would believe that. By the time the bus arrived at the Valley School, Zach had decided to tell the truth.

Zach spotted Josh and Kip locking up their bikes. Instead of going over to the bike rack, Zach hurried to the side door entrance. If he got to class a little early, he could put together his Indian report and no one would hassle him about the game.

"Where were you?" Kip called. "Coach Ward sure was mad you didn't show up. The Sluggers whipped us 11 to 3."

Zach winced. That was the worst defeat all season. "Sorry guys," Zach confessed, "I forgot we had a game."

"You what?" Frankie's black eyes opened wide. "You forgot the game! Give me a break! We were counting on you, man." Frankie kicked the ground in disgust.

"I was checking out the gardens at the old age home and I just forgot."

"You're such a wimp!" Henry chimed in.

"I forgot, honest. I wanted to play but I lost track of the time." Zach made a step toward the side door.

"Get back here," yelled Skidder Malonowski. He was the team captain and the best infielder in the fifth grade. "Face it, you chickened out!" he sneered.

Before Zach could say another word, Josh stepped in front of Skidder. "Lay off," he said. "Zipper forgot. Don't you get it? It was an accident. He wanted to play."

Zach looked at Josh with a startled expression.

"I know what it's like to get teased," Josh said under his breath, "especially when you're innocent. My brother has dumped on me since the moment I got born."

"Thanks, pal," Zach said. He was about to apologize for ripping up the marijuana poster when the bell above the side door blasted three sharp rings. Mr. Maggio opened the door and instructed the students to proceed directly to their classrooms.

Zach hurried toward his homeroom. Mrs. Ginsberg had put a wire basket on the counter by the pencil sharpener for the social studies reports. Zach was the last to turn in his project. He wiped it off as best he could and put it face down in the basket. Mrs. Ginsberg picked up the folder on top of the pile.

"Whose report?" she asked, holding the soggy cover at arm's length.

Zach swung his legs under his chair. "That's mine."

"I can't accept this report. It's covered with peanut butter."

"My sandwich leaked."

"And I don't see a title page." Mrs. Ginsberg continued trying to unstick the pages.

"I forgot to make a title page, but everything else is there," Zach assured her. "I even cut out pictures of Indians from *National Geographic* for extra credit."

Mrs. Ginsberg shook her head and wiped her long, red fingernails with a tissue. "I'm sorry, Zipper. I'm afraid I'll have to give you an incomplete. You can not hand in a report in this condition and expect to get full credit."

"But it's my sister's fault. She made the sandwich," Zach protested. "I handed the report in on time, didn't I?"

"The report is on time but it is missing a title page and it is currently unreadable. If you recopy your rough draft and hand it in on Monday, I will only deduct five points from your final grade."

Zach swung his feet even faster. "But Mrs. Ginsberg . . . ."

"There will be no further discussion of this matter." Mrs. Ginsberg picked up the pile of reports and put them in her canvas book bag. "And now class, it is time for the math quiz," she said cheerfully . . . .

Oppositional Defiant Disorder

In this disorder the youth presents an enduring pattern of negativistic, hostile, and defiant behaviors. Such behaviors do not violate social norms or the rights of others. These children often lose their temper, argue, and refuse to cooperate with adults. They deliberately do things to annoy other people and often blame others for their mistakes or behavior.

O. Henry (William Sydney Porter) (1862–1910)

O. Henry provides us an example of an oppositional defiant youth in his short story, "The Ransom of Red Chief." This story focuses on the playful defiant behaviors of a youth toward his kidnappers. Some of the behaviors may appear to violate social norms, which would indicate a conduct disorder rather than oppositional defiant disorder. However, in light of the context of the behaviors (he is a kidnap victim), the lack of any information regarding "Red Chief's" behavior outside the context of the story, and the playful nature of his behaviors, we have chosen to utilize the story to demonstrate the behavior of an oppositional youth.

(Refer to chapter 7 for biographical information on O. Henry.)

"The Ransom of Red Chief"

It looked like a good thing: but wait till I tell you. We were down south, in Alabama—Bill Driscoll and myself—when this kidnapping idea struck us. It was, as Bill afterward expressed it, "during a moment of temporary mental apparition"; but we didn't find that out till later.

There was a town down there, as flat as a funnel-cake, and called Summit, of course. It contained inhabitants of as undeleterious and self-satisfied a class of peasantry as ever clustered around a Maypole.

Bill and me had a joint capital of about six hundred dollars, and we needed just two thousand dollars more to pull off a fraudulent town-lot scheme in Western Illinois with. We talked it over on the front steps of a hotel. Philoprogenitiveness, says we, is strong in semi-rural communities; therefore, and for other reasons, a kidnapping project ought to do better there than in the radius of newspapers that send reporters out in plain clothes to stir up talk about such things. We knew that Summit couldn't get after us with anything stronger than constables and, maybe, some lackadaisical bloodhounds and a diatribe or two in the *Weekly Farmers' Budget*. So, it looked good.

We selected for our victim the only child of a prominent citizen named Ebenezer Dorset. The father was respectable and tight, a mortgage fancier and a stern, upright collection-plate passer and forecloser. The kid was a boy of ten, with bas-relief freckles, and hair the color of the magazine you buy at the newsstand when you want to catch a train. Bill and me figured that Ebenezer would melt down for a ransom of two thousand dollars to a cent. But wait till I tell you.

About two miles from Summit was a little mountain, covered with a dense cedar brake. On the rear elevation of this mountain was a cave. There we stored provisions.

One evening after sundown, we drove in a buggy past old Dorset's house. The kid was in the street, throwing rocks at a kitten on the opposite fence.

"Hey, little boy!" says Bill, "would you like to have a bag of candy and a nice ride?"

The boy catches Bill neatly in the eye with a piece of brick.

"That will cost the old man an extra five hundred dollars," says Bill, climbing over the wheel.

That boy put up a fight like a welter-weight cinnamon bear; but, at last, we got him down in the bottom of the buggy and drove away. We took him up to the cave, and I hitched the horse in the cedar brake. After dark I drove the buggy to the little village, three miles away, where we had hired it, and walked back to the mountain.

Bill was pasting court-plaster over the scratches and bruises on his features. There was a fire burning behind the big rock at the entrance of the cave, and the boy was watching a pot of boiling coffee, with two buzzard tail-feathers stuck in his red hair. He points a stick at me when I come up, and says: "Ha! cursed paleface, do you dare to enter the camp of Red Chief, the terror of the plains?"

"He's all right now," says Bill, rolling up his trousers and examining some bruises on his shins. "We're playing Indian. We're making Buffalo Bill's show look like magic-lantern views of Palestine in the town hall. I'm Old Hank, the Trapper, Red Chief's captive, and I'm to be scalped at daybreak. By Geronimo! that kid can kick hard."

Yes, sir that boy seemed to be having the time of his life. The fun of camping out in a cave had made him forget that he was a captive himself. He immediately christened me Snake-eye, the Spy, and announced that, when his braves returned from the warpath, I was to be broiled at the stake at the rising of the sun.

Then we had supper; and he filled his mouth full of bacon and bread and gravy, and began to talk. He made a during-dinner speech something like this:

"I like this fine. I never camped out before; but I had a pet 'possum once, and I was nine last birthday. I hate to go to school. Rats ate up sixteen of Jimmy Talbot's aunt's speckled hen's eggs. Are there any real Indians in these woods? I want some more gravy. Does the trees moving make the wind blow? We had five puppies. What makes your nose so red, Hank? My father has lots of money. Are the stars hot? I whipped Ed Walker twice, Saturday. I don't like girls. You dassent catch toads unless with a string. Do oxen make any noise? Why are oranges round? Have you got beds to sleep on in the cave? Amos Murray has got six toes. A parrot can talk, but a monkey or a fish can't. How many does it take to make twelve?"

Every few minutes he would remember that he was a pesky redskin, and pick up his stick rifle and tiptoe to the mouth of the cave to rubber for the scouts of the hated paleface. Now and then he would let out a war-whoop that made Old Hank the Trapper shiver. That boy had Bill terrorized from the start.

"Red Chief," says I to the kid, "would you like to go home?"

"Aw, what for?" says he. "I don't have any fun at home. I hate to go to school. I like to camp out. You won't take me back home again, Snake-eye, will you?"

"Not right away," says I. "We'll stay here in the cave awhile."

"All right!" says he. "That'll be fine. I never had such fun in all my life."

We went to bed about eleven o'clock. We spread down some wide blankets and quilts and put Red Chief between us. We weren't afraid he'd run away. He kept us awake for three hours, jumping up and reaching for his rifle and screeching: "Hist! pard," in mine and Bill's ears, as the fancied crackle of a twig or the rustle of a leaf revealed to his young imagination the stealthy approach of the outlaw band. At last, I fell into a troubled sleep, and dreamed that I had been kidnapped and chained to a tree by a ferocious pirate with red hair.

Just at daybreak, I was awakened by a series of awful screams from Bill. They weren't yells, or howls, or shouts, or whoops, or yawps, such as you'd expect from a manly set of vocal organs—they were simply indecent, terrifying, humiliating screams, such as women emit when they see ghosts or caterpillars. It's an awful thing to hear a strong, desperate, fat man scream incontinently in a cave at daybreak.

I jumped up to see what the matter was. Red Chief was sitting on Bill's chest, with one hand twined in Bill's hair. In the other he had the sharp case-knife, we used for slicing bacon; and he was industriously and realistically trying to take Bill's scalp, according to the sentence that had been pronounced upon him the evening before.

I got the knife away from the kid and made him lie down again. But, from that moment, Bill's spirit was broken. He laid down on his side of the bed, but he never closed an eye again in sleep as long as that boy was with us. I dozed off for a while, but along toward sun-up I remembered that Red Chief had said I was to be burned at the stake at the rising of the sun. I wasn't nervous or afraid; but I sat up and lit my pipe and leaned against a rock.

"What you getting up so soon for, Sam?" asked Bill.

"Me?" says I. "Oh, I got a kind of pain in my shoulder. I thought sitting up would rest it."

"You're a liar!" says Bill. "You're afraid. You was to be burned at sunrise, and you was afraid he'd do it. And he would, too, if he could find a match. Ain't it awful, Sam? Do you think anybody will pay out money to get a little imp like that back home?"

"Sure," said I. "A rowdy kid like that is just the kind that parents dote on. Now, you and the Chief get up and cook breakfast, while I go up on top of this mountain and reconnoitre."

I went up on the peak of the little mountain and ran my eye over the contiguous vicinity. Over towards Summit I expected to see the sturdy yeomanry of the village armed with scythes and pitchforks beating the countryside for the dastardly kidnappers. But what I saw was a peaceful landscape dotted with one man ploughing with a dun mule. Nobody was dragging the creek; no couriers dashed hither and yon, bringing tiding of no news to the distracted parents. There was a sylvan attitude of somnolent sleepiness pervading that section of the external outward surface of Alabama that lay exposed to my view. "Perhaps," says I to myself, "it has not yet been discovered that the wolves have borne away the tender lambkin from the fold. Heaven help the wolves!" says I, and I went down the mountain to breakfast.

When I got to the cave I found Bill backed up against the side of it, breathing hard, and the boy threatening to smash him with a rock half as big as a cocoanut.

"He put a red-hot boiled potato down my back," explained Bill, "and then mashed it with his foot; and I boxed his ears. Have you got a gun about you, Sam?"

I took the rock away from the boy and kind of patched up the argument. "I'll fix you," says the kid to Bill. "No man ever yet struck the Red Chief but he got paid for it. You better beware!"

After breakfast the kid takes a piece of leather with strings wrapped around it out of his pocket and goes outside the cave unwinding it.

"What's he up to now?" says Bill, anxiously. "You don't think he'll run away, do you, Sam?"

"No fear of it," says I. "He don't seem to be much of a home body. But we've got to fix up some plan about the ransom. There don't seem to be much excitement around Summit on account of his disappearance; but maybe they haven't realized yet that he's gone. His folks may think he's spending the night with Aunt Jane or one of the neighbors. Anyhow, he'll be missed to-day. To-night we must get a message to his father demanding the two thousand dollars for his return."

Just then we heard a kind of war-whoop, such as David might have emitted when he knocked out the champion Goliath. It was a sling that Red Chief had pulled out of his pocket, and he was whirling it around his head.

I dodged, and heard a heavy thud and a kind of sigh from Bill, like a horse gives out when you take his saddle off. A niggerhead rock the size of an egg had caught Bill just behind his left ear. He loosened himself all over and fell in the fire across the frying pan of hot water for washing the dishes. I dragged him out and poured cold water on his head for half an hour.

By and by, Bill sits up and feels behind his ear and says: "Sam, do you know who my favorite Biblical character is?"

"Take it easy," says I. "You'll come to your senses presently."

"King Herod," says he. "You won't go away and leave me here alone, will you, Sam?"

I went out and caught that boy and shook him until his freckles rattled.

"If you don't behave," says I, "I'll take you straight home. Now are you going to be good, or not?"

"I was only funning," says he, sullenly. "I don't mean to hurt Old Hank. But what did he hit me for? I'll behave, Snake-eye, if you won't send me home, and if you'll let me play the Black Scout to-day."

"I don't know the game," says I. "That's for you and Mr. Bill to decide. He's your playmate for the day. I'm going away for a while, on business. Now, you come in and make friends with him and say you are sorry for hurting him, or home you go, at once."

I made him and Bill shake hands, and then I took Bill aside and told him I was going to Poplar Cove, a little village three miles from the cave, and find out what I could about how the kidnapping had been regarded in Summit. Also, I thought it best to send a peremptory letter to old man Dorset that day, demanding the ransom and dictating how it should be paid.

"You know, Sam," says Bill, "I've stood by you without batting an eye in earthquakes, fire and flood—in poker games, dynamite outrages, police raids, train robberies, and cyclones. I never lost my nerve yet till we kidnapped that two-legged skyrocket of a kid. He's got me going. You won't leave me long with him, will you, Sam?"

"I'll be back sometime this afternoon," says I. "You must keep the boy amused and quiet until I return. And now we'll write the letter to old Dorset."

Bill and I got paper and pencil and worked on the letter while Red Chief, with a blanket wrapped around him, strutted up and down, guarding the mouth of the cave. Bill begged me tearfully to make the ransom fifteen hundred dollars instead of two thousand. "I ain't attempting," says he, "to decry the celebrated moral aspect of parental affection, but we're dealing with humans, and it ain't human for anybody to give up two thousand dollars for that forty-pound chunk of freckled wildcat. I'm willing to take a chance at fifteen hundred dollars. You can charge the difference up to me."

So, to relieve Bill, I accepted, and we collaborated a letter that ran this way:

Ebenezer Dorset, Esq.:

We have your boy concealed in a place far from Summit. It is useless for you or the most skillful detectives to attempt to find him. Absolutely, the only terms on which you can have him are these: We demand fifteen hundred dollars in large bills for his return; the money to be left at midnight to-night at the same spot and in the same box as your reply—as hereinafter described. If you agree to these terms, send your answer in writing by a solitary messenger to-night at half-past eight o'clock. After crossing Owl Creek on the road to Poplar Cove, there are three large trees about a hundred yards apart, close to the fence of the wheat field on the right-hand side. At the bottom of the fence-post, opposite the third tree, will be found a small pasteboard box.

The messenger will place the answer in this box and return immediately to Summit.

If you attempt any treachery or fail to comply with our demand as stated, you will never see your boy again.

If you pay the money as demanded, he will be returned to you safe and well within three hours. These terms are final, and if you do not accede to them no further communication will be attempted.

Two Desperate Men

I addressed this letter to Dorset, and put it in my pocket. As I was about to start, the kid comes up to me and says:

"Aw, Snake-eye, you said I could play the Black Scout while you was gone."

"Play it, of course," says I. "Mr. Bill will play with you. What kind of a game is it?"

"I'm the Black Scout," says Red Chief, "and I have to ride to the stockade to warn the settlers that the Indians are coming. I'm tired of playing Indian myself. I want to be the Black Scout."

"All right," says I. "It sounds harmless to me. I guess Mr. Bill will help you foil the pesky savages."

"What am I to do?" asks Bill, looking at the kid suspiciously.

"You are the hoss," says Black Scout. "Get down on your hands and knees. How can I ride to the stockade without a hoss?"

"You'd better keep him interested," said I, "till we get the scheme going. Loosen up."

Bill gets down on his all fours, and a look comes in his eyes like a rabbit's when you catch it in a trap.

"How far is it to the stockade, kid?" he asks, in a husky manner of voice.

"Ninety miles," says the Black Scout. "And you have to hump yourself to get there on time. Whoa, now!"

The Black Scout jumps on Bill's back and digs his heels in his side.

"For heaven's sake," says Bill, "hurry back, Sam, as soon as you can. I wish we hadn't made the ransom more than a thousand. Say, you quit kicking me or I'll get up and warm you good."

I walked over to Poplar Cove and sat around the post-office and store, talking with the chaw-bacons that came in to trade. One whiskerando says that he hears Summit is all upset on account of Elder Ebenezer Dorset's boy having been lost or stolen. That was all I wanted to know. I bought some smoking tobacco, referred casually to the price of black-eyed peas, posted my letter surreptitiously, and came away. The postmaster said the mail-carrier would come by in an hour to take the mail on to Summit.

When I got back to the cave Bill and the boy were not to be found. I explored the vicinity of the cave, and risked a yodel or two, but there was no response.

So I lighted my pipe and sat down on a mossy bank to await developments.

In about half an hour I heard the bushes rustle, and Bill wabbled out into the little glade in front of the cave. Behind him was the kid, stepping softly like a scout, with a broad grin on his face. Bill stopped, took off his hat, and wiped his face with a red handkerchief. The kid stopped about eight feet behind him.

"Sam," says Bill, "I suppose you'll think I'm a renegade, but I couldn't help it. I'm a grown person with masculine proclivities and habits of self-defense, but there is a time when all systems of egotism and predominance fail. The boy is gone. I sent him home. All is off. There was martyrs in old times," goes on Bill, "that suffered death rather than give up the particular graft they enjoyed. None of 'em ever was subjected to such supernatural tortures as I have been. I tried to be faithful to our articles of depredation; but there came a limit."

"What's the trouble, Bill?" I asks him.

"I was rode," says Bill, "the ninety miles to the stockade, not barring an inch. Then, when the settlers was rescued, I was given oats. Sand ain't a palatable substitute. And then, for an hour I had to try to explain to him why there was nothin' in holes, how a road can run both ways, and what makes the grass green. I tell you, Sam, a human can only stand so much. I takes him by the neck of his clothes and drags him down the mountain. On the way he kicks my legs black and blue from the knees down; and I've got to have two or three bites on my thumb and hand cauterized.

"But he's gone"—continues Bill—"gone home. I showed him the road to Summit and kicked him about eight feet nearer there at one kick. I'm sorry we lose the ransom; but it was either that or Bill Driscoll to the madhouse."

Bill is puffing and blowing, but there is a look of ineffable peace and growing content on his rose-pink features.

"Bill," says I, "there isn't any heart disease in your family, is there?"

"No," says Bill, "nothing chronic except malaria and accidents. Why?"

"Then you might turn around," says I, "and have a look behind you."

Bill turns around and sees the boy, and loses his complexion and sits down plump on the ground and begins to pluck aimlessly at grass and little sticks. For an hour I was afraid of his mind. And then I told him that my scheme was to put the whole job through immediately and that we would get the ransom and be off with it by midnight if old Dorset fell in with our proposition. So Bill braced up enough to give the kid a weak sort of a smile and a promise to play the Russian in a Japanese war with him as soon as he felt a little better.

I had a scheme for collecting that ransom without danger of being caught by counterplots that ought to commend itself to professional kidnappers. The tree under which the answer was to be left—and the money later on—was close to the road fence with big, bare fields on all sides. If a gang of constables should be watching for any one to come for the note they could see him a long way off crossing the fields or in the road. But no, siree! At half-past eight I was up in that tree as well hidden as a tree toad, waiting for the messenger to arrive.

Exactly on time, a half-grown boy rides up the road on a bicycle, locates the pasteboard box at the foot of the fence-post, slips a folded piece of paper into it, and pedals away again back toward Summit.

I waited an hour and then concluded the thing was square. I slid down the tree, got the note, slipped along the fence till I struck the woods, and was back at the cave in another half an hour. I opened the note, got near the lantern, and read it to Bill. It was written with a pen in a crabbed hand, and the sum and substance of it was this:

Two Desperate Men.

Gentlemen: I received your letter to-day by post, in regard to the ransom you ask for the return of my son. I think you are a little high in your demands, and I hereby make you a counter-proposition, which I am inclined to believe you will accept. You bring Johnny home and pay me two hundred and fifty dollars in cash, and I agree to take him off your hands. You had better come at night, for the neighbors believe he is lost, and I couldn't be responsible for what they would do to anybody they saw bringing him back. Very respectfully,

Ebenezer Dorset

"Great pirates of Penzance," says I; "of all the impudent—"

But I glanced at Bill, and hesitated. He had the most appealing look in his eyes I ever saw on the face of a dumb or talking brute.

"Sam," says he, "what's two hundred and fifty dollars, after all? We've got the money. One more night of this kid will send me to a bed in Bedlam. Besides being a thorough gentleman, I think Mr. Dorset is a spendthrift for making us such a liberal offer. You ain't going to let the chance go, are you?"

"Tell you the truth, Bill," says I, "this little ewe lamb has somewhat got on my nerves too. We'll take him home, pay the ransom, and make our get-away."

We took him home that night. We got him to go by telling him that his father had bought a silver-mounted rifle and a pair of moccasins for him, and we were to hunt bears the next day.

It was just twelve o'clock when we knocked at Ebenezer's front door. Just at that moment when I should have been abstracting the fifteen hundred dollars from the box under the tree, according to the original proposition, Bill was counting out two hundred and fifty dollars into Dorset's hand.

When the kid found out we were going to leave him at home he started up a howl like a calliope and fastened himself as tight as a leech to Bill's leg. His father peeled him away, gradually, like a porous plaster.

"How long can you hold him?" asks Bill.

"I'm not as strong as I used to be," says old Dorset, "but I think I can promise you ten minutes."

"Enough," says Bill. "In ten minutes I shall cross the Central, Southern, and Middle Western States, and be legging it trippingly for the Canadian border."

And, as dark as it was, and as fat as Bill was, and as good a runner as I am, he was a good mile and a half out of Summit before I could catch up with him.

Conduct Disorder

In this disorder there is a repetitive pattern of behavior that either violates the basic rights of others or violates societal norms or rules. Behaviors include physical aggression, hostility, lying, truancy, vandalism, stealing, and the use of alcohol and drugs. Such young people lack genuine concern for the feelings of others and seldom have feelings of guilt or remorse.

Claude Brown (1927–2002)

Claude Brown was born in Harlem, New York in 1927. His father was an alcoholic dockworker. Brown began getting into legal problems at the age of eight. His father frequently beat him and his siblings when they got into trouble. His mother battled with the juvenile court to get him into state juvenile programs. Brown spent years in juvenile detention centers and state training schools for stealing and selling drugs, but his life changed when a drug addict shot him. The shooting incident, along with the encouragement of his mother and some friends, helped him to leave his life of crime behind, and in 1959 he entered Howard University in Washington, D.C., where he began writing.

Brown wrote about what he knew best, and in 1965 he published his life story, *Manchild in the Promised Land*. This autobiographical novel has been in print for over thirty years and had sold over four million copies as of 2000. Brown's work has been widely praised for its portrayal of the generation of African Americans whose parents left the sharecropping lifestyle of the South for the cities of the North.

Brown's description of his days of stealing and drug dealing provide an excellent example of the features of conduct disorder. He describes using physical aggression, lying, being truant from school, using alcohol, selling drugs, and stealing—all of which are common characteristics of conduct disorder.

Manchild in the Promised Land

I remembered sitting on the stoop with Danny, years before, when a girl came up and started yelling at him. She said that her mother didn't want her brother to hang out with Danny any more, because Danny had taught her brother to play hookey. When the girl had gone down the street, I asked Danny what hookey was. He said it was a game he would teach me as soon as I started going to school.

Danny was a man of his word. He was my next-door neighbor, and he rang my doorbell about 7:30 A.M. on the second day of school. Danny said he would have taught me to play hookey the day before, but he knew that Mama would have to take me to school on the first day. As we headed toward the backyard to hide our books, Danny began to explain the great game of hookey. It sounded like lots of fun to me. Instead of going to school, we would go all over the city stealing, sneak into a movie, or go up on a roof and throw bottles down into the street. Danny suggested that we start the day off by waiting for Mr. Gordon to put out his vegetables; we could steal some sweet potatoes and cook them in the backyard. I was sorry I hadn't started school sooner, because hookey sure was a lot of fun.

Before I began going to school, I was always in the streets with Danny, Kid, and Butch. Sometimes, without saying a word, they would all start to run like hell, and a white man was always chasing them. One morning as I entered the backyard where all the hookey players went to draw up an activity schedule for the day, Butch told me that Danny and Kid had been caught by Mr. Sands the day before. He went on to warn me about Mr. Sands, saying Mr. Sands was that white man who was always chasing somebody and that I should try to remember what he looked like and always be on the lookout for him. He also warned me not to try to outrun Mr. Sands, "because that cat is fast." Butch said, "When you see him, head for a backyard or a roof. He won't follow you there."

During the next three months, I stayed out of school twenty-one days. Dad was beating the hell out of me for playing hookey, and it was no fun being in the street in the winter, so I started going to school regularly. But when spring rolled around, hookey became my favorite game again. Mr. Sands was known to many parents in the neighborhood as the truant officer. He never caught me in the street, but he came by my house many mornings to escort me to class. This was one way of getting me to school, but he never found a way to keep me there. The moment my teacher took her eyes off me, I was back on the street. Every time Dad got a card from Mr. Sands, I got bruises and welts from Dad. The beatings had only a temporary effect on me. Each time, the beatings got worse; and each time, I promised never to play hookey again. One time I kept that promise for three whole weeks.

The older guys had been doing something called "catting" for years. That catting was staying away from home all night was all I knew about the term. Every time I asked one of the fellows to teach me how to cat, I was told I wasn't old enough. As time went on, I learned that guys catted when they were afraid to go home and that they slept everywhere but in comfortable places. The usual places for catting were subway trains, cellars, unlocked cars, under a friend's bed, and in vacant newsstands.

One afternoon when I was eight years old, I came home after a busy day of running from the police, truant officer, and storekeepers. The first thing I did was to look in the mailbox. This had become a habit with me even though I couldn't read. I was looking for a card, a yellow card. That yellow card meant that I would walk into the house and Dad would be waiting for me with his razor strap. He would usually be eating and would pause just long enough to say to me, "Nigger, you got a ass whippin' comin'." My sisters, Carole and Margie, would cry almost as much as I would while Dad was beating me, but this never stopped him. After each beating I got, Carole, who was two years older than I, would beg me to stop playing hookey. There were a few times when I thought I would stop just to keep her and Margie, my younger sister, from crying so much. I decided to threaten Carole and Margie instead, but this didn't help. I continued to play hookey, and they continued to cry on the days that the yellow card got home before I did.

Generally, I would break open the mailbox, take out the card, and throw it away. Whenever I did this, I'd have to break open two or three other mailboxes and throw away the contents, just to make it look good.

This particular afternoon, I saw a yellow card, but I couldn't find anything to break into the box with. Having some matches in my pockets, I decided to burn the card in the box and not bother to break the box open. After I had used all the matches, the card was not completely burned. I stood there getting more frightened by the moment. In a little while, Dad would be coming home; and when he looked in the mailbox, anywhere would be safer than home for me.

This was going to be my first try at catting out. I went looking for somebody to cat with me. My crime partner, Buddy, whom I had played hookey with that day, was busily engaged in a friendly rock fight when I found him in Colonial Park. When I suggest that we go up on the hill and steal some newspapers, Buddy lost interest in the rock fight.

We stole papers from newsstands and sold them on the subway trains until nearly 1 A.M. That was when the third cop woke us and put us off the train with the usual threat. They would always promise to beat us over the head with a billy and lock us up. Looking back, I think the cops took their own threats more seriously than we did. The third cop put us off the Independent Subway at Fifty-Ninth Street and Columbus Circle. I wasn't afraid of cops, but I didn't go back into the subway—the next cop might have taken me home.

In 1945, there was an Automat where we came out of the subway. About five slices of pie later, Buddy and I left the Automat in search of a place to stay the night. In the center of the Circle, there were some old lifeboats that the Navy had put on display.

Buddy and I slept in the boat for two nights. On the third day, Buddy was caught ringing a cash register in a five-and-dime store. He was sent to Children's Center, and I spent the third night in the boat alone. On the fourth night, I met a duty-conscious cop, who took me home. That ended my first catting adventure.

Dad beat me for three consecutive days for telling what he called "that dumb damn lie about sleeping in a boat on Fifty-Ninth Street." On the fourth day, I think he went to check my story out for himself. Anyhow, the beatings stopped for a while, and he never mentioned the boat again.

Before long, I was catting regularly, staying away from home for weeks at a time. Sometimes the cops would pick me up and take me to a Children's Center. The Centers were located all over the city. At some time in my childhood, I must have spent at least one night in all of them except the one on Staten Island.

The procedure was that a policeman would take me to the Center in the borough where he had picked me up. The Center would assign someone to see that I got a bath and was put to bed. The following day, my parents would be notified as to where I was and asked to come and claim me. Dad was always in favor of leaving me where I was and saying good riddance. But Mama always made the trip. Although Mama never failed to come for me, she seldom found me there when she arrived. I had no trouble getting out of Children's Centers, so I seldom stayed for more than a couple of days.

When I was finally brought home—sometimes after weeks of catting—Mama would hide my clothes or my shoes. This would mean that I couldn't get out of the house if I should take a notion to do so. Anyway, that's how Mama had it figured. The truth of the matter is that these measures only made getting out of the house more difficult for me. I would have to wait until one of the fellows came around to see me. After hearing my plight, he would go out and round up some of the gang, and they would steal some clothes and shoes for me. When they had the clothes and shoes, one of them would come to the house and let me know. About ten minutes later, I would put on my sister's dress, climb down the back fire escape, and meet the gang with the clothes.

If something was too small or too large, I would go and steal the right size. This could only be done if the item that didn't fit was not the shoes. If the shoes were too small or large, I would have trouble running in them and probably get caught. So I would wait around in the back yard while someone stole me a pair.

Mama soon realized that hiding my clothes would not keep me in the house. The next thing she tried was threatening to send me away until I was twenty-one. This was only frightening to me at the moment of hearing it. Ever so often, either Dad or Mama would sit down and have a heart-to-heart talk with me. These talks were very moving. I always promised to mend my bad ways. I was always sincere and usually kept the promise for about a week. During these weeks, I went to school every day and kept my stealing at a minimum. By the beginning of the second week, I had reverted back to my wicked ways, and Mama would have to start praying all over again.

The neighborhood prophets began making prophecies about my life-span. They all had me dead, buried, and forgotten before my twenty-first birthday. These predictions were based on false tales of policemen shooting at me, on truthful tales of my falling off a trolley car into the midst of oncoming automobile traffic while hitching a ride, and also on my uncontrollable urge to steal. There was much justification for these prophecies. By the time I was nine years old, I had been hit by a bus, thrown into the Harlem River (intentionally), hit by a car, and severely beaten with a chain. And I had set the house afire.

While Dad was still trying to beat me into a permanent conversion, Mama was certain that somebody had worked roots on me. She was writing to all her relatives in the South for solutions, but they were only able to say, "that boy musta been born with the devil in him." Some of them advised Mama to send me down there, because New York was no place to raise a child. Dad thought this was a good idea, and he tried to sell it to Mama. But Mama wasn't about to split up her family. She said I would stay in New York, devil or no devil. So I stayed in New York, enjoying every crazy minute.

Mama's favorite question was, "Boy, why you so bad?" I tried many times to explain to Mama that I wasn't "so bad." I tried to make her understand that it was trying to be good that generally got me into trouble. I remember telling her that I played hookey to avoid getting into trouble in school. It seemed that whenever I went to school, I got into a fight with the teacher. The teacher would take me to the principal's office. After I had fought with the principal, I would be sent home and not allowed back in school without one of my parents. So to avoid all that trouble, I just didn't go to school. When I stole things, it was only to save the family money and avoid arguments or scoldings whenever I asked for money.

Mama seemed silly to me. She was bothered because most of the parents in the neighborhood didn't allow their children to play with me. What she didn't know was that I never wanted to play with them. My friends were all daring like me, tough like me, dirty like me, ragged like me, cursed like me, and had a great love for trouble like me. We took pride in being able to hitch rides on trolleys, buses, taxicabs and in knowing how to steal and fight. We knew that we were the only kids in the neighborhood who usually had more than ten dollars in their pockets. There were other people who knew this too, and that was often a problem for us. Somebody was always trying to shake us down or rob us. This was usually done by the older hustlers in the neighborhood or by storekeepers or cops. At other times, older fellows would shake us down, con us, or Murphy us out of our loot. We accepted this as the ways of life. Everybody was stealing from everybody else. And sometimes we would shake down newsboys and shoeshine boys. So we really had no complaints coming. Although none of my sidekicks was over twelve years of age, we didn't think of ourselves as kids. The other kids my age were thought of as kids by me. I felt that since I knew more about life than they did, I had the right to regard them as kids.

In the fall of 1945, I was expelled from school for the first time. By the time February rolled around, I had been expelled from three other schools in Harlem. In February, Mama sent me downtown to live with Grandpa on Eldridge Street. Papa enrolled me in a public school on Forsythe and Stanton Streets. It was cold that winter, and I usually went to school to be warm.

For weeks, everybody thought things were going along fine. The first day I didn't come home from school, Papa ignored it, thinking that I had gone uptown. But the next day, Mama received a card from Bellevue Hospital's psychiatric division informing her that I was undergoing psychiatric observation and that she was allowed to visit me on Wednesdays and Sundays. My grandfather knew nothing about any of this, so when Mama (his oldest daughter) came to him wanting to know what her son was doing in Bellevue, Papa asked, "How did he get there?" They both came over to Bellevue believing I had gone crazy. Dad didn't bother to come, because as he put it, "That's where he should have been years ago." I was glad Dad didn't come, because he might not have believed that I was falsely accused of trying to push a boy in school out of a five-story window. Mama had already heard my teacher's version of the window incident, and now I was trying to explain my side of the story. My teacher had told her that I persuaded a boy to look out of the window to see an accident that hadn't taken place. Because of the window's wide ledge, I was holding his legs while he leaned out of the window. The boy started screaming and calling for help. When he got down out of the window, the boy said I had been trying to push him out of the window. Just because we had fought the day before and I was the only one who saw the accident, I ended up in the nutbox.

I don't think my story completely convinced Mama or Papa, but they gave me the benefit of the doubt. Mama told me that I would have to stay in the hospital for a few weeks. Her eyes were filled with tears when she said good-bye, and I tried to look sad too, but I was actually happy. I thought about how nice it was going to be away from Dad. Also, there were a few of my friends there, and we were sure to find something to get into. I had already had a couple of fights and won, so this was going to be a real ball.

I had lots of fun in the nutbox, and learned a lot of new tricks, just as I thought. I didn't know it at the time, but many of the boys I met in Bellevue would also be with me at Wiltwyck and Warwick years later. Some of those I had bullied in the nutbox would try to turn the tables later on in life. Some would succeed.

There were a few things around to steal. There were plenty of guys to fight with and lots of adults to annoy. The one drawback that the nutbox had was school and teachers. But I found the nutbox to be such a nice place that I was sad when Mama came to take me home.

When I returned home, I was told that my former school had refused to readmit me. This was the best news I had heard since I started going to school. I thought that I had finally gotten out of going to school. But two weeks later, I was enrolled in another school in Harlem.

Within two months from the time I had left Bellevue, I found myself in Manhattan's Children Court for the first time. The reason was that I had been thrown out of two more schools, and there weren't any more in Manhattan that would accept me. The judge told Mama that if I was still in New York State when the fall semester began, he would send me someplace where I would be made to go to school. After Mama had promised the judge that I would not be in New York when September rolled around, we went home.

This was the first time that Mama had been in court, and she was pretty angry about the whole thing. All the way uptown on the bus, Mama kept telling me that I should be ashamed of myself for making her come down to that court and face those white people. Every ten or twelve blocks, Mama would stop preaching just long enough to look at me and say, "Child, maybe that head doctor was right about you," or, "Boy, why you so damn bad?" She didn't understand what the psychiatrist was talking about when he was telling her about my emotional problems. Since she couldn't understand the terms he was using, Mama thought he was telling her in a nice way that I was crazy. Of course, she didn't believe him. "That ole big-nose, thick-eyeglasses white man, he looked kinda crazy his own self," she said. No, she didn't believe him, whatever it was that he had said—but sometimes she wondered if that man might have been right.

Eating Disorders

The eating disorders are marked by serious disturbances in eating behavior. There are two forms of these disorders: anorexia nervosa and bulimia nervosa.

Eating disorders are not generally included in the category of disorders of infancy, childhood, or adolescence. They are included here because they often begin during adolescence.

Bulimia Nervosa involves repeated episodes of binge eating followed by behaviors adopted to compensate for the binge eating. Common compensating behaviors include self-induced vomiting, misuse of laxatives, use of diuretics, fasting, and excessive exercising.

Anorexia nervosa involves a refusal to maintain a minimally normal body weight. Individuals suffering from this disorder are extremely afraid of gaining weight. This disorder commonly begins during middle to late adolescence and is more common in females. In both anorexia and bulimia there is a disturbance in the perception of body shape and weight.

Marya Hornbacher (b. 1974)

Marya Hornbacher has battled most of her life with eating disorders. Her eating disorders began at a very early age with bulimia, when at the age of nine she threw up her snack just to see what would happen. She found that after she began purging she was unable to stop. After a period she was unable to continue to fool her family and began a series of hospital stays in an attempt to control her eating disorders. By the age of eighteen Hornbacher had developed a full-blown case of anorexia and weighed only 52 pounds.

Today Marya Hornbacher works as a freelance editor and writer. She won the White Award for best feature story of 1993 for "Wasted." She lives in Minneapolis, Minnesota with her husband. In recent interviews she admits that she continues to struggle with her eating disorders.

The current selection is from her outstanding book, also entitled
Wasted, which is an account of her life with bulimia and anorexia
and is an excellent example of both of these devastating disorders.

Wasted

Bulimia

I became bulimic at the age of nine, anorexic at the age of fifteen. I couldn't
decide between the two and veered back and forth from one to the other until
I was twenty, and now, at twenty-three, I am an interesting creature, an Eating
Disorder Not Otherwise Specified. My weight has ranged over the past thirteen years from 135 pounds to 52, inching up and then plummeting back
down. I have gotten "well," then "sick," then "well," then "sicker," and so on up
to now; I am considered "moderately improved," psychologically stabilized,
behaviorally disordered, "prone to habitual relapse." I have been hospitalized
six times, institutionalized once, had endless hours of therapy, been tested and
observed and diagnosed and pigeonholed and poked and prodded and fed and
weighed for so long that I have begun to feel like a laboratory rat.

* * *

It was that simple: One minute I was your average nine-year-old, shorts
and a T-shirt and long brown braids, sitting in the yellow kitchen, watching the
Brady Bunch reruns, munching on a bag of Fritos, scratching the dog with my
foot. The next minute I was walking, in a surreal haze I would later compare to
the hum induced by speed, out of the kitchen, down the stairs, into the bathroom, shutting the door, putting the toilet seat up, pulling my braids back with
one hand, sticking my first two fingers down my throat, and throwing up until
I spat blood.

Flushing the toilet, washing my hands and face, smoothing my hair, walking back up the stairs of the sunny, empty house, sitting down in front of the
television, picking up my bag of Fritos, scratching the dog with my foot.

How did your eating disorder start? The therapists ask years later, watching me pick at my nails, curled up in a ball in an endless series of leather chairs.
I shrug. Hell if I know, I say.

* * *

Shortly after I became bulimic, I went to the library one day to check out
a book on anorexia nervosa called *The Best Little Girl in the World*. I wanted
to be her: withdrawn, reserved, cold, wholly absorbed in her own obsession,
perfectly pure. Shutting everything out. It is in fact a rather romanticized account, written by a doctor intent upon demonstrating not the experience of
having an eating disorder but rather his own genius in curing them. The book
said you could die of an eating disorder. That didn't bother me. What it did *not*
say was that it did not kill you right away, it would live with you the rest of your

life, and *then* kill you. I wish I would've known that. I decided that if I did nothing else with my life, I would be an anoretic when I grew up. Bulimia seemed a good place to start.

As it turned out, I was very good at it.

My nighttime baby-sitter Kelly would watch me and laugh as I boasted, I bet you I can eat this entire loaf of bread. No you can't, she'd say. Determined, I'd start popping bread in the toaster, heart pumping. I remember the toast, the butter I spread on it, the crunch of toast against teeth and the caress of butter on tongue. I remember devouring piece after piece, my raging, insatiable hunger, the absolute absence of fullness. I remember cheerfully heading off for my bath. Night, I said. Locking the bathroom door, turning the water on, leaning over the toilet, throwing up in a heave of delight.

* * *

In sixth grade, I began to "take days off" from eating, to "cleanse my system." I tossed my lunch in the lunchroom trash can, keeping only the carrot sticks or the apple. When I think about it now, I can see how I began to withdraw into myself, away from the laughter and noise of my friends, focusing instead on the sensations of hunger, the lovely spinning feeling in my head, the way I would veer in and out of conversations. While my mouth jabbered, my eyes wandered off into space as my thoughts returned to the ache in the pit of my stomach, the heart pounding feeling of absolute power.

Eventually I'd break down and eat. And eat and eat and eat. I'd stop off at the neighborhood market on my way home from school to buy jars of hot fudge, caramel, marshmallow cream, eating each jar with a spoon. The binge provided a perfectly reasonable excuse to stop eating again. Or I'd walk home with two neighborhood friends and go to Sarah's house, to sit in her cozy kitchen. There, we'd have a small communion of hysterical laughter, followed by sudden silence and food. As we talked over homework, or lay sprawled on the white couch in front of the television, we'd eat: little white buttered buns, ice cream with chocolate syrup, potato chips, Double Stuf Oreos, microwaved frozen hamburger patties, Fruit Roll-Ups, Flintstones vitamins. Eventually, the two of them would stop eating. I wouldn't. Just before dinnertime we'd part ways. I'd go home, throw up, eat dinner with my parents, fight with one or the other, do homework, snack, bathe (throw up), and off to bed.

* * *

Something changed the year I entered junior high. For one thing, bulimia took over my life. It stopped being a moonlighting gig, something I just happened to feel like doing when things in my head were particularly crazy, or when I was angry or lonely or sad or flat. It began to have a force and took on a life of its own. From this point on, there are no memories that are not related to food or my body or barfing. It became a centripetal force that sucked me in, something I knew and needed. Badly. All the time. I did not put a bite of food in my mouth without considering if, when, and where I would throw up. I did not ever look in the mirror without thinking, *Fat.*

Consider, for instance, junior high parties. They started at seven and ended at ten. If you were lucky, they ended a little bit later. You wore a dress that made you look thin. You tried on every single piece of clothing you or your mother owned in search of the thing that would make you look thin. Fifteen-odd kids gather awkwardly in the basement of someone's gorgeous, enormous house. You all start eating. This is relatively normal, this is what people do at parties. They eat the Doritos and pretzels and Ruffles and nobody eats the veggies. You nibble on cookies and Hershey's kisses that somebody's mother has put in a cut-crystal bowl. Somebody's mother is hovering in the doorway, nervously glancing at the mixture of boys and girls. A pizza is ordered. Someone puts a movie in the VCR.

However. If you are bulimic, when the lights go out and cute kiddie couples pair off, slurpily kissing and fumbling on the couches, you will walk up the plush-carpeted stairs, heart pounding, face flushed with fear that the food is going to be digested before you can get it out. You will ask the sweet perfectly-made-up hovering mother where the bathroom is. She will point it out to you, smiling sweetly. You will go into the bathroom, take note of the brass fixtures on the sink, the Laura Ashley print wallpaper, the fresh flowers in a Waterford vase, the wicker magazine rack holding *Conde Nast Traveler* and *Forbes.* You will take a mental inventory of all of these things and scrutinize your face in the mirror. You will beg God to keep your face normal after you puke as you turn on the water full force to drown out the retching and splashing, hoping to hell that the walls are thick so nobody hears. You will lift the toilet seat, carefully slide your fingers inside your mouth and down your throat, and puke until you see orange. The Doritos. You ate them first because you, like most bulimics, have developed a system of "markers," eating brightly colored food first so you can tell when it's all out, and it all comes out in reverse order: the pizza, cookies, Ruffles, pretzels, Doritos, all swimming in dark swirls of Coke.

You straighten, flush. You turn the water down, put your hands under it, scrub with the Softsoap in a special matching Softsoap cover. You scrub hard, sniffing your hands and forearms. You look at your face. Thank you, God. No puffiness, eyes a little watery, but not red or bulging. You rinse your mouth with water, then look under the sink for mouthwash, find it, slosh it around. Redo your lipstick. Smile at the mirror, eyes bright and wide. Open the door, go downstairs.

Your friends turn and say, laughing, "Why was the water on?" In Minnesota houses, water pipes run downward through the center of the house and end in the basement. Three floors away, you can hear water running. You laugh, and say, "I'm paranoid about people hearing me pee." Everyone laughs. Your boyfriend, teasing, says, "We heard anyway."

You freeze, still smiling.

"No, I'm just kidding," he says. You laugh nervously, take your place beside him, sit on your hands to hide the shaking, the nicks on the knuckles of the first two fingers of your right hand.

Self-induced vomiting . . . causes abrasions on the back of the dominant hand or knuckles. Calluses form, creating what in medical parlance is called "Russell's sign."

Anorexia

The anoretic operates under the astounding illusion that she can escape the flesh, and, by association, the realm of emotions. The summer before I left for boarding school was the last time I would ever fully understand that I was a human being, and occasionally care about myself as such. I was about to become an anoretic. That is to say, I, the girl I knew as myself, was about to disappear. She was about to become no more than the blank spaces in the mirror where my body had once been. She was about to become no more than a very small voice.

* * *

Anorexia started slowly. It took time to work myself into the frenzy that the disease demands. There were an incredible number of painfully thin girls at Interlochen, dancers mostly. The obsession with weight seemed nearly universal. Whispers and longing stares followed the ones who were visibly anorexic. We sat at our cafeteria tables, passionately discussing the calories of lettuce, celery, a dinner roll, rice. We moved between two worlds. When we pushed back our chairs and scattered to our departments, we transformed. I would watch girls who'd just been near tears in the dorm-room mirrors suddenly become rapt with life, fingers flying over a harp, a violin, bodies elastic with motion, voices strolling through Shakespeare's forest of words.

* * *

Eating disorders are addictions. You become addicted to a number of their effects. The two most basic are important: the pure adrenaline that kicks in when you're starving—you're high as a kite, sleepless, full of a frenetic, unstable energy—and the heightened intensity of experience that eating disorders initially induce. At first, everything tastes and smells intense, tactile experience is intense, your own drive and energy themselves are intense and focused. Your sense of power is very, very intense. You are not aware, however, that you are quickly becoming addicted. And there's the rub. As with drugs, the longer you do it, the more you need to achieve that original high.

* * *

Part of this had to do with the self-perpetuating nature of eating disorders: The worries about your weight do not decrease no matter how much weight you lose. Rather, they grow. And the more you worry about your weight, the more you are willing to act on that worry. You really do not have to have an excessive level of body loathing to rationally convince yourself that starvation is a reasonable means to achieve thinness. Normally, there is a self-protective mechanism in the psyche that will dissuade the brain from truly dangerous activity, regardless of how desirable the effects of that activity may be. For example, a woman may wish to lose weight but have an essential respect for her physical self and therefore refrain from unhealthy eating. I had no such self-protective mechanism, no such essential self-respect. When you have no sense of physical integrity—a sense that your own health is important, that your body, regardless of shape, is something that requires care and feeding and a basic respect for the biological organism that it is—a very simple, all-too-common, truly frightening thing happens: You cross over from a vague wish to be thinner into a no-holds-barred attack on your flesh.

You stop seeing your body as your own, as something valuable, something that totes you around and does your thinking and feeling for you and requires an input of energy for this favor. You begin seeing it instead as an undesirable appendage, a wart you need to remove. "I *have* a body," you are likely to say if you talk about embodiment at all; you don't say, I *am* a body. A body is a separate entity possessable by the 'I'; the 'I' and the body aren't, as the copula would make them, grammatically indistinguishable. . . . Bodies get treated like wayward women who have to be shown who's boss, even if it means slapping them around a little.

When you believe that *you* are not worthwhile in and of yourself, in the back of your mind you also begin to believe that *life* is not worthwhile in and of itself. It is only worthwhile insofar as it relates to your crusade. It is a kamikaze mission. Life and self are far less important than your single-minded goal. "Thinness" was as good a name as any for my goal. Twenty pounds, I said. No matter what.

By winter, I was starving. Malnutrition is not a joke. Whether you're skinny or not, your body is starving. As the temperature dropped, I began to grow fur, what is technically called lanugo. Your body grows it when you're not taking in enough calories to create internal heat (it's interesting how we think of calories as the Antichrist, rather than as an energy source). I liked my fur. I felt like a small bear. I grew fur on my belly, my ribs, the small of my back, my cheeks, fine downy fur, pale white. My skin grew whiter, more so than usual, when the sun became translucent, as it does in winter far north. I began to look a bit haunted. I stood in the shower, feeling the bones in my lower back, two small points at the top of my rear. I took hold of my pelvic bones, twin toy hatchets. I took Fiberall and Dexatrim. I drank gallons of water. I was perpetually cold.

Mornings, I'd haul myself out of bed at 5 A.M., put on running clothes, walk through the purple light latticed with the black arms of trees, open the doors to the long hall of the main building, and run. This was the strangest thing. I have always hated solitary exercise. When I was younger, I played soccer, racquetball, and swam on the swim team, but I had always, always hated solo running. I was very proud of myself for forcing my body to run. And run. Malnutrition precipitates mania. So does speed. Both were at play here, in large doses. But so was masochism—the subjection of the self and/or body to pain and fear, ultimately resulting in a transitory sense of mastery over pain and fear. Every morning, I ran five miles, up and down this hall, touching the door at each end, the mark of an obsession. I had to touch the door or else it didn't count. You make up these rules, and if you break the rules, God help you, you have to run an extra mile to make up for it. When I was done, I'd go downstairs to the workout room and weigh myself.

The workout room was packed with girls. On the scale, on the bikes, on the weights, the rowing machine. Nothing wrong with a little exercise. But in such a small community, you can't help but notice the changes. The same girls, shrinking, day after day. I saw them, later, on campus, shivering in classrooms, at readings, at concerts, wrapped in wool. I'd weigh myself and leave. There was no mutual recognition. You can talk food all day with friends, but you keep your secrets. On the surface, you're doing this companionably, you're a friggin' unstoppable dieting army and you'll all go down together. On the underside, you're all competing with one another to be the thinnest, most controlled, least weak, and you have your own private crusade on which no one can join you, lest they be as fucked up as you.

By midwinter, I would run in the morning, eat grapefruit after grapefruit for breakfast (someone told me it had only eight calories. When I found out that was wrong, I ran ten miles to make up for all that grapefruit), go to class. At lunch I would speed-walk up and down the hallway while reading a book, then go to class. At the end of the day, run again, five more miles, go to the cafeteria, eat carrot sticks with mustard. Soon I made a new rule: now I had to run *after* dinner as well. By January I was running twenty-five miles a day, on a knee that was beginning to split.

In the hospital, anoretics are always amazed that they could possibly have had the energy to run, to sit on the exercise bike for hours, pedaling madly toward the vanishing point in their heads. They talk about this in group, depending on their state of mind, with either a sad sort of pride, or shock. The latter is rare. You only hear the latter from women who have come to some understanding that they have been living in an altered state, a state that cannot be maintained. The former tend to maintain their grandiose illusion that they are superhuman.

I was beginning to harbor that delusion myself, that I was superhuman. When you coast without eating for a significant amount of time, and you are still alive, you begin to scoff at those fools who believe they must eat to live. It seems blatantly obvious to you that this is not true. You get up in the morning, you do your work, you run, you do not eat, you live.

You begin to forget what it means to live. You forget things. You forget that you used to feel all right. You forget what it means to feel all right because you feel like shit all of the time, and you can't remember what it was like before. People take the feeling of *full* for granted. They take for granted the feeling of steadiness, of hands that do not shake, heads that do not ache, throats not raw with bile and small rips from fingernails forced in haste to the gag spot. Stomachs that do not begin to dissolve with a battery-acid mixture of caffeine and pills. They do not wake up in the night, calves and thighs knotting with muscles that are beginning to eat away at themselves. They may or may not be awakened in the night by their own inexplicable sobs.

You begin to rely on the feeling of hunger, your body's raucous rebellion at the small tortures of your own hands. When you eventually begin to get well, health will feel wrong, it will make you dizzy, it will confuse you, you will get sick again because sick is what you know.

* * *

The hospitalizations at Methodist have a tendency to blur, one into another, since I was there three times in less than a year. Hospitalizations in general are blurry. The days are the same, precisely the same. Nothing changes. Life melts down to a simple progression of meals. They become a way of life fairly quickly. You used to be a normal girl with a normal life. Now you are a patient, a case, a file full of forms. You may welcome this transition. It may seem inevitable to you. You have been removed from the world. You have been found flawed and wanting. You could have told them this years ago. It is all right, in a way, because there is nothing so sure, so safe, as routine. There is nothing so welcome to the anoretic or bulimic, much as she protests and howls, as a world wherein everything, everything, revolves around food.

And there is nothing so wonderfully conducive to eating disorders as treatment.

There are the certainties. You will be given slippers—little socks with rubber treads on the soles—and a paper gown. From the doorway to your room, the room will have a bathroom on the left. You will turn the doorknob, but it will be locked. To your right, built into the wall, a small closet. Three drawers beneath a mirror hung too high to see your butt or even your waist. You will be forced to focus instead on your arms, your shoulder bones, the flesh of your cheeks or throat.

Ahead of you, on the left side of the room, two beds, a curtain shoved back to the wall in between. Apparently you will be sharing the room with another patient. Perhaps the two of you will conspire. On the right side of the room, against the wall, sit two hospital chairs, vinyl-covered, gray metal frames. One of these beds is for you. It will be a hard bed, but you are exhausted. In the hospital you will sleep deeper than you ever have, or ever will again. There will be a little table by your bed with buttons on it. You can turn on the radio, call a nurse, flip the light. None of you ever use the nurse call button, even if you are having a heart attack, because you aren't really sick. To call a nurse would be ostentatious, as if you thought you really warranted worry, as if you were so weak as to want to get well. There will be a window in your room that will look out over rooftops and winding streets. Depending on what time of the year you are there, the trees will be either full or bare.

There will be a main room, which will have a television and a long bank of windows looking out over the city on one wall. The rest of the walls will have Plexiglas windows through which you will be watched. The room will have one or two couches, end tables, institutional carpeting covering the concrete floor. You will carry your pillow with you everywhere, in its rough white case. You will sit on it, because the floor will hurt the bones poking out through your ass. Or you will lie on the floor on your belly and move the pillow frequently, from under your rib cage to under your elbows to under your pelvic bones. There will be decks and decks of old cards, board games, news magazines. There will be no fashion magazines, and your friends and family will be warned not to bring them to you, because they are bad for you. They may not bring food or drink. If you are lucky, you will be in a hospital where they are allowed to bring decaffeinated coffee. The coffee is never caffeinated—you might be using caffeine to artificially boost your metabolism, or if you are experienced, your heart rate. In Methodist, not even decaffeinated coffee will be allowed, because you might be using it to boost your weight, knowing as you do that you are retaining fluids.

There will be nurses, several of them, on rotating shifts. They will be nice, or they will not. There will be bathroom times, usually every two hours on the hour. At those times, a few nurses with heavy, jangling key rings will open the door for you and lean back against the closet door. Everything rests on the nurse: The very nicest of them will let you leave the door open just a crack, a token, and she will talk to you while you pee to keep your mouth too busy to lean down and puke between your legs. Most of them will stand there, door wide, but will avert their eyes and talk to you. They always cross their arms. They act nonchalant. Some of them are not that much older than you. You hope they feel horrible. Some nurses will let you turn the water on while you go, so that the noise of your piddling into the little plastic container—called a "hat"—which measures your fluid output is not so thunderous. There are also the awful nurses, who swing the door wide and *watch.* These are the ones who diet. You hear them talking on the nurses' station when they think you aren't listening—idiots, you're *always* listening—about their fat thighs. These are the ones who do terrible, cruel things to their hair, perming it into thin strands of curled straw and dyeing it colors not found in nature. And they stare at you, your pants around your knees, your arm folded over your belly to hide what you can, and when you ask them, "Can I please turn on the water?" they will say not simply no but "Why?" And you will say, "Because this is a little embarrassing." And they will say, "Why?" And you will drop it, sitting there, attempting to will your body into silence.

Taking a dump will become an obsession. Taking a dump will be a topic of conversation, often a topic of terrific bawdy glee among the patients, sitting curled up on the couches, or beached, after meals, laid out on the floor, hands on the belly, groaning, distended, in no small measure of pain. The nurses will eventually get embarrassed and silence you: Let's move on to another subject, they'll say, and silence will seep over the room again. The fact of the matter is that you cannot take a dump. None of you can take a dump. You will beg for laxatives, but they cannot give you laxatives because more than half of you are addicted to them already, and they could kill you. You personally are not addicted to laxatives at that point, and the whole idea of using them for weight loss will seem utterly stupid to you, because it's not *real* weight you lose by shitting all day long. It's just *water* weight, which isn't as *good*. Of course you do not know then that in less than six months, you and your disdainful ass will move into the bathroom for days at a time because yes, you too! will be eating whole boxes of chocolate Ex-Lax three times a day. Your bodies are in shock. Your intestines, not used to having food in them, or keeping it, will grip the six meals a day like a vise, tighten on the food, refuse to digest. You will lie in bed at night, picturing each item you've eaten, stuck somewhere, arranged in order of consumption: In your large intestine, Tuesday's meals, compacted but still whole; in your small intestine, Wednesday's and Thursday's, part of Friday's: in your stomach, Saturday's and Sunday's: Monday's meals are stuck in your esophagus and lunging toward the back of your throat. If you go too long without taking a dump—say, six to ten days—they will take you away to another part of the hospital and give you a barium enema. This is a nightmare. Barium is an explosive.

Your day will go like this: You will wake up in the wee hours of the morning with dreams of a boa constrictor wrapping around your arm. It will be a blood pressure cuff. You will, in hazy tones, ask the nurse how your pressure and pulse read. She may or may not tell you, depending on whether she's a regular nurse on the unit (won't tell) or a sub (will). You will sink back into sleep. In the morning, if you are me, you will wake up very early. This will get you in trouble because they will think you are waking up early to have unmonitored time to yourself, to exercise. You are simply used to waking up early, but you take their suggestion nonetheless and spend these early hours listening to the sheets hiss as your legs move up and down.

When the light turns from dark blue to pale gray, a nurse will come to the door to wake you up. Good morning, she'll say. You'll mumble, Morning. You will stand up too fast because you never, never get it through your thick head that your body is fucked up. You will sway and sometimes fall over, which will put you on watch for the rest of the damn day. You will put on your paper gown, shivering, and get back under the covers to wait until it's your turn.

When it's your turn, a nurse will come to the door and usually hold your elbow as you go down the hall. You will stand on the high-tech scale that was probably constructed for eating-disorder units because the numbers face away from you. When you peer over to look at them, you find your weight reads in kilos. You don't know metric. You are furious. You are in a state of total dis-array, as is everyone else on the unit. Most of you have known your weight minute by minute for some time. It has become the center of your life, and this not-knowing simply will not do. You beg to know your weight, because you're new. When you've been there a little longer, you will listen to other new women beg with the same desperation, and you will exchange little knowing glances with the others in the hall. They never tell you. Your life comes apart at the seams.

You live, all of you, in a state of constant, crazed anxiety. You know you're going to gain weight. There's really no way to get around it. You can play all sorts of little games, and you will still gain weight. There is no way to describe the tiny, constant implosions of your chest when this thought hits you, as it does, often, day in, day out.

You take a shower in a stall with no curtain. You have to sit down on the little stool in the shower. You argue with the nurse about this. "Why?" you ask. Most of the nurses will turn away in the chair where they keep watch, but not all. You will learn quickly which nurses you hate, which ones not to hate. The ones you hate will watch. Because you are a little bitch, you will ask the one you hate most, "What, are you jealous?" She will attempt to shake her head in scorn.

But she is jealous. Most of them are not. Most of them think you're piti-ful. But a very few have, shall we say, eating issues of their own. You have a trump card.

Your forbidden things will be kept in a little plastic cubby in the nurses' station: Razors, matches, cigarettes. You will be allowed, upon request, to shave your legs. Most of you will shave your legs every day. You will also ago-nize daily about what you will wear, and you'll apply your makeup perfectly, and curl and tease your hair, as if you had somewhere to go, as if you will not spend your day and the next and the next on the eighth floor of a hospital, with no one to see you but the nurses and the other fuck-ups in the cage. Almost all of you have been spending at least an hour daily refining your appearance since puberty. It is part of your routine, and your routine must be maintained, if only in name.

You will sit in the main room playing solitaire on the floor. You like morn-ings, because you feel peaceful then. You look forward to you day. Every day, the routine is as such: Breakfast, morning check-in, physical therapy, snack, morning class, lunch, occupational therapy, snack, free time, dinner, visiting hours, snack, evening check-in, bed.

It's like being at camp.

You will not realize until you get to treatment just how deep and abiding your obsessive love of food really is. It's not the way most people like food—the feeling of fullness, of communion with friends and family. Food *qua* lover. I re-member the day I met Jane as she sat on a couch, doing something to an apple with her mouth that was positively erotic. She was still pretty sick. I asked:

What are you doing to that apple? She looked up at me, startled, her tongue on the wet, white flesh. She laughed and said, "I'm making love to it." It was funny, but true. With both anorexia and bulimia, food becomes the object of your desire. You either prefer the desperate hunger of unfed passion, or the battering cycle of food moving in and out and in and out of your body in a rhythm that you never want to end.

Treatment, that first time, turned out to be divine. I had it easy. I was classified as bulimic, so I did not have to gain too much weight. I got to avoid the weird agony some of the other women were going through, though I would later experience the frenzied panic at weight gain upon my frequent returns. Treatment, that time, turned out to be a grand buffet. They feed you normal food, and lots of it. In earlier years, eating disorder facilities were big on force-feeding and providing massive quantities of high-calorie food, but they soon figured out that this treatment gave way to almost immediate relapse. Now they give you a nutritionist who attempts to convince you that food is simply a necessary thing, neither Christ nor Antichrist. After the first week, when I flat-out refused to eat anything—it was more a statement than an actual fear of food—I went through the motions that we all went through, bitching and moaning about how awful it was to have to eat, balking at the slightest drop of grease on our poached fish, taking as long as we possibly could to finish our food. The fact was, I was in seventh heaven. My life revolved around meals. Never believe an eating-disordered person who says she hates food. It's a lie. Denied food, your body and brain will begin to obsess about it. It's the survival instinct, a constant reminder to eat, one that you try harder and harder to ignore, though you never can. Instead of eating, you simply *think* about food all the time. You dream about it, you stare at it, but you do not eat it. When you get to the hospital, you have to eat, and as truly terrifying as it is, it is also welcome. Food is the sun and moon and the stars, the center of gravity, the love of your life. Being forced to eat is the most welcome punishment there is.

In a little eating room, a nauseating late-1980's aesthetic will prevail. Heavy on the mauve. There will be a schoolroom clock on the wall, round glass face glinting with the ugly light of those long, humming fluorescent bulbs. You will stand in the doorway for a minute, looking for your tray. It will have your menu beside it. You will spot it, like spotting the face of a lover in a crowd, move toward it, feign disgust, pull your chair back, sit down. At first, you will honest-to-god be mortified, and really not hungry. Your stomach is shrunken, you are very simply afraid of food, and you will cry in despair. But as the body begins to come alive again, you begin to feel hunger, a racking sort of hunger, and you will damn near cry for joy.

Your menu: you have been given a chart, which tells you how many calories you have to eat per day. It breaks that number down into categories: Proteins, breads, milks, vegetables, fruits, desserts, "satieties" (fats). These numbers dance like sugarplums in your head. The obsessive-compulsivity that you used to channel into hyperactive management of time and work is rerouted to a place where it can do some *real* good, and it twitches in your face like a tic when you sit down, each day, with your chart and your menu. You spend hours poring over it, trying out every possible combination of items that might fulfill your quotas. You love the neat X in the box, the tidy circle around optional items, butter and jam, French or ranch. You will look forward to every meal, every snack, with a completely ridiculous level of excitement. All of you will pretend to dread them. All of you are full of shit.

This time around, it will be summer. At meals and snacks, someone will turn on the radio, which sits on the counter running along one wall, under the cupboards where they keep the Ensure, you will remember Ensure, a nutritional liquid that you will get when you do not finish your food within the allotted time: half an hour for meals, fifteen minutes for snacks. As soon as you walk into the room, a nurse will look up at the clock and write down a time on the white dry-erase board on the wall. A nurse will sit down at the head of the table to watch you. She will not eat. She will not read a magazine. She will simply watch you. If she is young, she will join in the conversation, if there is one. Usually there won't be because you are all peering suspiciously at your food. If she is old, she will not talk. When the conversation inevitably turns to food, weight, exercise, she will speak. That's a nonissue, she'll say. You will find this incredibly ironic.

She will scrutinize your eating habits. If you are scraping the tines of your fork against your teeth, even silently, if you curl your lip back from the food in an involuntary sneer, if you are pushing your food around on your plate, or eating things in a particular order, day after day, as I did—liquids first, followed by vegetables, starch, fruit, entrée, and dessert—if you do any of these things, the nurse will pipe up: Marya, that's a behavior. When you are new, you'll ask, A *behavior?* You will sit there, trying to keep your lip as far from the food as possible without being obvious, thinking of all the connotations of a *behavior.*

Or if you commit a cardinal sin—spitting food daintily into your napkin, folding it expertly under the table, casually slipping the pats of mandatory butter into your pocket, hiding the last bites of food under your tongue (hiding it in your cheek never works, your cheeks are sunken and stretched)—you will find yourself in serious shit. If you do not finish your meal on time, you will be kept after. You will sit, with one or two other girls, while the nurse calculates the number of calories left on your plate. How are you figuring this? You cry. How do you know how much Ensure to give me? That's too much! That's bullshit! Watch your language, Marya, she warns as she pours the white liquid into a little plastic cup with measuring marks along the side. You will be given ten minutes to finish the Ensure. I'd speed it up, she'll advise, watching you sip as slowly as you can. You're making a choice, she'll say. This is supposed to be empowering. If you do not finish, you will be tube-fed.

You will remember the silence, the ding of tin fork to plate. You will remember the radio, KDWB bouncing along. Everyone will come to know every song on the playlist backward and forward. You will remember a table of women, intently staring at their food, glancing at one another's plates, unconsciously mouthing the words to the songs between slow bites.

When I got to treatment the first time, I was not one of the emaciated ones. I was definitely slim, far thinner than is normal or attractive, but because I was not *visibly* sick, the very *picture* of sick, because I did not warrant the coveted title of Anoretic, I was embarrassed. Ignore the fact that my diastolic pressure had a habit of falling through the floor every time I stood up, putting me on watch for sudden cardiac arrest, or the fact that my heart puttered along, slow and uneven as an old man taking a solitary walk through the park. Ignore the fact that I had a perforated esophagus and a nasty little habit of coughing blood all over my shirt. In treatment, as in the rest of the world, bulimia is seen as a step down from anorexia, both in terms of medical seriousness and in terms of admirability. Bulimia, of course, gives in to the temptations of the flesh, while anorexia is anointed, is a complete removal of the bearer from the material realm. Bulimia hearkens back to the hedonistic Roman days of pleasure and feast, anorexia to the medieval age of bodily mortification and voluntary famine. In truth, bulimics do not usually bear the hallowed stigma of a skeletal body. Their self-torture is private, far more secret and guilty than is the visible statement of anoretics, whose whittled bodies are admired as the epitome of feminine beauty. There is nothing feminine, delicate, acclaimed, about sticking your fingers down your throat and spewing puke. Denial of the flesh, however, is not only the obvious culmination of centuries of bizarre ideas about the dainty nature of women but also an active realization of religious and cultural ideals.

And yet this is a culture where we seesaw madly, hair flying and eyes alight, between crazed and constant consumption, where the insatiable hunger is near universal, as is the fanatical belief in the moral superiority of self-denial and self-control. Culturally, we would be diagnosed as bulimic, not anorexic, daily veering back and forth between two extreme points, bingeing and purging. The frenzied adoration of the anorexic body, and the violent hatred of fat, on ourselves and on others, reveals not that anorexia is beautiful, nor that fat is particularly despicable, but that we ourselves are intolerably torn, and we have to chose sides.

* * *

The near-total cessation of food happened very quickly. I had not necessarily intended to cut back on eating: when I left for Washington, I was already at such a low intake level that it did not occur to me that I could, or should, lower it further still. But I did, eliminating what seemed a few superfluous bits of food. On the surface, I did it as catharsis; food suddenly seemed to be a burden, a strain on my limited time, and I pruned my diet just a bit, a few nips and tucks here and there. In reality, I did it as a test of my own endurance. I wanted to see how long I could go, running on fumes. I wanted to find the bare minimum required to subsist.

Remember, anoretics do eat. We have systems of eating that develop almost unconsciously. By the time we realize we've been running our lives with an iron system of numbers and rules, the system has begun to rule us. They are systems of Safe Foods, foods not imbued, or less imbued, with monsters and devils and dangers. These are usually "pure" foods, less likely to taint the soul with such sins as fat, or sugar, or an excess of calories. Consider the advertisements for food, the religious lexicon of eating: "sinfully rich," intones the silky voiced announcer, "indulge yourself," she says, "guilt-free." Not complex foods that would send the mind spinning in a tornado of possible pitfalls contained in a given food—a possible miscalculation of calories, a loss of certainty about your control over chaos, your control over self. The horrible possibility that you are taking more than you deserve.

But systems, like corsets, keep shrinking, tightening around the body, pressing the breath out of you. They tighten further still until you cannot move at all. Even then they do not stop.

This is how my system of eating had worked when I was in Minneapolis: Food was divided into units. A unit consisted of eighty calories, the equivalent of your average slice of bread. Of course I made the system up in my head, and do not, to this day, understand why this particular system held such significance for me. This is how we work, we all have our systems. A friend of mine used to divide food arbitrarily into liquids and solids—solids including soup, bread, pasta, rice; liquids including chocolate, vegetables, and chicken—and would've argued with any rational being who tried to explain to her the alternative nature of "liquid" or "solid."

It's just a pattern we have, and we need it fiercely. I would have a hard time putting into words the passion we have for our systems. They are as near and dear to us as any saving God. We know them better than we know the alphabet, we know them in the deepest part of the brain, the way we know how to write, even in the dark. They are the only things that stand between us and total disintegration into chaotic, needy softness, the only things that keep the uncertainty of things at bay. We take a certain sick pride in the fact that we know the caloric and fat content of every possible food on the planet, and have an understandable disdain for nutritionists who attempt to tell us the caloric content of anything, when we are the gods of caloric content and have delusions of nutritional omniscience, when said nutritionist will attempt to explain the average woman needs a daily diet of 2,000 or more calories when we ourselves have been doing JUST FUCKING FINE on 500.

When I got out of Lowe House, I was (1) quite thin at 101 pounds, and (2) eating a consistent diet of 31.25 units, according to my calculations. By winter of that year in Minneapolis, I decided that 16 units would suffice. I cut my caloric intake in half and deleted my intake of fat altogether. By the summer before leaving for Washington, I was down to 10. When I got to Washington, I decided immediately to cut two units—just two, what difference does a measly two units make?—putting me at eight. By October, I went to six units, and by December, I was down to four.

Four units. Line up four apples and think about how you you'd feel after a few days of eating that and nothing else. Or four slices of bread. Or one carton of yogurt and an orange. Or two bagels. Or a pile of carrot sticks and a bowl of cereal. I was eating 320 calories a day.

The term "starvation diet" refers to 900 calories a day. I was on one-third of a starvation diet. What do you call that? One word that comes to mind: "suicide."

Factor in, here, that most people have a funny habit of sleeping. I did not have this habit. Certainly not in Washington. I was afraid I'd miss something. I was manic, and starving, and starving explodes mania into a sort of psychedelic passion for wakefulness, a deluded disdain for such base needs as sleep. Most people sleep seven hours a night. That's seven hours where their bodies are essentially at rest and don't require as much energy in the form of food. Most healthy people can go seventeen hours on, say, 2,000+ calories, putting them at about 117.64706 calories per waking hour.

Put me, and a lot of people like me, at, say, twenty-one hours awake, three hours tossing in half-sleep, at 15.238095 calories per waking hour.

By the way, I also became a little obsessed with numbers in Washington.

Discussion Questions

1. List several points of lucidity demonstrated by London's narrator in "Told in the Drooling Ward." Does this narrator's lucidity dispel any of the myths about mental retardation?

2. Research has determined that a significant number of the victims of eating disorders are young women. Why? What can be done to help young women avoid eating disorders?

3. Discuss some of the physical problems that Ms. Hornbacher experienced as a result of her eating disorder. Is it possible for permanent damage to the body to result from eating disorders? If so, list several examples.

4. Why is Zipper's nickname Zipper? Is this an appropriate nickname for a young man with ADHD? Why or why not? Make a list of other nicknames that might fit this disorder.

5. Conduct disorder includes behaviors that violate the rights of other people. Is it possible to violate the rights of the men who violated the law by kidnapping Red Chief? Why or why not?

6. There has been much discussion about excessive use of medication with children diagnosed with ADHD. Do you agree or disagree that too much medication has been used in the treatment of ADHD? Why or why not? Discuss ways to deal with ADHD children other than using medication alone.

SOCIAL DEVELOPMENT ISSUES JOURNAL

Social Development Issues, sponsored by the Inter-University Consortium for International Social Development (IUCISD), is a refereed journal published three times a year that serves as a scholarly forum linking multiple disciplines, nations, and cultures. The Journal's purpose is to promote consideration of issues that affect social justice as well as the development and well being of individuals and their communities. The Journal is committed to the advancement of social, cultural, political, and economic theories including policy and practice (and their interrelationship) within a global context.

Each issue includes reviews of noteworthy new books.

Individual Journal subscriptions include membership in IUCISD and the Consortium's newsletter. For more information about the Consortium see the Web site at **http://www.iucisd.org**.

A sample of recent topics in the Journal:

❚ Globalization and the social responsibility of the state in developing countries
❚ The links between education, employment, and demographic change
❚ Social development and the feminist tradition
❚ From social development to transformation
❚ South African nongovernmental organizations
❚ Income growth and inequality in Singapore
❚ Women and war: protection through empowerment in El Salvador

Social Development Issues Journal

Shanti K. Khinduka IUCISD President	**Frank Raymond** IUCISD President-Elect Journal Board President University of South Carolina

All SDI editorial team members listed below are affiliates of Washington University in Saint Louis

Michael Sherraden Editor	**Amanda Moore McBride** Associate Editor	**Timothy Broesamle** Managing Editor	**Anupama Jacob** Production Editor

Subscribe and join today. Libraries may order direct or through their subscription agency.

The *Social Development Issues Journal* is published three times a year by Lyceum Books. The subscription rate is $40.00 per year for individuals; $60.00 for institutions and libraries. There is a $21.00 fee for all foreign postage. All subscription inquiries should be sent to Social Development Issues Journal, 341 N. Charlotte Street, Lombard, Illinois 60148. Your e-mail inquiries can be sent to **lyceumsubscribe@comcast.net**

If you would like to join the Inter-University Consortium for International Social Development, please click on: **http://www.iassw.org**

School Social Work Journal

School Social Work Journal is a refereed publication intended primarily for school social work practitioners, educators, and students in the public schools. Articles in the Journal are directly related to the improvement of social work practice in the schools. These articles report original research, integrative and comprehensive reviews, conceptual and practical positions, effective assessment and intervention methodologies, and model service delivery programs. Each issues includes reviews of noteworthy new books.

To learn more about the Illinois Association of School Social Workers, visit the Web site: **http://www.iassw.org**

A sample of recent topics in the Journal:

I Caring for Grandparent-Headed Families
I Junior high school predictors of high school dropout.
I Ethics and Confidentiality
I Youth Mentoring
I Drug traffic intervention through school and community centers.
I Abuse in adolescent dating relationships.
I Ecological Strategies and Socially Isolated Youth
I The impact of violence on school achievement and behavior.
I Challenges and service needs of urban children.
I The development of a tool for school social work collaboration.

Each issue includes reviews of noteworthy new books.

The *School Social Work Journal* is published fall and spring by the Illinois Association of School Social Workers. The subscription rate is $20.00 per year for individuals; $40.00 for institutions and libraries. There is a $10.00 fee for all foreign postage. All subscription inquiries should be sent to School Social Work Journal, 341 N. Charlotte Street, Lombard, Illinois 60148.

E-mail inquiries can be sent to **lyceumsubscribe@comcast.net**

BEST PRACTICES IN MENTAL HEALTH
An International Journal

A new and innovative journal available Spring 2005

Best Practices in Mental Health: An International Journal is a refereed publication intended primarily for mental health teachers, researchers, and practitioners and which will also provide valuable guidance for students in the field. Best practices are high priorities of the U. S. National Institute of Mental Health (NIMH), and the journal will publish articles, commentary, and research reports that promote the latest developments. By having an international scope, the journal will be able to publish the best mental health practices and research from around the world. A distinguished international editorial board will insure that the journal publishes materials which seek to replicate and improve promising practices wherever found and to promote intervention research. The journal is published twice a year. A year's subscription is $40.00 for individuals and $60.00 for libraries and institutions. Online access is being developed for library/institutional subscribers. All subscription inquiries should be sent to: Best Practices in Mental Health, 341 N. Charlotte Street, Lombard, IL 60148. E-mail inquiries can be sent to **lyceumsubscribe@comcast.net**.

For up-to-date information see the Lyceum Web site,
www.lyceumbooks.com.